COLSTON SYMPOSIUM ON OBSERVATION AND INTERPRETATION 1957

Back Row (*left to right*) *:* R. Edgley, J. F. Nye, E. W. Bastin, D. J. O'Connor, R. Englman, J. O. Wisdom, G. Süssmann, S. Zienau, A. J. B. Cruickshank, N. L. Cooper, J. Cohen, S. F. Mason, E. Götlind, W. Mays, U. Öpik

2nd Row: R. H. Brown, G. Kneebone, F. Bopp, M. B. Hesse, P. Alexander, R. B. Braithwaite, W. C. Kneale, M. Scriven, D. M. Mackay, A. M. K. Müller, D. R. Cousin, E. H. Hutten, F. C. Frank, P. Feyerabend

3rd Row: P. T. Landsberg, L. Rosenfeld, J.-P. Vigier, D. Bohm, G. Ryle, C. Darwin, S. H. G. Barnett, S. Körner, A. J. Ayer, H. J. Groenewold, W. B. Gallie, D. H. Everett, M. Polanyi

Observation and Interpretation in the Philosophy of Physics

With Special Reference to Quantum Mechanics

Edited by

S. Körner

in collaboration with M. H. L. Pryce

Proceedings of the
Ninth Symposium of the Colston Research Society
held in the University of Bristol
April 1st - April 4th, 1957

DOVER PUBLICATIONS, INC.
NEW YORK NEW YORK

Published in the United Kingdom by Constable and Company Limited, 10 Orange Street, London W.C. 2.

This new Dover edition, first published in 1962, is an unabridged and unaltered republication of the work first published by Butterworths Scientific Publications in 1957 under the former title: *Observation and Interpretation; A Symposium of Philosophers and Physicists.*

This edition is published by special arrangement with Butterworth and Company Limited, 88 Kingsway, London W.C. 2, England.

Manufactured in the United States of America

Dover Publications, Inc.
180 Varick Street
New York 14, N. Y.

Foreword

THE name of Edward Colston, the great seventeenth-century philanthropist and educationalist, is associated in Bristol with a number of scholastic and charitable institutions. It was adopted by a group of public-spirited citizens when, in 1899, they established the 'University College Colston Society', with the aim of fostering the young and struggling University College. For a decade it played a part in the movement which culminated in the institution of the University of Bristol in 1909.

The Society then changed its name and made its object more precise: it became the 'Colston Research Society' and devoted itself to the encouragement of original work in the University. It made grants for the purchase of apparatus and for the other expenses of research. As resources increased activities expanded and, notably, in the later thirties the Society financed a full-scale Social Survey of Bristol.

After the war a new reconsideration of policy led to the decision to devote the major part of the Society's efforts to the promotion of an annual symposium, the first being held in 1948. The rapid growth of the symposium as a means for the advancement of knowledge is one of the remarkable features of the intellectual life of recent years. Usually such meetings are fostered by bodies interested in one particular field of learning. As the list of titles (on the page opposite) shows, no such limitation applies to the symposia of the Colston Research Society. That the subject should be one at an interesting and active stage of development is the main factor in making a choice. The fact that the symposium is held in one of the younger seats of learning, with its home in an historic city, is a stimulus not only to the University but also, we believe, to the visiting guests who have come from many countries. The publication of the proceedings ensures the communication of the papers and discussions to wider circles.

It was my privilege to be President of the Colston Research Society for the year 1956-57, during which the ninth symposium was promoted by the Society. The subject was 'Observation and Interpretation' and the proceedings are printed in this, the ninth volume of the Colston Papers.

S. H. G. BARNETT

Preface

THE contributions to this volume, whether by philosophers or physicists, are concerned with questions belonging to the philosophy of physics—for the most part to the philosophy of Quantum Mechanics. Sir Charles Darwin's paper alone, unlike the others, was delivered before an audience in which philosophers and physicists were a small minority.

It is my pleasant duty to thank the Colston Research Society for asking me to organize the symposium and my colleague Professor Pryce for his collaboration. Without his expert advice it would have been neither possible nor proper for me to accept the Society's invitation. Warm thanks are also due to Mr. R. H. Brown, the Hon. Secretary of the Colston Research Society, and to my colleagues Mr. R. Edgley, Dr. P. Feyerabend, Mr. I. W. Pleydell-Pearce and to the Warden and staff of Manor Hall, where the meeting took place. All these helped in many ways. Dr. Feyerabend undertook the arduous task of supervising the recording of the discussions from tape-recorder to the printed page.

It would be ungracious and ungrateful not also to mention the courtesy and efficiency of the contributors, the printers and the publishers during all stages in the preparation of the volume.

S. KÖRNER

Previous volumes in the Colston Papers are:

Vol. I.	1948	*Cosmic Radiation*—Editor, Professor F. C. Frank
Vol. II.	1949	*Engineering Structures*—Editor, Professor A. G. Pugsley
Vol. III.	1950	*Colonial Administration*—Editor, Professor C. M. MacInnes
Vol. IV.	1951	*The Universities and the Theatre*—Editor, Professor D. G. James
Vol. V.	1952	*The Suprarenal Cortex*—Editor, Professor J. M. Yoffey
Vol. VI.	1953	*Insecticides and Colonial Agricultural Development*—Editors, Professor T. Wallace and Dr. J. T. Martin
Vol. VII.	1954	*Recent Developments in Cell Physiology*—Editor, Dr. J. A. Kitching
	1955	No Symposium held in this year
Vol. VIII.	1956	*The Neurohypophysis*—Editor, Professor H. Heller

Contents

SIXTH SESSION

Chairman: Professor R. B. Braithwaite

SEVENTH SESSION

Chairman: Professor M. Fierz

Speakers

Professor A. J. Ayer, Department of Philosophy, University College, London.

Professor D. Bohm, Department of Physics, The Technion, Haifa, Israel.

Professor F. Bopp, Institut für theoretische Physik, Universität München, Germany.

Professor R. B. Braithwaite, King's College, Cambridge.

Dr. P. K. Feyerabend, Department of Philosophy, University of Bristol.

Professor M. Fierz, Universität Basel, Switzerland.

Professor W. B. Gallie, Department of Philosophy, University of Belfast.

Professor H. J. Groenewold, Natuurkundig Laboratorium der Rijks-Universiteit te Groningen, Holland.

Mr. W. C. Kneale, Exeter College, Oxford.

Professor S. Körner, Department of Philosophy, University of Bristol.

Professor M. Polanyi, Department of Economic and Social Studies, University of Manchester.

Professor K. R. Popper, The London School of Economics and Political Science, University of London.

Professor L. Rosenfeld, The Physical Laboratories, University of Manchester.

Professor G. Ryle, Magdalen College, Oxford.

Dr. G. Süssmann, Institut für theoretische Physik, Universität München, Germany.

Professor J.-P. Vigier, Institut Henri Poincaré, Paris, France.

Sir Charles Darwin, K.C.B., M.C., F.R.S., was the Guest Speaker at the Annual Reception of the Society on Wednesday, April 3rd.

List of Members

other than the speakers

Alexander, P., Department of Philosophy, University of Leeds.

Bach, S. J., Department of Physiology, University of Bristol.

Bastin, E. W., King's College, Cambridge

Cohen, J., Department of Philosophy, University College, Dundee.

Cooper, N. L., Department of Philosophy, Queen's College, Dundee.

Cousin, Professor D. R., Department of Philosophy, University of Sheffield.

Crombie, A., All Souls, Oxford.

Cruickshank, A. J. B., Department of Chemistry, University of Bristol.

Devonshire, A. F., Department of Physics, University of Bristol.

Englman, R., Department of Physics, University of Bristol.

Everett, Professor D. H., Department of Chemistry, University of Bristol.

Fowler, G. N., Department of Physics, University of Bristol.

Frank, Professor F. C., Department of Physics, University of Bristol.

Gibbs, D. F., Department of Physics, University of Bristol.

Götlind, E., Department of Philosophy, University of Uppsala, Sweden.

Hesse, Mary B., Department of History and Philosophy of Science, University College, London.

Hush, N., Department of Chemistry, University of Bristol.

Hutten, E. H., Department of Physics, Royal Holloway College, University of London.

Kneebone, G., Department of Mathematics, Bedford College, University of London.

Landsberg, P. T., Department of Natural Philosophy, University of Aberdeen.

Mackay, D. M., Department of Physics, King's College, University of London.

Mason, S. F., Department of Chemistry, University of Exeter.

Mays, W., Department of Philosophy, University of Manchester.

Müller, A. M. K., Institut für theoretische Physik, Technische Hochschule, Braunschweig, Germany.

Nye, J. F., Department of Physics, University of Bristol.

O'Connor, Professor D. J., Department of Philosophy, University of Liverpool.

Öpik, U., Department of Physics, University College of Wales.

Pleydell-Pearce, I. W., Department of Psychology, University of Bristol.

Powell, Professor C. F., Department of Physics, University of Bristol.

Scriven, M., Minnesota Center for the Philosophy of Science, U.S.A.

Seymour, R. C., Department of Chemistry, University of Bristol.

Shepherdson, J. C., Department of Mathematics, University of Bristol.

Thurston, H. A., Department of Mathematics, University of Bristol.

Werle, J., University of Warsaw, Poland.

Wisdom, J. O., London School of Economics and Political Science, University of London.

Zienau, S., Department of Physics, University College, London.

FIRST SESSION

Chairman: Professor S. KÖRNER

R. B. BRAITHWAITE: On unknown probabilities.

A. J. AYER: The conception of probability as a logical relation.

On unknown probabilities

by

R. B. BRAITHWAITE

LET us consider the case of throws with a coin which is irregular in shape or non-uniform in density or both. It might, for instance, be an ancient Greek drachma with the head face in bolder relief than the tail face, or it might be the fake 'coin' which J. E. Kerrich constructed by attaching a disc of lead to a disc of wood of the same size for the probability experiments with which he whiled away his internment in Denmark during the war (**9**). Most people would wish to say that there was a numerically measurable probability of unknown amount that a throw with this coin would yield heads. Throws of an irregular coin are paradigmatic of the situation which arises in all the sciences when there is a set of events some but not all of which have a certain property A, and in which we wish to say that there is a perfectly definite probability that any one of these events has $\boldsymbol{A}$, but we don't know at all what number, on the conventional scale between 0 and 1, to assign to this probability. What is meant by speaking of a probability which is numerical but whose numerical value is unknown?

All those who would hold any form of an objective frequency theory for the sense of 'probability' as it is used in these cases have a straightforward answer to this question. The probability of a throw with the coin yielding heads is an objective numerical property of coin-throwing situations with that coin which, although unknown at the moment, may be discovered by throwing the coin a large number of times and considering the frequency of heads not only in the whole set of throws but in various subsets selected out of the whole set. All frequentists agree that to speak of the coin as having an unknown probability p of yielding heads when thrown is perfectly legitimate in that there is an empirical procedure for determining p, that is, an empirical criterion for estimating its value. Disagreement on this point among frequentists is confined to disagreement as to the way in which the *meaning* of the statement that the probability is p is related to the empirical *criterion* for estimating its value. Those who follow von Mises or Reichenbach would define the probability as the limiting value of actual frequencies used in the criterion. I myself (in **1**, Ch. V, VI, and briefly in **2**, **3**) prefer to tidy up the logic of the 'hypothetical infinite population' language of working mathematical statisticians or, which comes to much the same thing, the logic of the application to empirical data of the abstract mathematics of measure theory used by statistical mathematicians. This leads to treating the statement that there is a probability p that the coin will fall heads as being a scientific hypothesis containing a parameter p as a theoretical concept, such a statistical hypothesis differing from a universal hypothesis only in that its meaning is determined not by a rule by which it can be definitively rejected, but by a rule by which it can be provisionally rejected, by empirical data. But the differences between various frequentist schools are minor ones compared with their common agreement that the meaning of the statement that the probability of a member of a set of events having a certain empirical property is given, one way or another, in terms of the observable frequencies by which the statement can be tested.

Though a frequency theory is completely adequate, in my opinion, to analyse the notion of probability in statements which occur within a science, there are other uses of the word 'probability' and its cognates which I should not attempt to analyse in terms of empirical frequencies. Many of these uses are, I think, not quantitative: to say that one scientific hypothesis is more probable, on given evidence, than another, does not require supposing that there are numbers measuring the two probabilities, one greater than the other; it is rather to say that it is more *reasonable*, on the evidence, to believe one rather than the other, or that one is more *supported* by the evidence than the other. The logical relation theories of Harold Jeffreys and J. M. Keynes were attempts to analyse such comparisons of reasonableness or support in numerically measurable terms: for reasons one of which is being expounded by A. J. Ayer their theories seem to me unacceptable.

But there is a third type of theory, primarily adapted to probabilities of single events, which would make such probabilities measures of the actual degrees of belief, whether rational or irrational, of the asserter of the probability statement. Methods of measuring degrees of belief in terms of the odds at which the believer would be prepared to bet on the event happening were propounded by F. P. Ramsey in 1926, published posthumously in 1931 (**10**), and by Bruno de Finetti in 1928, published in a series of writings in Italian from 1930 onwards and expounded in lectures in French at the Institut Henri Poincaré in 1935, published in 1937 (**5**, see also **6**, **7**). These subjectivist theories have recently received attention in writings by American economists and statisticians on principles of rational choice, in particular in a book by L. J. Savage (**11**) developing a whole theory of mathematical statistics on a subjectivist basis derived mainly from de Finetti's work.

Ramsey did not think that the subjectivist theory he suggested was the whole truth about all uses of probability; he admitted that the frequentists might be right in their analysis of its use within a science, and he related the betting rates measuring partial beliefs to the hypothetical empirical frequencies to which they would be 'most appropriate' (**10**, pp. 157, 188). De Finetti's system, however, is a thoroughgoing subjectivism which he would apply to all contexts in which 'probability' is meaningfully used. For de Finetti the probability of an event having a certain property A, in the opinion of a man K at a time t, is the rate at which K would choose to bet on either the event's having A or the event's not having A if, at time t, he were compelled to bet with another man L, who was in a position to choose both the amount of the stake and which of the two should back the event's having A (expanded from **6**, p. 83). Since it is impossible to bet on anything except an event or set of events it is only probabilities of these that are meaningful for de Finetti; so we cannot speak of probabilities of hypotheses (Savage is not so self-denying). And since a probability is a betting rate which de Finetti cannot consider without knowing, he cannot speak of 'unknown probabilities'. But he wishes to hold that his subjectivist theory is adequate to explain the use of probability in science, so he is obliged to give a different account of the irregular-coin situation from that given by other probability theorists. It is this which I wish to discuss in this paper. De Finetti develops it by using a difficult piece of mathematics: I shall give the barest bones of his mathematical argument, using the language and balls-in-bags model of the frequentists, that are essential for discussing his logic.

Suppose there are a number of bags, each containing black and white balls, and that in a proportion u of these bags the proportion of black balls is p in each bag and in a proportion v of these bags this proportion is q in each bag, with $u+v = 1$. Then $up+vq$ is the proportion among all the possible draws from one or other of the bags of those draws which yield a black ball. Suppose the ball drawn is replaced after the first draw and a second draw made in the same way, and consider the possible results of the two draws together. The proportion among these possible results of those which yield two black balls is $(up+vq)^2$. In frequentist probability language the two draws are independent: in each the probability of drawing a black ball is $up+vq$ independently of the result of the other draw.

Now suppose that a restriction is imposed requiring that the second draw shall be made from the same bag, whichever it is, from which the first draw has been made. The proportion among the possible results of the two draws of those which yield two black balls is now up^2+vq^2, which is greater than $(up+vq)^2$ by $uv(p-q)^2$. In frequentist probability language the two draws are not independent: the probability of drawing a black ball at the second draw after a black ball has been drawn at the first draw is greater than it would have been had the first draw been of a white ball, since the drawing of a black ball at the first draw increases the probability that the bag being drawn from is the one which contains the greater of the two proportions u, v of black balls.

If draws are continued indefinitely, the first method will yield, for every x, $0 \leqslant x \leqslant 1$, a probability $f_1(x)$ that the black-ball proportion among n draws is less than or equal to x which is the same as if all the draws were made (with replacement after each draw) from a single bag containing a proportion $r = up+vq$ of black balls. The Law of Great Numbers establishes that, as n increases, the graph of $f_1(x)$—the 'cumulative distribution function'—plotted against x, approaches asymptotically a step-function with one step occurring at $x = r$ (see Fig. 1). This step-function, the limiting form of the 'binomial' cumulative distribution function, holds of a situation in which all the draws are independent and of constant probability r.

If draws are continued indefinitely according to the second method, i.e. with the requirement that every draw shall be from the same bag, whichever that may be, the graph of the cumulative distribution function $f_2(x)$ plotted against x approaches asymptotically a step-function with two steps, the first occurring (if $p < q$) at $x = p$ and the second at $x = q$, the heights of these steps being respectively u and v (see Fig. 2). This, the limiting form of a 'weighted binomial' cumulative distribution function, is a weighted average (a 'mixture') of two binomial cumulative distribution functions.

This reasoning can be straightforwardly extended to the case in which there is a proportion u_1 of the bags all having the same proportion p_1 of black balls, a proportion u_2 all having the same proportion p_2 of black balls, . . . a proportion u_m of the balls all having the same proportion p_m, with $u_1+u_2+ \ldots +u_m = 1$. The limiting form of the cumulative distribution function will then have m steps at the points $x = p_1$, $x = p_2$, ... $x = p_m$, the heights of each step being u_1, u_2, ... u_m respectively. By choosing m sufficiently large and the m p's and m u's suitably the graph can be made to approximate with any degree of approximation to *any* function $f(x)$ specified in the interval $0 \leqslant x \leqslant 1$, which takes the values $f(0) = 0$, $f(1) = 1$ and whose slope is nowhere descending. For example, the function $f(x) = x$ is approximated to by

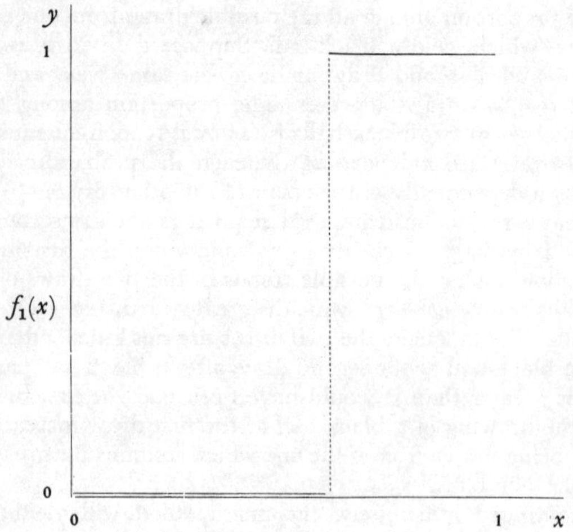

FIG. 1

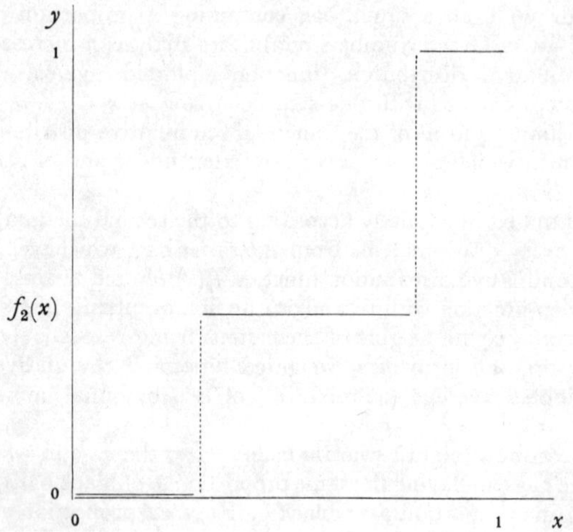

FIG. 2

the limiting form of the cumulative distribution function for the case in which there are $m+1$ bags each containing m balls of which 0, 1, 2, ... m are black respectively, when m is a large number. The weighted cumulative distribution function is here the average with equal weights of $m+1$ binomial cumulative distribution functions representing situations in which the draws are independent and of probabilities 0, $1/m$, $2/m$, ... $(m-1)/m$, 1 respectively.

The characteristic of a set of events, considered in respect to a property A, which is necessary and sufficient for their cumulative distribution function to be of the *simple* binomial type is that the events should all be probabilistically independent of one another (with respect to the property A). De Finetti discovered a characteristic of a set of events which he proved to be necessary and sufficient for their cumulative distribution function to be of the *weighted* binomial type, a characteristic which he called *équivalence* or (in 7) *exchangeability* (Savage calls it *symmetry*). A set of n events is *exchangeable* (with respect to a property A) if, for every $m \leqslant n$, the probability of any m-fold subset all having the property A is the same whatever m-fold subset is chosen. Exchangeability is a weaker characteristic than independence: for a set to be independent not only must the probability of an m-fold subset all having the property A be the same for any m-fold subset (exchangeability), but this probability must be the mth power of the probability of one event's having the property A.

De Finetti uses this weaker notion of *exchangeable events* to account for whatever he takes to be of value in the notion of *independent events of equal but unknown probability*. He rejects the frequentists' parallel between the irregular-coin situation and the situation of drawing balls from a bag containing black balls in an unknown proportion. In the latter case, 'there is no doubt that we can speak of the probability of the different proportions and of probabilities conditional upon one of these proportions . . . the statement that there are so many white and so many black balls in the [bag] refers to an objective fact which can be verified directly, and the probability conditional upon an objective given event is well defined'—for de Finetti in terms of a conditional bet which is only to hold if some specific event happens. But in the coin situation 'we have no right to consider as distinct hypotheses the supposition that the irregularity [of the coin] has a greater or less influence on the "unknown probability", for this "unknown probability" cannot be defined and hypotheses concerning it have no objective significance' (5, p. 49: my free translations).

How then does de Finetti describe the coin situation which we frequentists describe by saying that the throws are independent and of constant but unknown probability? He says that this 'nebulous and inexact' notion should be replaced by that of exchangeable events. Exchangeability of a set of n events (with respect to a property A) has a perfectly good meaning on de Finetti's view of probability: it means that, for every $m \leqslant n$, his betting rate on any m-fold subset of the set all having the property A will be the same for each m-fold subset. Exchangeability is sufficient for the Law of Great Numbers to ensure that the cumulative distribution function $f_n(x)$ for n throws of the coin should approach asymptotically, with increasing n, a unique limiting function $f(x)$. And this is all we need for saying that, for a large n, the probability $f_n(x)$ that the proportion of heads in n throws is less than or equal to x does not appreciably vary with n. By using this probability, which for de Finetti has a perfectly good meaning as a betting rate, we can arrive at the result we want that 'a sufficiently rich experience always leads us to take as probable frequencies or distributions in the future which are close to those which have been observed' (5, p. 50) without our having to use the illicit notion of the observed frequencies enabling us to estimate the value of an 'unknown probability' p of the coin falling heads.

Now it seems to me that de Finetti's examination of the properties of the characteristic of sets called *exchangeability*, and his mathematically elaborate proof that exchangeability is a sufficient condition for the probability functions of the set to be weighted binomials, are an important contribution to the theory of weighted binomials, a theory which is fundamental in connexion with sampling from stratified populations and in 'minimax' treatments of statistical inference. But I cannot believe that de Finetti avoids considering unknown probabilities by using exchangeability. For what is meant by considering an unknown probability is surely considering a proposition stating that a probability has a value p, without specifying what that value is. And de Finetti's exposition considers such propositions in connexion with exchangeability just as much as does the customary exposition in connexion with independence with equiprobability.

To say that a set of n events are exchangeable with respect to the property A, is to say that there are n numbers $p_1, p_2, \dots p_n$ which are such that: for any subset with one member the probability of the unique member of the subset having A is p_1 (i.e. that the probability of any one member of the set having A is p_1); for any subset with two members, the probability of both members of the subset having A is p_2, and so on up to the probability of all the n members of the set having A being p_n. Thus to make an assertion or a hypothesis about the exchangeability of events of the set is to assert or to suppose the existence of n numbers, without of course specifying what these numbers are. The only difference between an assertion of exchangeability and one of independence with constant probability is that the latter asserts exchangeability together with the relations $p_2 = p_1^2$, $p_3 = p_1^3$, $\dots p_n = p_1^n$. This does not require considering any unknown probabilities not involved in an assertion of exchangeability: indeed an assertion of independence with constant probability refers to only one distinct unknown probability p_1 whereas an assertion of exchangeability refers to an unlimited number of distinct unknown probabilities if it is to be applied, as de Finetti wishes, to sets of unlimitedly many events.

And there is no difference between the way in which de Finetti uses exchangeability and the way in which other probability theorists use independence in deducing the limiting forms of the distribution functions concerned. From the premiss of exchangeability what is deduced is that the limiting form is a graph rising from the point $x = 0, y = 0$ to the point $x = 1, y = 1$. From the stronger premiss of independence with constant probability what is deduced is that the limiting form jumps from $y = 0$ to $y = 1$ in a single step which occurs at some unspecified value of x. To deduce the shape of the graph in the first case requires putting values for p_1, p_2, ... into the premisses; to deduce the position of the jump in the second case requires putting in a value for p_1 only. The parallelism in the two deductions derives from the fact which de Finetti has established—that the first case is a mixture of cases of the second.

De Finetti speaks of the notions of 'unknown probability', 'hypothesis about the value of an unknown probability', 'experience which confirms or refutes an evaluation of probability' as all being 'totally illusory' (**6**, p. 86). I think that his argument is best regarded as directed not against unknown probabilities as such, but against thinking of statistical inference as the testing of a probability evaluation by experience. This contention is best expressed in the passage where he writes: 'Whatever may be the influence of observation upon prediction of a future event, it does not in any way imply that we *correct* an original evaluation of probability p which has been *refuted* by experience, by substituting for it another value p' which *conforms* to this experience and so is probably *closer to the real probability value*; on the contrary, the influence is shown only in the fact that, when experience has told us the result B of the first n trials, our judgement will no longer be expressed by the probability p but by the conditional probability which our original opinion would assign to the future event considered as conditional upon the eventuality B' (**5**, pp. 54f.: his italics). De Finetti proposes to allow experience to influence our probability judgements about the future not indirectly by means of an 'intermediate mysterious notion' of an objective probability which is 'a part of the physical world and exists outside ourselves' (**5**, pp. 59, 57), but directly by the use of conditional probability judgements whose conditions we know have been fulfilled. In logicians' language he wishes to treat what W. E. Johnson has called *eduction* and Rudolf Carnap *predictive inference* without regarding it as a process of inductive inference leading to a law followed by a deduction from the law; and like Johnson (**8**) and Carnap (**4**, p. 568), he gives an improved form of Laplace's Rule of Succession for eduction. [The formulae of Johnson and of Carnap, who both use equivalents to exchangeability, are essentially the same as de Finetti's]. Why de Finetti, *quâ* logician, thinks exchangeability important is that exchangeability without independence allows a place for the influence of experience, whereas for the 'special case of independence . . . the influence of past observation is strictly nil' (**5**, p. 62). So I regard de Finetti's contribution to inductive logic as being that of proving that a set of events which are exchangeable without being independent, a condition which is necessary for an eductive formula to be profitably applied, are equivalent, so far as any probability argument is concerned, to mixtures of sets of events which are both exchangeable and independent, and for each of which separately an eductive formula yields nothing of interest.

De Finetti in fact has shown that the type of dependence between events required for the use of an eductive formula is explicatable in terms of sets of independent and equiprobable events. He has effected an *analysis* of such dependent events in terms of independent events in the same sense of 'analysis' as that in which Fourier analysed all periodic functions in terms of simple harmonic functions. It follows from Fourier's Theorem that any musical note (i.e. any periodic sound) can be produced by a suitable combination of tuning forks each yielding a 'pure' note. Similarly de Finetti's theorem proves that any phenomenon of dependence permitting the application of an eductive formula can be produced by suitably combining phenomena of independence: the principle of the dependence arises, in a sense, out of the principle of the combination involved (in technical terms, out of the 'measure' used in the differential element of the Stieltjes integral concerned). De Finetti, while protesting against treating the throwing-an-irregular-coin situation as being analogous to the drawing-from-many-bags situation, has provided the best possible argument for treating them on a parity, as we frequentists do.

De Finetti's subjectivist system will allow experience to influence our probability judgements about the future in the way I have described. But it cannot allow experience to influence our probability judgements of exchangeability or of independence, which for him are judgements of equalities of betting rates; so we can never pass from regarding the throws with the irregular coin as being exchangeable but not independent to regarding them as being both exchangeable and independent, or vice versa. But if the irregular-coin situation can be treated as having a balls-in-bags model, there are empirical criteria for preferring the hypothesis of non-independence, corresponding to the draws being all made from the same bag, to the hypothesis of independence, corresponding to the draws being made from the contents of all the bags lumped together. [The former situation will be distinguished from the latter by the fact that the variance of the means in sets of draws will be greater in the former than it would be in the latter]. De Finetti says that he cannot understand what meaning a frequentist, who defines probability in terms of sets of events, can give to an assertion of the constancy and independence of the probabilities of the single events in the sets (**7**, p. 223). My answer, as a frequentist, is that, for the mass phenomena for which a frequency analysis holds, an assertion of independence with constant probability asserts an empirical hypothesis whose meaning is determined by rules giving the empirical circumstances under which it would be rejected.

From a subjectivist viewpoint an unknown probability must be regarded as the unknown betting rate of a semi-omniscient God or a personified Nature, who, although It does not know whether the coin will fall heads on any particular occasion, does know the by-and-large frequencies with which heads will fall in sets and subsets of throws. De Finetti explains the formal laws of the probability calculus as being laws for the *coherence* of his betting rates preventing the man with whom he is compelled to bet being able certainly to win from him. But the thing with which we are all compelled to bet is Nature, and to succeed in our betting we must adapt our betting rates to Its. This can only be done by trying out various hypotheses about Its betting rates, and seeing how we fare. That we have in the past been able, through experience, to learn sufficient of Nature's betting rates to be able successfully to bet with It is known as the progress of science.

REFERENCES

(**1**) BRAITHWAITE, R. B., *Scientific explanation* (Cambridge, 1953).

(**2**) BRAITHWAITE, R. B., 'The meaning of empirical probability statements', *Actes du XIème Congrès International de Philosophie* (1953), **14**, 136–8.

(**3**) BRAITHWAITE, R. B., 'Probability and induction', in *British philosophy in the mid-century*, ed. C. A. Mace (London, 1957).

(**4**) CARNAP, R., *Logical foundations of probability* (Chicago, 1950).

(**5**) DE FINETTI, B., 'La prévision: ses lois logiques, ses sources subjectives', *Annales de l'Institut Henri Poincaré* **7** (1937), 1–68.

(**6**) DE FINETTI, B., 'Le vrai et le probable', *Dialectica* **3** (1949), 78–92.

(7) De Finetti, B., 'Recent suggestions for the reconciliation of theories of probability', in *Second Berkeley Symposium on Mathematical Statistics and Probability*, ed. J. Neyman (Berkeley, 1951).
(8) Johnson, W. E., *Mind*, n.s., **41** (1932), 421–3.
(9) Kerrich, J. E., *An introduction to the theory of probability* (Copenhagen, 1946).
(10) Ramsey, F. P., *The foundations of mathematics and other logical essays* (London, 1931).
(11) Savage, L. J., *The foundations of statistics* (New York, 1954).

[De Finetti's pure mathematics of *exchangeability* has been further developed in
Hewitt, E. & Savage, L. J., 'Symmetric measures on Cartesian products', *Transactions of the American Mathematical Society*, **80** (1955), 470–501.]

The conception of probability as a logical relation

by

A. J. AYER

THERE is a fairly widespread view that, at least in one important sense of the term, probability is most properly attributed to statements: and that what is being asserted when it is said that a statement is probable, in this sense, is that it bears a certain relation to another statement, or set of statements, which may also be described as confirming, or supporting, or providing evidence for it. There are some, indeed, who maintain that this is the only sense in which it is correct to speak of probability; that what we 'really mean' when we assert anything to be probable is always that some statement bears the requisite relation to such and such a piece of evidence. Thus Keynes[1] assumes that every significant probability statement can be fitted into his formula '$a/h = p$', where a is the proposition which is said to be probable, h is the evidence on which it is probable, and p is the degree of probability that h confers on a, a quantity which may or may not be numerically measurable. And Kneale[2] takes it for granted that probability is relative to evidence: if this is often overlooked, it is because in talking about probability we seldom bother to specify the evidence on which we are relying: 'our probability statements are commonly elliptical'.[3] Other writers, like Carnap[4], distinguish this sense of probability from one in which to speak of the probability of an event is to attribute a numerical frequency to the distribution of some property among events of a given class. Carnap himself allows that we have a use for this conception of probability in terms of observed frequencies, or of the limits towards which they are supposed to tend. He calls it probability$_2$ to differentiate it from the other, logical, conception of probability, what he calls probability$_1$. It is, however, on the basis of probability$_1$ that he develops his inductive logic.[5]

Not all the advocates of this conception of probability agree with Keynes in regarding probability as an unanalysable logical relation. Certainly Carnap does not suppose his probability$_1$ to be unanalysable. But he does recognize that, on this interpretation of them, probability statements come to resemble statements of formal logic in the sense that if they are true they are analytic. This might, indeed, be disputed by philosophers like Kneale who wish to hold on to the synthetic *a priori*, and so to confine analyticity within more narrow limits: but they would at least allow

[1] J. M. Keynes, *A Treatise on Probability.*

[2] W. Kneale, *Probability and Induction.*

[3] *Op. cit.*, p. 10.

[4] R. Carnap, 'The Two Concepts of Probability'. *Philosophy and Phenomenological Research*, Vol. V, no. 4.

[5] Vide *The Logical Foundations of Probability.*

that statements of probability, in this sense, are not empirical. They are necessarily true, if they are true at all. For it is characteristic of any view of this type that the existence of a probability relation between statements is made to depend, not on any contingent matter of fact, but solely on the meaning of the statements concerned. And this is my ground for saying that the advocates of such views treat probability as a logical relation, whether they assent to this form of words or not.

Now it seems to me that there is a very simple objection to theories of this type, which has strangely escaped the notice of their supporters[6] and even of their critics. Let us suppose that a disciple of Keynes has decided to bet upon a horse-race and that he is considering the chances of a horse named 'Eclipse'. He is determined to be rational and so to bring his degree of belief in the horse's victory into exact accordance with the objective probabilities. He assembles the evidence: h_1 that Eclipse will be ridden by the champion jockey; h_2 that the going will be hard; h_3 that Eclipse is suited by the distance; h_4 that it went lame after its last race; h_5 that it has previously beaten the more fancied of its competitors; h_6 that it has recently dropped in the betting, and so forth. Assume that he evaluates all the relevant evidence that he can acquire, or, in other words, that, so far as his knowledge goes, he has not omitted any true proposition which, if it were conjoined with his other data, would make any difference to the resultant probability. So, taking a to be the proposition that Eclipse will win, he decides that the probability of a on $h_1 = p_1$, $a/h_2 = p_2$, $a/h_3 = p_3$, $a/h_1h_2 = p_x$, $a/h_{1-4} = p_y$, . . .; and finally that a/h_{1-n}, where h_{1-n} represents the totality of the relevant evidence at his command, $= p_z$. How is he to place his bet?

To common sense the answer is obvious. If his degree of belief in the proposition that Eclipse will win is to be rational, it must correspond to the probability p_z. He must find a means of comparing this with the odds that he is offered and bet accordingly. But what reason can he have, on his principles, for accepting the common-sense answer? In what way is the probability p_z better than the other probabilities, p_1, p_2, ... p_x, p_y, which he has also estimated? If his estimates are correct, all these statements of probability are necessary truths. And in that case how can any one of them be superior to the others? What one wants to say is that the probability p_z, since it is the only one that is estimated on the basis of all the relevant evidence, provides the best appraisal of what is actually likely to happen. But what can this mean to Keynes? An event will happen, or it will not. To say that it is likely to happen is, on his theory, only a misleading way of saying that the statement that it will happen is probable on the basis of certain other statements. But this leaves us free to choose these other statements in any way we like, provided only that we have sufficient warrant for accepting them. It may seem, indeed, that even this proviso sets a problem; for to say that we have sufficient warrant for accepting a given statement must mean, for Keynes, that it follows from, or is made probable by, another statement, or set of statements, which we have sufficient warrant for accepting: and then one appears to be threatened with an infinite regress. Keynes meets this difficulty, however, by assuming that there are certain statements which

[6] Professor Braithwaite reminds me that Keynes does notice the point which I am about to raise when he discusses the Weight of Arguments in chapter VI of his Treatise. But, since he concludes that probabilities are unaffected by the weight of evidence, he misses the force of the objection.

we can know directly to be true: and it is on statements of this sort that all rational judgements of probability must finally depend. This assumption may be questioned; but even if it be admitted, our original objection still holds. Once we have assembled some trustworthy data by these means, there can be no reason, on Keynes's system, why we should trouble to carry our investigations any further. The addition of more evidence may, indeed, yield a higher or lower probability for the statement in which we are interested. But unless we have made some logical mistake, this probability cannot be said to be more, or less, correct than the one that was yielded by the evidence with which we started. Neither can any sense be given to the claim that it is a better estimate of what is likely to happen.

Carnap has seen that there is a difficulty here, and he has tried to meet it by introducing what he calls 'the principle of total evidence'. 'Let $c(h, e)$', he says, 'be the degree of confirmation of the hypothesis h with respect to the evidence e. Let us suppose that we have a definition of the function c and, based upon this definition, a theorem "$c(h, e) = q$", which states the value q of c for given h and e. A principle which seems generally recognized, although not always obeyed, says that if we wish to apply such a theorem of the theory of probability to a given knowledge situation, then we have to take as evidence e the *total evidence* available to the person in question at the time in question, that is to say, his total knowledge of the results of his observations.'[7]

But why *have* we to take as evidence the total evidence available to us, whatever that may mean? What sort of principle is this? It can hardly be a *moral* principle. So far as morality goes, we might equally well choose to rely on the evidence which yielded the highest degree of confirmation for the hypothesis in which we were interested, or on that which yielded the lowest, or on whatever evidence we found most pleasing. Unless we miscalculate, the result at which we arrive will in each case be a necessary truth; and there can surely be no moral reason for preferring any one of these necessary truths to any other. It might, however, be thought that there was a practical reason: and indeed one may suppose that Carnap intended his principle of total evidence to be pragmatic. The suggestion would seem to be that we should trust hypotheses to the degree to which they are confirmed; and that by taking all the available evidence into account, we diminish the risk of falling foul of the facts, that is, of over- or under-estimating the likelihood of the actual occurrence of the event to which our hypothesis refers. Once again, this is in accordance with common sense: but how can it possibly be justified on Carnap's principles? The event will occur or it will not. To say that there is a probability, of a given degree, that it will occur is to say only that the hypothesis that it will occur is confirmed to that degree by such and such evidence. If this proposition is true, it is necessarily true: but so are all the other true propositions which, on the basis of greater, or less, or partly, or wholly different evidence, assign to the hypothesis a different degree of confirmation. There is no sense, therefore, in which the proposition which brings in all the available evidence can be superior to any of the others as a measure of probability. And this being so, there can be no practical reason why we should take it as a guide.

[7] R. Carnap, 'On the Application of Inductive Logic', *Philosophy and Phenomenological Research*, Vol. VIII, No. 1.

So far as I can see, the only way in which Carnap might hope to meet this objection would be to make his principle of total evidence a part of the definition of probability$_1$. He might claim that what we must be understood to mean by saying that a hypothesis is probable, in this sense, to a certain degree is just that it is confirmed, to this degree, by the totality of the evidence which is available to us. But what is this totality? If it be only 'the total knowledge of the results of our observations', then the difficulty will not be met. For, to revert to my example of the horse race, it may well be that the only information I have bothered to acquire, which is in any way relevant to the hypothesis that Eclipse will win, is that it is to be ridden by the champion jockey; and in that case I shall be justified in regarding the hypothesis as probable to the extent that this single piece of evidence confirms it, and betting accordingly. No doubt if I were to investigate further, as any sensible punter would, I should find evidence which would lead me to revise my estimate of Eclipse's chances. But why should I take the trouble? If what I mean by saying that it is probable to such and such a degree that Eclipse will win is that the hypothesis that it will win is confirmed to this degree by the totality of the relevant observations that I have actually made, then the fact that the probability might be different if I had extended my observations need not concern me. For, on this view, if I do not miscalculate, there is no sense in which this second estimate of probability could be any better than the first.

The answer to this might seem to be that the probability is to be defined by reference not to the results of all the relevant observations that one happens to have made, but to those of all the relevant observations that one could make if one chose. The totality of evidence that is available to me will not as a rule be limited to the evidence that I actually have. But then what are its limits? What means is there of deciding which are the observations that it is possible for me to make? Presumably, in the case of the horse race, the condition of the horse's lungs is relevant. Is this within the range of evidence that is available to me? Well, I could use X-rays to find it out. But what if I have not the skill? Then, I can employ a radiologist to do it for me. But what if I cannot discover a radiologist who is willing? What if he asks more money than I can afford to pay? Then, perhaps, I can find some way of forcing him to do it: perhaps I can steal the money. But will this always be possible? I do not see how there can be a general answer to such questions; nor, therefore, how there can be a rule for determining what is the totality of the available evidence. But in default of such a rule, this definition of probability would seem to be both vague in principle, and of little practical use.

Furthermore, it makes judgements of probability at least partly subjective. If the stable guards its secrets well, the totality of the evidence that is available to me will fall short of the totality of the evidence that is available to the horse's trainer. Let us make the implausible assumption that both he and I are in fact possessed of all the relevant evidence that is respectively available to us, and that we correctly calculate the degree of confirmation of the hypothesis that Eclipse will win, arriving naturally at different results. Both results will be valid, but the one that is valid for him will not be valid for me. If I take over his estimate I shall fall into error, for I shall then be asserting that the hypothesis is confirmed to the degree he says by the totality of the evidence that is available to *me*, when it is not in fact confirmed to that degree by the totality of the evidence that is available to me but only by the different totality of the evidence that is available to *him*. It follows also, on this view, that there is no such thing as *the* probability of a hypothesis: there are as many different probabilities as there are persons who have access to different quantities of evidence. This conclusion may or may not be objectionable in itself; but I think it would be regarded as disturbing at least by some of those who wish us to look upon probability as a logical relation.

It may be suggested that they can avoid this conclusion by assuming that everyone has access, in principle, to all the evidence that there is. Then to say that a statement is probable to such and such a degree will be to say that it is confirmed to that degree by the totality of true statements. There is no need to put in the proviso that these statements must all be relevant, since the inclusion of irrelevant truths will make no difference to the result. This does indeed yield an objective definition of probability, but it has the fatal disadvantage that the probability of every hypothesis becomes either 0 or 1. For the totality of true statements must include either the negation of the hypothesis in question, or the hypothesis itself.

To escape from this predicament, one would have to restrict the range of the available evidence in such a way that it excluded any statement, or set of statements, which entailed either the hypothesis or its negation. And then one might equate the probability of the hypothesis with the degree to which it was confirmed by the totality of true statements that satisfied this condition. One objection to this would be that in assessing probabilities we could never draw on any universal statement of law. For if the event, to which our hypothesis referred, were subject to causal laws, the relevant statements of law, when combined with the statements affirming the appropriate initial conditions, would always entail the hypothesis or its negation. We could indeed keep the statements of law if we excluded the singular statements which joined with them in producing the entailments; but this would be an absurd proceeding, since it is only through establishing singular statements that we ever acquire any evidence at all. And just for this reason, it may be said, we can afford to forgo the universal statements of law; for they draw all their support from the singular statements which are derivable from them; and these we shall have. Moreover, statistical laws, with frequencies of less than a hundred per cent, will not be excluded, though it may well be argued that they too will be superfluous, if all true singular statements are to be comprised in the available evidence.

A more serious objection to this definition of probability is that it allows us to have very little confidence in any of the judgements of probability that we actually make. For it can very seldom be the case that we in fact know every true singular statement that is relevant to the hypothesis in which we are interested. But in so far as the evidence at our disposal falls short of the total evidence, we cannot infer that the hypotheses which it is supposed to confirm are at all likely to be true. For all that is meant by their being likely to be true is that they are confirmed, to whatever degree, by the total evidence; and this is not in our possession. What we want to say is that, even if we can never be sure of having all the requisite evidence, nevertheless by acquiring more evidence, and incorporating it into our calculations, we bring our estimates of probability nearer to the truth. And clearly this is the view that Carnap holds. But I am not at all sure that he, or anyone else who conceives of probability as a logical relation, is entitled to hold it. For, as we have already remarked, each necessary truth to the effect that a given hypothesis is confirmed by some collection of evidence to such and such a degree is in itself as good as every other: we can pick out a special set of these propositions and say that they alone are to be regarded, by definition, as statements of probability; but then it will follow that the others, which fall outside this privileged set, are not statements of probability at all; there will be no justification for treating them even as approximations to the measures of objective probability for which we are in search.

Perhaps this difficulty could be met by introducing the concept of second-order probabilities. They might then be defined in such a way that one could assign a probability to the hypothesis that a given statement of confirmation was a statement of probability: and this probability would be made to increase, as one added to the evidence on which the statement of confirmation was based.

It seems to me, however, that such devices do not, in the end, remove the fundamental weakness of the logical theory. It has been well remarked by Kneale that 'no analysis of the probability relation can be accepted as adequate, i.e. as explaining the ordinary usage of the word "probability", unless it enables us to understand why it is rational to take as a basis for action a proposition which stands in that relation to the evidence at our disposal'.[8] And, even if the other objections to it can be met, I maintain that the view which we have been considering fails this test. For, if we are presented only with a stock of necessary facts to the effect that certain statements, or groups of statements, bear logical relations to each other in virtue solely of their meaning, I do not see what reason there could be for differentiating between the items of this stock as bases for action. I am not clear even what could be meant within the terms of this theory, by saying that one of them was a better basis for action than another. It is true that one may select a subclass of these necessary propositions and decide to *call* its members statements of probability; but in so doing one will beg the question. For the use of the word 'probability', in this connexion, itself implies that it is most rational to act on the basis of the propositions which have thus been selected: and this has not been proved.

In conclusion, I do not wish to say that probability, in the sense which here concerns us, is in no way relative to evidence. It seems clear that an appeal to evidence is needed to justify the belief that such and such an event is more or less likely to happen; and also that it is rational in such cases to take all the evidence at our disposal into account, the ground for this being, I suppose, that experience has shown us that our forecasts are more often right when this is done than when it is not. It does not follow, however, that statements of probability, in this sense, are statements *about* the relations of hypotheses to their evidence; and I do not think that they are. Nor, in the sense in which probability is the guide of life, do I think that statements of probability can be logically true.

[8] *Probability and Induction*, p. 20.

Discussion

Hutten. I disagree sharply with Professor Ayer's view that the logical theory of probability is untenable and that it is the idea of total evidence which makes this theory untenable. There are two objections against this—first of all, it seems to me, that Professor Ayer has forgotten his Hume, because if you make too much of the idea of total evidence, you require really another version of justification of induction. We all know that a statement of probabilities changes with the evidence and nobody worries about this. A probability statement is always relative to the evidence and only if one wants to justify induction as a whole, or something like that, then the idea of total evidence may be involved. In other words, 'total evidence' in this *absolute* sense brings back all the old difficulties of induction. The second objection is that if you reject probability in the sense of degree of reasonable belief you have, of course, to reject the application of the concept of probability in all those cases in which we should say that we should probably not catch the train tomorrow, or something like that, which surely you would not want to do. It is an historical accident that when the Chevalier de Méré asked Pascal to help him recover his betting losses the subject of probability became closely related to the relative frequency of an event within a series of events. But everybody knows that relative frequency is not the whole of probability; furthermore the frequency theory is, as again everybody knows, logically inconsistent which shows that it, too, gets into difficulties.

Ayer. There are two points, I think, that Hutten has made: first about the probability of statements changing with their evidence, and secondly whether the logical theory does apply to the probability that I shall catch my train tomorrow. Well, one might say, why worry about total evidence? It started from my argument that in that system, if you were betting on a horse race or if you were trying to assess whether you were likely to catch your train, it would be sufficient just to look up one piece of evidence and to stop there. For example, if I looked up an old time-table I should already have some evidence and there would be no reason whatever to look for further evidence, because the statement that, on the evidence I have, the degree of reasonable belief is such and such is a logical truth, and there's nothing in the system which would oblige me to add to my logical truths. If one realized this one could still try to save the logical theory by bringing in the principle of total evidence; and here my puzzle has been—perhaps it is more of a puzzle than actual opposition to the logical theory—that I don't see how we can make the principle work. If the total evidence is the totality of facts available to me, then, as I have shown, we are left in exactly the same position as we were before, because I needn't bother to add to it; if the total evidence is evidence that could be available to me, then you get a logical difficulty, which you might meet artificially by making restrictions, as I pointed out. But even then it didn't seem clear to me how on this theory, it could be rational to take the total evidence. We can only say that there's a practical justification, that by going on the total evidence you are more likely to be right. But within the logical theory this can mean nothing, because saying that you are more likely to be right simply means that the proposition that you are right is confirmed by such and such evidence, so that this doesn't get you any further at all. And I perfectly agree with Hutten about statements of probability changing, and about the fact that we add to our evidence as our knowledge changes, but my problem is that I can't fit this fact in with the logical theory. And on the second question I would say that 'catching my train tomorrow' is in exactly the same position as the horse-racing. Of course, I am not at all clear what I should put in the place of the logical theory—perhaps a Braithwaitean combination between the frequency view and the subjective view.

Kneale. It seems to me that Professor Ayer has put in a very clear way a puzzle which must have worried a lot of us. But I think it is a puzzle which arises from approaching probability in a rather queer way—a way that I myself have followed sometimes. He suggests that the trouble arises from the theory of Keynes that probability is a logical relation, but I hold that a similar puzzle can be produced for anyone who holds the frequency theory. The frequency theorists try to define probability in the technical sense as the limit towards which fractions of relative frequency tend, as you go on examining more and more specimens in a collective. But how do they apply their theory to particular cases? It's quite clear that a particular thing may have a number of different properties all of which are in some sense relevant to the question 'Is it *Z*?' Assume that the thing we are dealing with is an *A* thing and that the frequency of *Z* things among the *A* things is a half. But it may also be a *B* thing and the frequency of *Z* things among the *B* things may be a third. And so on. You see how this argument can be developed in the same way as that of Professor Ayer. So I don't think the difficulty is one specially for people like Keynes. It's rather a difficulty of reconciling the ordinary popular, everyday use of the word 'probable' and the technical usage which the philosophers hurry on too rapidly to try to define. Unfortunately the philosophers often start their books by talking about the technical sense, and sometimes they even 'pooh pooh' the non-technical sense, the 'common or garden' sense. Then, having worked out their own accounts of the technical sense, they begin to have qualms and say 'But now how are we to relate this to what happens in ordinary life?' What I suggest is that we should start from the other end and begin by examining the 'common or garden' usage of the word 'probable' and then see how the technicai usages are connected with this. Now the most obvious thing about the usage of the word 'probable' in ordinary life is that it is an evaluative term. To say that a proposition is probable is not just to make a statement of fact. It is rather more like saying that it's right to do so and so. Now, if you look at it in this way you will see that the circumstances in which it is sensible to commend an opinion by saying that it is probable are circumstances in which you are unable to say straight out: 'It's true'. When you can prove a proposition by producing conclusive evidence, you don't want to commend it in this way. But the situations in which you can't say straight out 'It's true' are normally situations in which you haven't access to all the information that would be required for a demonstration. There is always some practical limit to what we can muster. Sometimes the reason for stopping is that one is pressed by enquiries of other sorts. At other times, the reason may be that one hasn't the money to pay for new apparatus. Now at the point where one has to stop because one can't get any more information, it seems appropriate to bring in remarks of the kind 'Most *A* things are *Z*', 'It's not very likely that a *B* thing would be *Z*', and so forth. In short, one begins to consider how the various features of the thing one is dealing with are relevant to the question whether it is *Z*. And it is only at this point that we get to the technical notion of probability, i.e. the probability of an *A* thing being *Z*. But here the word 'probability' has lost its commendatory force and is really being used as equivalent to 'the chances of an *A* thing's being *Z*'. When this is realized, I think, Professor Ayer's problem disappears.

Braithwaite. I agree with Mr. Kneale that the ordinary use of probability has a commendatory meaning, but I don't agree that one ought not to consider other meanings until this commendatory meaning has been cleared up. The situation as I see it is rather like this. There is one sense of 'probable' as a monadic predicate attributed to a proposition; and a use of 'probable' in this sense always includes a commendatory element, since it is equivalent to making some remark about what it is reasonable to believe, and to say that a belief is reasonable certainly includes commending it (at least partially). Perhaps probability in the 'technical sense' as it originated in the seventeenth century—the probability of a coin falling heads being $\frac{1}{2}$, etc.—may originally have included some commendatory element, but this element has, as it were, been sterilized by the fact that numerical values are involved in these probability statements. Why probability logicians have devoted most of their attention to these numerical probability statements is that they are about the probabilities concerned first in games of chance and later in questions of insurance and matters arising within the natural sciences, and the interpretation of these probabilities raises subtle difficulties. My own view is that here there are two important but different uses of probability, one being a numerical use (Mr. Kneale's 'chance') which I should analyse in terms of frequencies, the other having the commendatory element emphasized by Mr. Kneale but being essentially non-numerical and equivalent to reasonableness of belief. Here how much evidence one ought to find out before allowing that a belief is reasonable is essentially a question of moral philosophy, analogous to the question as to how much economics a voter ought to learn before he supports the economic programme of a political party.

Ayer. I think Mr. Kneale is quite right in saying that the same difficulty arises for the frequency theory. The frequency theorists try to get out of it by saying that they don't apply probabilities to single events, but of course, when it comes to the *Anwendungsproblem* they have to, and then I suppose the rational thing to do in picking out the relevant frequency is to assign the event to the narrowest class that has a stable frequency; but how this can be justified—this is a problem which may be no more easily solved than by the logical theorists. At the same time, there is one other point: Mr. Kneale seemed to think that this collecting of evidence was simply a practical matter which stopped where you chose and that there was no real difficulty; but my objection is that on the logical theory which he defends, and perhaps also on the frequency theory, there would be no reason ever to collect any evidence at all, because once you've got one single piece of evidence you would have a nice probability statement which is necessarily true—why on earth should you bother to go on at all? He says you go on until you get tired—but why should you? And one final point: it seems to me that Dr. Hutten may be right in suggesting that one should divorce the question of rationality from probability altogether—that one shouldn't equate, as Keynes does, the degree of rational belief with the greatest likelihood. Because if you equate them, you seem bound to fall into these difficulties.

Feyerabend. So far the discussion has only succeeded in blurring the very clear objections which Professor Ayer has produced against the logical theory. His objections are: Given a statement of the form $P(h, e) = p$ and a series of singular statements e', e'', e''' etc. the singular statements express evidence which may be partly known, partly unknown, partly relevant and partly irrelevant. Now the question arises (a) why should we include into '*e*' all the known relevant evidence? and (b) why should we try to extend our knowledge of relevant evidence and add also the further evidence which we may acquire, to '*e*' in the above probability-statement? And Ayer's point is simply that the demand to include into '*e*' all the known evidence and the second demand to extend our knowledge of relevant evidence cannot be justified in terms of the degree of rational belief attached to some hypothesis. Now first of all it must be pointed out against Mr. Kneale, that within the frequency theory this difficulty does not exist. For in many cases the reference-classes are fixed by the problem at issue. If e.g. the problem consists in the question what is the life-expectation of male university teachers who are unmarried, then this problem is in itself sufficient to fix the reference-class, viz.: male university teachers who are unmarried. But even in those cases where the problem does not fix the class it is not necessary to leave the domain of relative frequencies, as the relevant details can be accounted for in terms of relative frequencies. It is different with the logical theory. Why do I want to include into '*e*' the evidence that the die with which I am playing is loaded? Because if I did not, my degree of rational belief would differ from the relative frequencies. Hence it is relative frequencies (or empirical laws—in the case of the horse-race) to which we have to refer if we want to justify our demands that all the relevant evidence should be used and that evidence must be produced until all the relevant evidence is exhausted (the statement that it is exhausted is in itself an empirical statement). In order to justify these demands we must appeal to relative frequencies, i.e. we must leave the realm of probability conceived as a logical relation. Hence, whereas the frequency theory can, with respect to the problem posed by Professor Ayer, look after itself, the logical theory cannot, but must resort to relative frequencies and this is exactly Professor Ayer's point.

Polanyi. When saying something about the probability of a die falling with any particular side on top, I am postulating an assumption which has not been discussed so far—the assumption of randomness—which is an axiomatic conception applicable to experience and which introduces lots of difficulties. In the case of quantum mechanics, the position with which we are faced from the beginning is precisely this: that certain events are occurring in a random fashion, and that we must proceed to talk about the probability of events and not about the probability of statements about events. It is also relevant that in the tradition of probability considerations in the natural sciences, as for example in the process of induction described in the *Design of Experiment* by R. A. Fisher, we pursue the intention to find out something, not about the probability of statements, but about the probability of a certain state of affairs.

Bohm. As the discussion shows, there seem to be these two limiting views on probability—the subjective, or logical view, and the objective, or the frequency view—and that each of these views is subject to important difficulties. Now, you cannot be sure by considering just the frequencies alone that they will necessarily repeat. If, for example, you throw a die a thousand times and get about five hundred heads, it may well turn out that in the next thousand throws the result is quite different. Of course, we know by experience that this is not so. Nevertheless just by considering frequencies alone we cannot prove that it will not be so. This raises the question of randomness, which Professor Polanyi has introduced. If we want to solve this problem we must try to understand the laws of probability as a limiting case of laws which hold at some deeper level; we must proceed from some hypothesis concerning the general structure of the universe which will explain why probabilities are usually a good way to deal with events which tend to repeat themselves. In other words, as I will discuss tomorrow, one may say that there are many levels of reality or being and that, for example, at one level the facts which can be found out are not enough to determine exactly what will happen at that level. Moreover there is an element of randomness in the sequences of events in that level which is due to events that take place or to things that exist at another level. As a result randomness is just as much a necessity as whatever causal determination may exist. For example, if we decide to measure repeatedly the position of an electron which is in a certain quantum state, we will discover a random fluctuation; but then at a deeper level there may well be laws which govern those fluctuations that are lawless at a higher level. The essential point is that if the universe has such a structure—an infinite structure—then it will be true that data taken at a certain level will necessarily give imprecise predictions because of random fluctuations. There will be, within the random fluctuations, a tendency towards the validity of the law of the larger numbers, coming from the many factors existing at lower levels. Nevertheless by going to the lower level you could in principle obtain a better prediction. It is in this way, I think, that one should give a basis for the theory of probability—not purely by considering the empirical evidence in terms of relative frequency, nor just by considering purely logical statements of expectation, but rather by actually making some theory as to the structure of the world which explains why statements of probability as well as statements of logical inference are so often correct.

Öpik. I would like to make an attempt at resolving the controversy about the logical concept of probability by suggesting a reason why we ought to get as much evidence as possible under the circumstances for our probability estimate: if we have a certain amount of evidence it's in principle possible, although there may be a practical difficulty, to calculate from that evidence a probability of a certain event happening or a certain statement being true. Now if our evidence contains two statements, H_1 and H_2, we may justify the use of both of them rather than of, say, H_1 alone by saying that in this way we are likely to get a more useful probability and by that I mean a probability which is nearer either to zero or to unity than we would have only from one piece of evidence[1]; and the probabilities near to zero or to one are more useful, on their basis our predictions will more frequently come true. Moreover in everyday life it is sometimes possible to get so much more information that we can predict with complete certainty whether or not an event will occur. If, for example, we could find out everything about that horse, about the man who is going to ride it, and so on, we would probably end with complete certainty.

Gallie. I would like to make a small contribution on the same lines as Dr. Öpik to try to meet Professor Ayer's difficulties. I would suggest that his difficulty arises because he bases probability statements on true statements, whereas what one wants are not just true observation statements but apposite observation statements. I could make a lot of true remarks about the horse which have no relevance to the race—such as, for instance, that it has a fly in its ear; hence a lot of observation statements are inapposite. Now in the same way in which certain true statements can be shown to be inapposite, so certain probability statements are manifestly incomplete for the purpose in hand. One can show a person that if he wants to win he must consider probabilities B, C, and D as well as A. And, beginning to work from the other end, one can, I think, thus provide a reason for continuing to examine probabilities.

Rosenfeld. I should like to speak as a common gardener. We have heard a great deal about a difficulty raised by Professor Ayer, but I must confess I have not yet understood that there is any difficulty in the problem which he raises. For instance, when deciding whether to back a horse or whether to catch a train, it seems to me it is clearly indicated by the formula $P(h, e) = p$ that the assignment of a probability to an event is to be determined by the evidence which is available at the time when the decision is to be taken, and I am only repeating what Mr. Kneale has said before, when I am saying that this is a practical question which is itself part of the evidence e in the formula. I think that this standpoint of the gardener is not so different from the standpoint of the physicist who analyses an event or a given situation. Then I think there is a continuous process going from a rough estimate of probability which is just an expression of a feeling about likelihood to the accurate determination of a law of nature and it is very difficult to say whether here probability disappears and is replaced by certainty. This itself is a probability judgement after all, and the decision about the formulation of a law of nature or, let us say, about the accuracy to which measurements must be made in order to get a decision which satisfies the physicist is again a practical decision which may turn out very differently in different circumstances. For instance, when Joule tried to find the law of dependence of the heat given out by a conductor as a function of the intensity of the current, he made only a few measurements—extremely rough measurements—and

[1] Dr. Öpik has afterwards realized that there are cases where this is not true, but he has produced a purely formal mathematical argument by which he claims to show that if we increase the amount of information on which we calculate probabilities to guide our actions, then the expectation of gain resulting from these actions will increase. This he considers the practical reason for getting as much information as possible.

from this he concluded that it was a law of proportionality to the square of the current. Obviously, in this case, he had decided beforehand that the law should be a simple relationship involving low exponents and for the purpose of determining the exponent this kind of accuracy was enough. So I don't think the scientific point of view is so very different from the point of view of ordinary common sense. And the formula $P(h, e) = p$ also shows us that when probability is expressed as a relationship between an event and some body of evidence it expresses a relationship, a judgement about an event which includes the observer very essentially; and that is so in ordinary life, as well as in physics, as we have learned in quantum theory. This now raises the problem of objectivity. Are all those judgements of probability subjective, as seems to be suggested when one considers them from this practical approach? It is difficult to decide this question as the meaning of the word 'subjective' is not very clear, but I nevertheless think it's a bit dangerous to call those probability statements 'subjective'; because, if carried out with reasonable precautions, they will fall out the same for all possible observers in the same circumstances and faced with the same problems, and therefore they will be 'objective' in the very obvious sense that they are the same for all observers. This is an empirical fact which we cannot justify by any philosophical disquisition. From the point of view of logical definition of the concept of probability and the rules of calculation with probability this of course implies some logical requirements to the effect that when one passes from one probability to the other, when the evidence changes, one obtains the same results when the evidence is added up in different ways. But, as I see it, one must take the concept of probability as something which happens to work in practical experience.

Vigier. It seems to me that the main question has been raised by Professor Polanyi when he spoke of randomness. For the trouble with both the definition of Carnap and the definition of von Mises is that they cannot explain why probability works in nature. I disagree with what Professor Rosenfeld just said because I think that probability calculation works whether there are observers or not. Suppose I play the game of dice and instead of throwing the dice with my own hands I build a complex machine to throw them. In this case the result will still correspond to the calculations of probability, whether there are observers or not. Hence, the real physical problem consists in the question under what conditions the calculus of probability works. That is a question of the correlation and the complexity of all the causes outside the context, which act on the phenomenon. For example, you could try and justify the validity of the laws of probability in the case of the game of dice just by studying the laws of motion of the dice, the twists of the hand, and by showing that because of the complexity of those causes the laws of probability will apply correctly. That would be a mechanistic way of justifying the objective validity of those laws based upon too narrow a point of view. For nature should be considered as infinitely complex, which implies that no given set of laws can be sufficient for justifying the validity of the laws of probability. Outside each context there exist more complex things which act on the phenomena in question, and it is this very complexity which allows us to apply the calculus of probability, rather than specific features of information or peculiarities of the observers.

Wisdom. Supposing you have a race in which the horse is being ridden by a superlative jockey but is also known to be lame, and let us have no further hypothesis, to make the situation as simple as possible. I took it that the basic point of the theory discussed by Professor Ayer was that there is a logical relation, in both cases: one of probability of the horse winning in relation to the best jockey, and another logical relation of probability in relation to lame horses, and that his question that seems to have no answer is, why should you choose one of these rather then the other? And, secondly, why should you try to take account of both pieces of information? To this there may be a fairly simple answer on pragmatic lines. True enough, these probability relations are logically necessary and analytic. But that does not mean that one cannot use them for particular ends. For example one uses rules of inference in logic in order to arrive at conclusions. You start with a set of premises and if you apply one rule of inference which is of an analytic sort, you can get to one conclusion, and if you use another rule of inference you can get to another conclusion. Now of course there is no reason why you should choose one inference rather than the other unless you specify what sort of conclusion you are trying to arrive at. Hence the choice is simply a practical matter depending on where one is trying to go. Something perfectly analogous holds in the case of probability, so that the fact that the relations are logical doesn't seem to me to exclude choosing one rather than the other or even trying to combine them. Now when it's a question of combining them, there is no possible answer to the question why you should take all the evidence into account rather than some of it, unless one admits that after all we do know something, that we do start off with certain bits of knowledge, established hypotheses, and so forth.

Fierz. It seems to me that one ought to distinguish between two types of probability which have not been sufficiently kept apart in our discussion. Probability of the first kind is exemplified by the transition probabilities of quantum mechanics. Here you have a model of the actual behaviour of the things you are investigating and you introduce probabilities as objective properties of the model. In the case of the die the situation is not quite so clear, as one has always to postulate a die which exhibits a special probability, say 1/6 to fall with 3 up. Probability of the second kind is exemplified by the probability of a judgement to the effect that such a model is true or by the probability of assumptions about a single event such as e.g. the assumption that I shall die tomorrow. Such a probability is not an intrinsic property of myself—because either I shall die tomorrow or I shall not die tomorrow—but it is a degree of reasonable belief, and probability in this sense is completely different from the kind of probability I mentioned before.

Thurston. Towards the beginning of Professor Ayer's paper he mentioned various pieces of evidence h_1, h_2 and so forth about the horse and talked about probabilities P on h_1, P on h_2 and so forth, of the horse winning its race. Then he went on to consider the question of whether these were satisfactory, of which is the most satisfactory—and I think he even mentioned the word 'truth'. Now it seems to me that if you just consider these probabilities as only what they claim to be, that is as probabilities on a given piece of evidence, then there is no question of them being satisfactory or unsatisfactory, they just are. It's only if you have in the back of your mind some idea, some probability which you consider to be the probability of the event independent of a particular piece of evidence, that you have to worry about these things. I think, if you give up the quest for it then part of your problem disappears. You're left only with the problem of which of these P on H_1 or H_2 or H_3 or up to n should you use in placing your bet. Now we all seem agreed here that the thing to do is to take account of all the evidence you can get. In order to produce a motive for this, Professor Ayer introduced what he called a principle of complete evidence. This seems to be too strong a principle as you can do what you want with a weaker principle. Suppose you make the following suggestion: If you have one body of evidence A, another body of evidence B, and A includes all in B and some besides, then P on A is a better thing to take than P on B. This principle is a good deal weaker than the principle of complete evidence and I think weak enough that it doesn't run into the logical difficulties, but it is strong enough to urge you to find as much evidence as you can and to use it.

Süssmann. I would like to remark that probabilities can never be obtained on the basis of mechanics alone and that mechanics can only help us to derive probabilities if certain initial probabilities are given. Hence we must introduce new statistical axioms, non-mechanical axioms, if we want to incorporate probability into physics.

Öpik. I fail to see that there are two concepts of probability as was asserted by Professor Fierz. Rather it seems to me that there are two ways of applying the same concept of probability, and in the case of the neutron it would seem to me that the application is a good deal more precise, than in the case of, say, asking the question whether a person will die on the next day or not. I think one can perfectly well calculate the probability of a person dying on the next day. Suppose I know nothing about the person except his age, then I can use available statistics and calculate the probability of that person dying on the next day. But one can find out a good deal more about the person and make a much better calculation, and there is no very definite limit to what I can learn and therefore the results of such calculations vary according to the amount of trouble I am prepared to take. Now in the case of the neutron there is a very sharp and strict limit to which we can go in collecting our information and therefore, after we have got the maximum information about the neutron, we can then get a perfectly definite value for the lifetime, and the reason why other physicists get the same value is that in the very nature of things, they can go to precisely that limit and no further.

Bohm. I would like to discuss the point that Dr. Süssmann made. I believe that you can on the basis of causal laws come to a better and better approximation to probability. If we consider e.g. a causal law involving a very large number of co-ordinates, each one very sensitive to the effect of the others, then we get some very complex, more or less, random motion. It can then be shown that in practically all the boundary conditions that exist, this gives a good model of probability. In other words, for most of the time the number of variables which will be in a certain place will be very close to a certain number which we call the probability. You will also get a very good approximation to the property of randomness. For you can calculate all the essential characteristics of randomness for example, the degree of correlation between the different variables and show that even in this determinate motion the degree of correlation may be very small. Hence you don't get a perfect representation of probability but an arbitrarily good approximation. This, I think, is better than a perfect representation, because I don't believe that the theory of probability is perfectly correct. I think that it is part of the cause of the difficulty inherent in the conception of probability that it does not apply with complete correctness any more than the conception of perfect determinism applies in this way. Rather, both of these conceptions must be regarded as opposite approximations to the same problem. This brings me to the second question that was raised just after that, the question of the maximum amount of information possible. I think that nature is split approximately into levels in such a way that certain methods of experimentation or a certain method of working can provide us with a certain maximum information in that level and that all people who work within that level will finally reach agreement on that maximum degree of information that is possible. In this way, they will obtain an objective probability. Nevertheless, new methods of measurements may bring them below or beyond these limits, such new methods might then lead to a new maximal information and to new probabilities.

Scriven. It is not clear to me why one should have to say that there are two definitions of probability, although I don't have quite the same reasons as Mr. Öpik for this. I wonder whether one could say that there are two concepts of number, one concept in which we talk about classes of things which we cannot count as they contain so many things, and the other in which we can set the circumstances where it is possible to count and give an exact number. Now in the case of probability one might also say that the probability of a hypothesis can't be given exactly, because the conditions are not precise enough; but that in certain cases where the conditions are very rigid then one can assess a numerical value which one calls a statistical probability. I would not agree that there is anything commendatory about either of these assessments, it's commendatory only in the same way in which a true statement or the assertion that a statement is true is commendatory. Hence we shall have to say in the light of this problem that the estimates of probability are relative not only to evidence at hand, but also to hypotheses in mind. The idea of appositeness which Mr. Gallie seemed to me to have brought out very well is an extremely important one; it won't do to take the modified principle of relevance that was suggested because quite clearly it's false, and we can add a very large number of true statements to the evidence we have, and not at all increase the probability of our predictions. What you have to do is to add apposite statements, and what counts as an apposite statement depends on the hypotheses that you have in mind. In line with this I then would like to ask Professor Ayer a final question. I am not clear why the reason for taking more apposite evidence is not simply that predictions based upon such judgements give results which in fact more frequently turn out to be correct than those which are based upon very little of the apposite evidence.

Cruickshank. I just want to disagree with Dr. Öpik to some extent concerning whether or not there is only a single concept of probability or two. I feel sure that we have really been talking about two different sorts of probability this afternoon. I see it this way: when we speak about the probability of a certain single event having a certain single result, then the situations in which such a statement can reasonably be made are, I think, always purposive situations. This inevitably implies a certain degree of subjectivity unless one assumes the condition that all observers have the same purpose in mind is specified in a logical relation. Whereas, if we speak about a group of events such as the result of a very large number of throws of a die then we have quite a clear concept of an objective probability: if we assume that the die follows classical mechanics, and we specify a machine which is going to throw it in a certain way, then we can set up a distribution of results which will approximate more or less to a gaussian distribution.

Landsberg. I should like to draw attention to the distinction between closed and open systems, which is, I think, helpful in a widely ranging discussion of probability, such as we are having here. The physicist is usually concerned with a system which is isolated (or 'closed' as regards all its main extensive physical properties such as energy, mass, etc.). When he is not concerned with an isolated system, as for instance when the system is in contact with a large heat or particle reservoir, then the surroundings are at least clearly defined as regards their essential physical properties (reservoirs, sources and sinks of heat, etc.). It then becomes possible to regard the system plus its surroundings as isolated, by some simple theoretical device such as supposing the extended system to be enclosed in a completely impervious container. This usually represents a good *approximation* to the actual system (which in fact interacts with the rest of the universe). For such a system a phase space can be devised in which possible physical states of the extended system are represented by points, and their occurrence can be weighted by some method which seems appropriate. Probabilities can thus be introduced for systems which are closed or can in principle be closed by regarding them as communicating only with defined surroundings. A simple example of such a system is a bar between reservoirs at different temperatures with a steady flow of heat along it. The question of the probability of a horse winning a race is in quite a different category. It is not amenable to this approach because an open system is involved whose surroundings are the whole rest of the universe (the winning horse may be struck dead by lightning just before the end of the race, for example). Such systems are surely too complicated for quantitative arguments and, just as the impervious container is introduced in the physicist's case, a model is called for which, while approximate, is at least simple. Some new conventions and abstractions would therefore seem to be required before the sample space of the probabilists can be defined, and numerical probabilities attain a more objective status.

Braithwaite. How many concepts of probability there are is to some extent a scholastic question, since they are all intimately related. If I had to answer the question as to how many senses there are, I should answer three—two numerical senses (one important in terms of frequencies, one less important in terms of betting rates) and one non-numerical sense in terms of reasonableness of belief. The three senses are logically related in that, for example, in some cases it cannot be said to be reasonable to bet at a specific betting rate unless it is reasonable to believe that this betting rate corresponds to the frequency. With regard to the notion of randomness emphasized by Professor Polanyi and others, it seems to me that to speak of an event's being a random event is not to attribute a property to the event: the word is used as a rubric or sub-title to indicate that the event is being considered as one of a class of similar events with reference to which the probability statement is being made. One remark about the connexion Professor Bohm wishes to make between the logical analysis of probability and what I will call general principles of reality. I believe that there is no such connexion. The question as to what is the correct analysis of the probability proposition—the statistical hypothesis—that the half-life of a radium atom is about 1700 years is entirely distinct from the question as to whether or not this hypothesis can be explained by non-statistical hypotheses at a deeper level. This latter question, which we are to discuss tomorrow, belongs to physics; but the former question belongs to logic.

Ayer. I am very grateful to Dr. Feyerabend for his support. He seems to me to have spotted exactly what I was trying to say, and indeed to have given the answer in advance to the points raised by lots of people, notably Professor Gallie, Professor Rosenfeld, Dr. Wisdom, Dr. Thurston and Dr. Scriven. I'll take Professor Rosenfeld. He talked about his gardening, and said that if he was going to stay at home tomorrow, he didn't fuss much about the weather: he tapped his barometer and got some evidence from that and left it there. If he was going out tomorrow, being a practical man, he took rather more trouble; he consulted weather reports or what not. That is to say, he got a different probability relevant to different available evidence. Now the whole question I wanted to raise is Why should he take this trouble? Why should he increase the amount of available evidence? And, to this, he gave, I think, no answer, unless the answer that it happened to work, which was the answer given by all the others, Gallie, Wisdom, Thurston—whose principle, I think, is a much better principle than the one of complete evidence, and also Scriven. Well now, I actually said in my paper what Scriven says, that it might be that the reason for taking more evidence was that experience has shown you are more often right when you do, but the whole point I wanted to make was that this couldn't be fitted into the logical theory. If you stick to the logical theory, and this is also my answer to Wisdom and Gallie, then there's no reason why one should do this at all. In fact, both Gallie and Wisdom—I don't think Scriven committed himself—veered into the frequency theory, and said 'There's no problem, all you do is use your past experience which has shown that lame horses lose races more often than horses ridden by a good jockey'. Well, yes indeed, if you are going to bring the frequency in, then you bring it in, but the point is that you then sacrifice the logical theory, and the main part of my argument is that the logical theory will not do by itself. One further point—Feyerabend said there was no difficulty about the frequency theory, that the one that Kneale has pointed out didn't hold, but I wasn't convinced by him there. He said that once you have determined your class on the frequency theory, then it's perfectly easy going. But surely, the difficulty Kneale brought out, and the one that I was impressed by, was how to determine your class, and this would seem to me to be a parallel difficulty to the one I raised with regard to the logical theory, and not as yet resolved by anybody in this discussion. Not many people approached it directly, and I don't think anybody has given a satisfactory answer to this, although I do think there is more hope of working it out in frequency theory terms than in logical theory terms. Dr. Öpik makes a very interesting suggestion which was different from the other ones. He said that the reason for going for more evidence was that you then get probabilities nearer to 1 or 0—he said that you were likely to get them, although what on earth he meant by 'likely' there I don't know. Now if this is supposed to be a way of using the logical theory, the word 'likely' must be used here in the logical sense, and in that case I don't think it will work, but even omitting this I don't think his argument will do because it might quite easily happen that if you took only a little evidence you would get a probability nearer to 1. As in the case of my horse race. Let's say that this is a really tremendously good jockey and the other jockey is pretty bad and even corrupt, and we know that he has been bribed and so on—if we don't know that the horse has gone lame, then we're going to have a probability very near to 1, and the bettor will be entirely satisfied; because if he gets more evidence then he will have to balance the chances of the lame horse ridden by the good jockey against those of the other horses, ridden by such corrupt jockeys, that they might even lose to a lame horse, and he will get a probability nearer to one-half, which will be dis-satisfying; therefore, he would have done better not to collect the further evidence. If we only take the principle of getting probabilities nearer to 1 or 0, we do not necessarily stop at one piece of evidence, but we are likely—in the unanalysed use of the term—to stop short at a point where no rational man would. And finally, I'm a little worried by this talk of objective probabilities, of probabilities intruding into nature, which some people seem to me to have put forward much too lightly. I think they might establish that there were two things—first of all, the calculus of chances as a purely *a priori* piece of mathematics which would be valid independently of people believing it or not. Secondly, they might hold that there were objective frequencies in nature, but the problem is how to obtain these frequencies and how to evaluate them.

SECOND SESSION

Chairman: Professor C. F. POWELL

D. BOHM: A proposed explanation of quantum theory in terms of hidden variables at a sub-quantum-mechanical level.

L. ROSENFELD: Misunderstandings concerning the principles of quantum theory.

A proposed explanation of quantum theory in terms of hidden variables at a sub-quantum-mechanical level

by

DAVID BOHM

THE quantum mechanics is now customarily formulated as a logically closed structure of theory; i.e., not only are the basic mathematical formulation and physical interpretation shown to form a logically consistent whole, but it is also shown that once we accept this formulation, we cannot even conceive of deviations from the general scheme of the theory. This is done with the famous uncertainty principle of Heisenberg, which shows that within the framework described above, no measurement can even be thought of, which would violate the basic principle of the quantum mechanics. And to this, we must add von Neumann's theorem, which showed that it would be inconsistent with the general laws of the quantum theory to suppose that one could conceive of variables even in a purely abstract way, which would be in states more precisely defined than the limits set by Heisenberg's principle.

On the basis of such analyses, there would seem to exist, at first sight, an overwhelming presumption against any effort to make a new kind of theory, which would aim at a degree of determinism higher than that possible in terms of the quantum theory. Thus, it is argued that efforts such as those of Einstein, to obtain a more nearly 'complete description of reality' are useless and foredoomed to failure.

On the other hand, a more careful analysis shows that there are serious flaws in the reasoning on which the above conclusions are based. In particular, we shall see that a new kind of theory is possible, which is more nearly determinate than the quantum theory, and which approaches the latter as an approximation and a limiting case, rather as the quantum theory itself approaches classical theory in the limit of high quantum numbers. The new theory would however be quite different from the quantum mechanics in a deeper sub quantum-mechanical level, where it would predict qualitatively new properties of matter. We shall see that there are good reasons for supposing that these new properties may be relevant for treating a new domain of phenomena not adequately treated in current theory. This domain is associated with very high energies, very short distances, (of the order of 10^{-13} cm or less) and with the creation and destruction of so-called 'elementary particles'.

We shall be able to give here only a very brief summary of the essential features of this kind of theory. To do this, let us begin with an attempt to understand the uncertainty principle of Heisenberg in terms of such a deeper theory. Now, it is already well known that there is in classical Brownian motion a close analogy to Heisenberg's principle (shown originally by Fürth). Thus, one has for the distance

(Δx) covered by such a particle in its random motions during the time interval, Δt, the relation

$$\overline{(\Delta x)^2} = a(\Delta t) \qquad \delta x = \sqrt{\overline{\Delta x^{\frac{1}{2}}}} = a^{\frac{1}{2}}(\Delta t)^{\frac{1}{2}}$$

which gives the root mean square of Δx. Let us define the mean velocity during the interval Δt as $\bar{v} = \delta x/\Delta t$. Then evidently $\bar{v}$ fluctuates at random, but its root mean square fluctuation is

$$\delta v = \sqrt{\frac{\overline{(\Delta x)^2}}{(\Delta t)^2}} = a^{\frac{1}{2}}(\Delta t)^{-\frac{1}{2}}.$$

Writing $p = mv$, where m is the mass of the particle, we obtain

$$\delta x \, \delta p = ma$$

which is independent of Δt.

We see then that there is an indeterminacy in the position and momentum of the particle, analogous to that deduced by Heisenberg for the quantum theory. Here, however, the constant, ma plays the same role that Planck's constant 'h' plays in Heisenberg's principle.

Now it must be admitted at the outset that the analogy of Brownian motion to the quantum mechanics is incomplete. In particular, the quantum theory involves two additional essential features, viz quantization and the wave-particle properties of matter, which are not present in Brownian motion. Nevertheless, we shall use the analogy as a starting point, and later we shall enrich our conceptions so as to include quantization and the wave-particle duality.

Now, returning to the Brownian motion, we see that in *the level of this motion*, there is a genuine and objective indeterminacy in the trajectory. For no property of the *Brownian particle nor of anything else existing at this level of size* determines this motion. Nevertheless, the motion is determined in a deeper level, i.e., that of the atomic motions. But here, it is determined by myriads of variables, (the atomic coordinates and momenta) which are moving in such a complicated way that they deliver an essentially random series of impacts to the Brownian particle, and thus cause the above described fluctuation in its orbit. The main point here is then that indeterminism and determinism can exist together, but in different levels.

Let us now go on to the quantum mechanics. Here, likewise, we accept Heisenberg's indeterminacy as a real and objective indeterminacy in the behaviour of matter at the quantum-mechanical level. But now we postulate a sub-quantum-mechanical level, containing qualitatively new and (for the present at least) unknown or 'hidden' variables. The precise character of the motions to which these variables refer is unimportant at the quantum-mechanical level (although as we shall see, it will become important in investigations of the deeper level). As in the case of the Brownian motion, all that is important in the present discussion is that these lower level variables shall be numerous enough and complex enough in their movements, so that they impart to the quantum-mechanical variables a certain degree of random motion, such that Heisenberg's principle ($\delta x \, \delta p \geqslant h$) is satisfied. Thus Planck's constant, h, will represent some statistical feature of the lower level motions, related perhaps to their temperature, but also depending on other properties of the motions. The universal character of Planck's constant suggests that, at least in the domain investigated thus far, the statistical conditions in the sub quantum level are everywhere essentially the same.

Now, it is well known that there are two kinds of classical Brownian motion. First of all, the particle may undergo a random displacement of its centre of mass, all the while retaining a fixed mode of being as a particle. Secondly, however, for a gas near the critical point, the particle itself may be constantly forming and dissolving, giving rise to the phenomenon known as 'critical opalescence'.

There is a considerable amount of evidence suggesting that the second kind of Brownian motion is a better representation of the quantum theory than is the first. To see why this is so, we begin by calling attention to the fact that the so-called 'elementary particles' (protons, electrons, neutrons, mesons, etc.) are now known to be capable of undergoing destruction and transformation into each other, in collisions and other processes involving very high energies (hundreds of millions of electron volts or more). When a similar transformability was discovered in atoms fifty years ago (in radioactive decay) this immediately suggested an inner structure of the atoms capable of explaining the transformations by various corresponding inner motions. And later, as we know, such a structure (involving electrons, protons, neutrons, etc.) was, in fact, discovered. Similarly, what suggests itself now is some kind of inner structure for electrons, protons and neutrons, etc., the motions of which could explain the transformation of these latter particles. Present experiments in the high energy domain indicate that if such an inner structure exists, it is very probably of the order of 10^{-13} cm. in radius (compare with 10^{-8} cm. for a typical atomic radius).

Now, the next problem is to define more precisely the nature of this inner structure. Present experiments (which we have no time to quote here) make it unlikely that it is made of still smaller particles. Moreover, the current quantum-mechanical field theory of these particles also suggests another model. For the field theory describes all motion in the quantum-mechanical domain in terms of 'creation' and 'destruction' of elementary particles. Thus, if an electron is scattered from one direction of motion into another, this is described as the 'destruction' of the original electron, and the 'creation' of another electron moving in the new direction. Hence, there is, in this theory, no particle which permanently retains a fixed identity as a particle. Indeed, if one looks more deeply into the field representation of the motion even for a free particle, one discovers that its motion is described mathematically as a destruction of the particle at a given point and its creation at a closely neighbouring point. Thus, the motion is analysed as a series of creations and destructions, whose net effect is to continually displace the particle in space. All of this suggests the Brownian motion model of an orbit as the continual forming and dissolving of particles fluctuating in a more or less random distribution around, as shown below

These fluctuations are assumed to be so rapid that in the large scale level or even in the atomic level, the track acts essentially like a continuously existing orbit. But

in processes whose energies are very high, the associated frequencies will be of the order of the frequency of formation and dissolution. Here the track ceases to act like a continuous orbit. The process of formation and dissolution will then be affected systematically, and the pattern of motion will in general be changed, so as to lead to a tendency to create new types of particles. In this way, high energy transformations of particles could be explained.

As long as the laws of the quantum mechanics are valid, we could not expect to test experimentally for whether the fluctuation process is really taking place in full detail as we have assumed it or not. For by hypothesis, it occurs in a region defined by $\delta x\ \delta p \sim h$. But according to Heisenberg's principle, this relationship also defines precisely the maximum degree of accuracy that is possible in any measurement. Hence, no experiment could disclose the existence of these fluctuations in detail, even if they should really be taking place.

On the other hand, we must remember that the uncertainty principle was based on an analysis of the process of measurement (e.g. in a microscope) which shows that the transfer of an indivisible and uncontrollable quantum from the observing apparatus to the observed system always intervenes to prevent measurements of unlimited accuracy. But to obtain Heisenberg's relationships in detail, one also had to assume that the present general laws of the quantum theory hold precisely in each process (quantization with $E = h\nu, p = h/\lambda$, wave-particle duality, and probability interpretation of wave function). If there is a sub quantum level, however, then the above quantum laws will *not* hold in the lower level, so that Heisenberg's conclusions will not necessarily follow, provided that the interaction between observing apparatus and observed system significantly involves these lower level laws. Thus, if there is some domain in which the quantum theory breaks down, Heisenberg's principle need not be valid, and the fluctuations might be observable in detail.

Is there any reason in terms of our model why the quantum theory should break down in some domain? The answer is—yes. To see why, let us return to classical Brownian motion. According to the discussion that we gave, the mean momentum of a particle fluctuates by a quantity of the order of $\Delta p = ma^{\frac{1}{2}}\Delta t^{-\frac{1}{2}}$. Thus, the shorter the time the bigger the fluctuation; and for $\Delta t \rightarrow 0$, we obtain infinite fluctuation. But this cannot happen, because the mean energy $\overline{E} = \overline{(\Delta p)^2}/2m = ma/2(\Delta t)$ is, according to the equipartition theorem, of the order of κT, where T is the temperature of the medium in which the particle is suspended; and κ is Boltzmann's constant. Thus, if we consider the mean fluctuation in the momentum, averaged over shorter and shorter times, we shall eventually reach an upper limit. Beyond this limit, the product $\delta p\ \delta x$ will then be *less* than the constant, *ma*.

Similarly, in the quantum domain, we may expect that for short enough times (and for distances that are correspondingly short), the fluctuations will be less than is implied by Heisenberg's principle. For such short times, the laws would then have to be more nearly determinate than those of the quantum theory, but over longer times, they would approach the quantum-mechanical degree of determinism as a limiting case.

We may surmise that the critical interval of time is of the same order of magnitude as that needed for the formation and dissolution of particles. This would place the beginning of the sub electronic and of the sub-quantum-mechanical levels at about the same point. In this case, the new sub-quantum laws would be relevant, in the treatment of the domain of the structure of elementary particles.

Independently of this surmise, however, one can see that the present divergences (infinite results) obtained in quantum electrodynamical calculations could be eliminated. For it can be shown that these infinities all come from quantum-mechanical fluctuations of very high frequencies. If in reality the high frequency fluctuations are a great deal less than is implied by the present quantum theory, the results will come out finite. Thus, the present divergences may be a consequence of extrapolating the quantum theory to unjustifiably short times.

We conclude from the preceding discussion that the argument on the basis of Heisenberg's principle against the possibility of a law more nearly determinate than the quantum theory is not relevant for the conditions under discussion here; for the conclusion follows only if we assume beforehand that there is no sub-quantum level. The same can be said of von Neumann's arguments, which are certainly logically consistent, but which depend in an essential way on the assumption that the general quantum-mechanical framework of law is valid universally and without approximation. What the introduction of the notion of a sub-quantum level does is then to contradict the basic assumptions on which the arguments of Heisenberg and von Neumann are founded.

But here it must be remarked that to go beyond Heisenberg's principle, we will in one way or another have to observe properties that are new relative to those appearing in the quantum-mechanical domain. One possible set of properties would of course be the precise positions and momenta of the particles to which the laws of the quantum-mechanics apply (e.g. electrons, protons, etc.). But as in the case of the Brownian droplets that are always forming and dissolving, the precise positions and momenta of these particles would have little significance, since within the limits corresponding to Heisenberg's principle, this behaviour would in any case not be determined by factors existing in the quantum level. In other words, even if we did make such accurate measurements of the entities of the quantum level, this would be little more than to demonstrate the existence of the sub-quantum-mechanical fluctuations. In order to study the essential laws determining the behaviour of matter to a precision going beyond the limits set by Heisenberg's principle, we must do experiments that directly reflect the properties of the sub-quantum-mechanical entities.

At present, we can have little idea of what the sub-quantum-mechanical entities described above may be, because the quantum laws do not depend significantly on their detailed properties. In any case, it is clear that little information about them can be obtained by trying to measure the properties of the entities of the quantum level to a precision greater than that permitted by Heisenberg's principle. Rather, some basically new kinds of experiments are needed, which reflect the new sub-quantum-mechanical properties more directly (as one most effectively studied the detailed properties of atoms, not by measuring large-scale properties such as pressure, temperature, etc. in very small regions of space, but rather by new kinds of experiments involving scintillation, cloud chambers, and other apparatus that was directly sensitive to the atomic structure of matter). One of the roles of the theory is then to guide us to such new kinds of experiments, to which it is very unlikely that we could come without the aid of some such theory.

In the absence of new kinds of experiments, we can still develop the theory further, by trying to explain more of the essential properties of matter in the quantum-mechanical level. We shall consider here only the special case of the one-body problem and will make some remarks about the many-body problem at the end of this talk.

Let us begin with the wave-particle duality. The model of a particle that is always forming and dissolving creates room, logically speaking, for a wave resembling that appearing in Schrödinger's equation.

First of all, there will be some probability function $P(\mathbf{x})$ proportional to the mean fraction of the time that a particle condenses into a small element of volume near $\mathbf{x}$. This probability will represent the statistical state of the motions in the sub-quantum level, which determine this process. We may therefore tentatively interpret the probability function of the quantum theory, $|\psi(\mathbf{x})|^2$, (where $\psi(\mathbf{x})$ is the wave function) as being the same as the probability $P(\mathbf{x})$ that we have just defined.

But at any given time, the wave function is determined by two quantities, not only an amplitude $R = P^{\frac{1}{2}}$ but also a phase, $\phi(\mathbf{x})$, where

$$(\psi(\mathbf{x}) = R(\mathbf{x})e^{i\phi(\mathbf{x})})$$

Indeed, the phase is much more directly connected with the wave properties of matter than is the amplitude. What then, does the phase signify, in the sub-quantum level?

To obtain a significance for the phase, we may suppose that some periodic process is taking place in the sub-quantum level. This may manifest itself, for example, as an inner oscillation of the particle, or else as a rotation (in case the particle is spinning). Thus, the phase, ϕ, may represent the phase of this oscillation, or one of the Euler angles of rotation of the body, or perhaps still some other periodic variable. Then, we assume that if the particle condenses out at the point, $\mathbf{x}$, it will do so with some mean phase, which like the probability itself, is determined by the conditions in the sub-quantum level. Thus, both the phase and the amplitude of the wave function represent statistical properties of the sub-quantum-level, and quantum mechanics begins to emerge as a kind of statistical theory of the lower level.

We now proceed to show that the theory can easily be extended further so as to yield the correct quantum conditions. To do this, we use an argument equivalent to one originally suggested by de Broglie.

Now a particle will be formed at the point $\mathbf{x}$ with some mean velocity $v(\mathbf{x})$ (which is in general a function of position). We suppose a certain homogeneity in the properties of the sub-quantum level, such that when a particle of a given type is formed, the behaviour of its phase considered in the frame of that particle (the Lorentz frame in which its mean velocity is zero) will be the same for all particles of that type. In particular, we make the plausible assumption that the mean rate of change of the phase in this frame is a constant, denoted by w_0 (which implies that the motion is on the average simply harmonic or else uniform rotation).

Now, it is an essential part of our theory as formulated thus far that the phase, ϕ, shall be a continuous function of position. But if we go to the mean rest frame of the particle (which is located at some point $\mathbf{x}$), then it seems natural to assume that for any fixed instant of time, t_0, the phase change, $\delta\phi$, will be zero (in the first order) for an arbitrary displacement δx_0 of the position. For if there were a non-zero phase change in such a displacement this would define a preferred direction, namely that of the gradient of the phase at that point, $\nabla\phi(\mathbf{x})$. In homogeneous space, there would, by definition however, be nothing in the sub-quantum level to favour one direction on the average over another; and since, in the Lorentz frame under discussion, the particle is on the average at rest, there is nothing in the quantum level that would do this either. Thus, in the neighbourhood of the particle, we can write

$$\delta\phi = \omega_0\, \delta t_0 \text{ independently of } \delta x_0$$

where δt_0 is the change of time as measured in the rest frame.

Let us now express the phase changes in terms of some fixed coordinate frame. To do this, we make a Lorentz transformation, writing

$$\delta t_0 = \frac{\delta t - \mathbf{v} \cdot \delta\mathbf{x}/c^2}{\sqrt{1 - v^2/c^2}}.$$

We get

$$\delta\phi = \frac{\omega_0}{\sqrt{1 - v^2/c^2}}(\delta t - \mathbf{v} \cdot \delta\mathbf{x}/c^2).$$

But we can now write for the energy of the particle $E = m_0c^2/\sqrt{1 - v^2/c^2}$ and the momentum $\mathbf{p} = m_0\mathbf{v}/\sqrt{1 - v^2/c^2}$ where m_0 is the rest mass. Thus, we obtain

$$\delta\phi = \frac{\omega_0}{m_0c^2}(E\, \delta t - \mathbf{p}_1\, \delta\mathbf{x})$$

Let us now consider how ϕ changes as one goes around a virtual circuit (in which the time as well as the position may change). If we add up all the phase changes in such a circuit the consistency of the theory requires that $\oint \delta\phi$ shall be an integral multiple of 2π (otherwise, we will contradict the hypothesis that there is a well-defined mean phase at each point in space). Thus we write

$$\oint \delta\phi = \frac{\omega_0}{m_0c^2}\oint (E\, \delta t - \mathbf{p}\, \delta\mathbf{x}) = 2n\pi.$$

If we write $m_0c^2/\omega_0 = h/2n$ we obtain $\oint (E\, \delta t - \mathbf{p}\, \delta\mathbf{x}) = nh.$

If we apply this result to a special circuit in which the time is constant, the above equation gives just the Bohr-Sommerfeld quantization condition. From the definition of the wave function, $\psi = Re^{i\phi}$, we see also that it is equivalent to the condition for the single-valuedness of the wave function (i.e., that $e^{i\phi}$ returns to its original value if we go around any circuit).

The property of quantization has thus correctly been explained, and in a way that suggests a rather deep relationship between relativity and the quantum theory.

To go further along these lines, we must enrich and define the theory to a still greater degree by trying to explain more of the essential features of the quantum mechanics (e.g. many-body problem, Fermi and Bose statistics, Dirac equation, field theory, etc.). Efforts now in progress have gone a long way towards this. Thus, there now exists an extension of the above theory to the many-body problem, which leads to a set of opposed kinds of particles that automatically satisfy the symmetry requirements on the wave function for fermions and bosons respectively. These particles are seen to arise as different sides of the sub-quantum level, which also guarantees a certain interaction between them. Moreover, further work indicates that when one supposes a rotation of these particles, one obtains the spin properties correctly. The details of these theories have however not yet been fully worked out.

After the programme of explaining the main features of the quantum level is completed, one can then further develop the theory by trying to explain the new experiments in the field of high energy particles. Finally, as the conception grows more and more detailed, it may suggest specific new kinds of experiments, which could directly prove the existence of entities in a sub-quantum level.

Misunderstandings about the foundations of quantum theory

by

LEON ROSENFELD

RECENT criticism of the foundations of quantum theory originates from a number of physical and epistemological misconceptions. To point out, with painful explicitness, the most serious of these might be helpful to those whom this criticism seems to have caught unprepared.

1. *'Interpretation of the formalism'*

The critics have put forward the novel suggestion that an alternative 'interpretation' could be found for the mathematical formalism of quantum theory. Physicists know what it means to interpret physical experience in terms of mathematical concepts; but to imagine that they might have to interpret somehow pre-existing mathematical symbols in physical terms is an idealistic construction alien to the spirit of science. A physical theory is a consistent set of relations between certain concepts; these concepts usually refer to magnitudes and are therefore associated with numbers, but they are primarily the mental representation of concrete physical realities and as such must be defined in words, linking them (either directly or indirectly) to *everyday experience*, i.e. to features of common observation not further defined. The ordinary language (spiced with technical jargon for the sake of conciseness) is thus *inseparably* united, in a good theory, with whatever mathematical apparatus is necessary to deal with the quantitative aspects. It is only too true that, isolated from their physical context, the mathematical equations are meaningless: but if the theory is any good, the physical meaning which can be attached to them is *unique*.

Historically, the false problem ('scheinproblem') of 'interpreting a formalism' appears as a short-lived decay-product of the mechanistic philosophy of the nineteenth century. So long as the luminiferous aether was firmly believed to be an indispensable constituent of the universe, the search for a dynamical theory of light was a real physical problem, and it was tackled by the great masters in a perfectly realistic way: their papers are in fact wonderful illustrations of this inseparable unity of physical representation and mathematical symbolism which characterizes true theoretical thinking. When it was realized, however, that the aether problem had no *unique* solution, a process of disintegration set in, in which the mathematical set of equations expressing the laws of electro-magnetic phenomena became detached from its 'dynamical interpretations'. The unity was then soon restored by recognizing the electromagnetic field as a primordial element of physical description, irreducible to dynamical concepts.

Now, quantum theory eminently possesses this character of uniqueness; every feature of it has been forced upon us as the only way to avoid the ambiguities which would essentially affect any attempt at an analysis in classical terms of typical quantum phenomena. The suggestion that such ambiguities might be circumvented by the introduction of 'hidden parameters' is empty talk: for such parameters, in order to be of any use, should be linked with observable quantities, i.e. with classical concepts: and this link, whatever it is, could not possibly violate the restrictions in the use of the latter concepts imposed by the existence of the quantum of action. Consider, for instance, essentially quantal concepts, like spin or parity, which cannot be defined in classical terms: the definite prescriptions which bring them into relation with observable phenomena are in full harmony with the law of the quantum of action.

2. *'Deterministic substratum'*

The critics are perturbed by the fundamentally statistical character of the causal relationships of quantum theory. There is, however, no logical justification for requiring a 'deterministic substratum' to a given set of statistical laws. There may or may not be such a substratum: this is a question to be decided by experience, not by metaphysics. Now, the peculiar *wholeness* of quantal processes, which implies the reciprocal lack of determination of canonically conjugate quantities, is an immediate consequence of the *physical content* of the law of quantification of action. No logically consistent formal device can therefore produce a deterministic substratum without doing violence to the immense body of experience embodied in the quantum laws.

3. *The point of view of Sirius*

The wholeness of quantal processes necessitates a revision of the concept of phenomenon. Since the concepts which in classical theory describe the state of a physical system are actually subject to mutual limitations, they can no longer be regarded as denoting *attributes* of the system. Their true logical function is rather to express *relations* between the system and certain apparatus of entirely classical (i.e. directly controllable) character which serve to fix the conditions of observation and register the results. A phenomenon is therefore a process (endowed with the characteristic quantal wholeness) involving a definite type of interaction between the system and the apparatus.

This new definition of the concept of phenomenon contains no arbitrary element: it is part of a terminology inherent in quantum theory and expressing a situation of fact, i.e. a situation which is not of our doing, but which we have learned from experience. It is perfectly true that this novel experience has profound epistemological implications. We must relinquish the illusion of being capable of unrolling a picture of the events on the Earth as they might be contemplated by some sharp-sighted, but not otherwise interfering, dweller of Sirius. But why should such a picture be at all possible? This is one of those metaphysical extrapolations which invariably lead us astray, because we attach absolute validity to presuppositions derived from limited experience. Only experience can teach us the limits of validity of such presuppositions, and in the present case, one of the lessons we have learned from the investigation of atomic phenomena is just that the quantum of action sets a limit to the unambiguous application of the mode of description of classical physics. To object to a lesson of experience by appealing to metaphysical preconceptions is unscientific.

The necessity of including the specification of the conditions of observation into the definition of the phenomenon has nothing to do with the question of the objectivity of the resulting mode of description. With respect to the latter question, the logical situation in quantum theory is exactly the same as in classical physics. If Micromegas paid us another visit, he would perfectly understand our statements about atoms; in fact, being like ourselves a highly organized compound of many atoms, he could not discuss atoms with us in any other terms than those of quantum theory.

4. *The curse of positivism*

According to our critics, the epistemological point of view of quantum theory undermines the sound belief in the reality of the external world, in which all physical thinking is rooted, and opens the door to the barren doctrine of positivism: we are no longer concerned with things, but only with the way to speak about things; science is degraded from a quest for truth to a verbal exercise. Dogmatic assertions that certain questions are meaningless bar the way to further inquiry; inability to understand the riddles of the quantum is hidden in the clouds of mystical renouncement.

This picture would be alarming if it were true. However, it is just another dream, a nightmare perhaps, of our critics. Obviously, it cannot result from a serious assessment of the immense broadening and enrichment of scientific thought which has resulted from the endeavour to formulate the laws of atomic phenomena. In fact, it is based on the most futile casuistics: the critics diligently excerpt from the writings in which the principles of quantum theory are discussed isolated sentences on which they put arbitrary interpretations. No wonder that they should find (as they freely confess) some difficulty in 'understanding Bohr': which, incidentally, does not prevent them from branding him as a positivist. There is no difficulty, at any rate, in understanding the critics' philosophy and exposing its unscientific character.

The realization of the mutual limitations imposed upon the use of classical concepts by the conditions of observation has forcefully reminded us of our own position in the world, and of the function of science in relation to this position. We are not merely contemplating the world, but acting upon it and thereby modifying its course. Accordingly, the scientific description of the phenomena is fundamentally concerned with the interaction of external agencies with the human observer; or, at least, in the narrower domain of physics, with material systems under the latter's control. The mode of description of classical physics appears, from this point of view, as a special case of wide validity, in which the quantitative effects of the interaction between observational devices and observed systems may be neglected: which does not mean, however, that the presence of these observational devices is not just as essential as in quantum theory for the very definition of the physical concepts.

It must again be stressed that there is in this view of the nature of science no arbitrary element: it is just an explicit statement of a situation which has always existed, even though it was not always so clearly recognized. Certainly, it puts an emphasis unknown to the outdated materialistic metaphysics of the nineteenth century on the active role of the observer in defining the phenomena: but in so doing, it brings the whole structure of science nearer to reality, in closer conformity with our real relationship to the external world.

There is an undeniable similarity between the epistemological conclusion drawn in such a straightforward, unambiguous way from the peculiar character of the quantum laws, and the insistence of the early positivists on the essential part played by our sensations in determining our knowledge of the external world. This only means that, to that extent, the early positivist movement was a healthy reaction against the shallow metaphysics of mechanistic materialism. But why should scientists be made responsible for the later positivists' blundering into a metaphysics of their own? No scientist would accept the extreme positivist contention that there is nothing more in statements about phenomena than the conceptual expression of relations between sensations: he would maintain that such statements refer primarily to real processes of the external world; our mental representation of these processes being itself, of course, subject to definite laws depending upon our sensorium.

To point out that certain relations between classical concepts cease to be meaningful in quantum theory has none of the sinister implications fancied by our critics: it is a plain statement of fact, founded in a law of nature. The words 'renouncement' or 'resignation' often used in this context are ambiguous in their emotional connotation: renouncement may be felt as privation or as liberation. Some critics seem to take the invitation to 'renouncement' as an attempt on their personal freedom: the right to indulge in metaphysical dreams is not disputed; only, this activity is not science.

5. *The insufficiency of quantum theory*

As any other scientific theory, quantum theory has its limitations. Our methods of field quantization break down when we attempt to apply them to processes confined within space-time regions of linear dimensions much smaller than 10^{-13} cm, or (what amounts to the same) involving momentum and energy exchanges much larger than a GeV. There is evidence that the 'particles' which we treat at present as the elementary constituents of nuclei have some kind of 'structure' extending over such small regions, and are susceptible of metastable excited states of some tenths of a GeV energy. These excitations are connected with several types of meson fields, which are coupled in various ways to each other and to the lepton fields. It is clear that we are here on the threshold of a new world with laws of its own, which we have not yet discovered.

The critics try to exploit this situation to their advantage, but it is just here that the dilettantism of their approach is most conspicuous. In fact, it is idle to 'hope' that the cure of our troubles will come from underpinning quantum theory with some deterministic substratum, unless this surmise could be justified by arguments derived from the analysis of the phenomena which have to be explained. For instance, these phenomena might reveal some limitation of the law of quantization of action: this would indeed give substance to the critics' belief in 'hidden' sub-quantal features. Unfortunately for them, all the evidence points with merciless definiteness in the opposite direction: however strange they may be in other respects, all the processes involving the unknown interactions invariably conform to the fundamental quantum law.

Moreover, recent developments have strikingly demonstrated the fruitfulness, for the interpretation of these processes, of concepts like parity and particle-antiparticle conjugation, which are specifically quantal, i.e. irreducible to classical representations. While our critics, in their numerous speeches and profuse writings, were prophesying the ultimate vindication of their views by future discoveries in the domain of high-energy processes, one major discovery, of truly universal import, about deep-lying symmetry properties of the fundamental laws of nature, did actually take place: and lo! its substance and meaning can only be formulated in terms of the essentially quantal concepts just mentioned. The true road to future progress in this domain is clearly marked: the new conceptions which we need will be obtained not by a return to a mode of description already found too narrow, but by a rational extension of quantum theory. This will indeed require a sound criticism of the foundations of the theory.

Discussion

Polanyi. Could Professor Rosenfeld tell us a little more about the general grounds on which quantum mechanics as it exists today is supposed to be forced upon us and Bohm's theories are hence excluded.

Rosenfeld. What I have said is that a scheme like Bohm's cannot be entirely logically consistent and compatible with the existence of the quantum of action. Of course if you drop the postulate of the quantum of action, as Bohm suggested to do, then all possibilities are open. I may perhaps illustrate what I mean by discussing a more specific point; Bohm interprets the gradient of the phase of his wave-function as a momentum. This use of the word momentum is not compatible with the quantal definition of momentum in terms of observation.

Bohm. I agree with Professor Rosenfeld that our theory cannot be entirely equivalent to quantum mechanics, but I also believe that every new theory must contradict the old theory in some respects. Quantum mechanics contradicts classical mechanics in very many important respects—for instance it says there are stationary states—and nevertheless it approaches classical mechanics as an approximation. Now Professor Rosenfeld believes that future progress will be made not by contradicting quantum mechanics but by building upon it as a foundation and perhaps by enriching it and adding new things to it. Perhaps some progress will be made in this way—I would not wish to say it is not a way to do it; but I believe that eventually we will come to a point where we contradict quantum mechanics and get consequences which simply are not consistent with the quantum of action.

Fierz. Though in general I share Professor Rosenfeld's view, I have nevertheless the feeling that what he said was a bit too dogmatic. It was an odd statement when he said that what Bohm is trying to do is *Zukunftsmusik*. This word was used to characterize the music of Wagner, but Wagner has written the opera and Mr. Bohm has not. On the other hand it may well be that on the basis of apparently wrong and irrational speculations a physicist discovers something that is correct and important. This was the case with Dirac's theory of the electron where the dogmatic postulate (which is also quite wrong) that his equations should be of first order, finally led to the correct theory. Rosenfeld also seems to have over-emphasized the empirical reference. For although in general physics may be described by saying that we start from experience, this is not true in every case. It is often by freely speculative methods that a certain result is obtained. An example is the way in which de Broglie found his wave equation—experiments about matter-waves were only made afterwards. It is of course desirable to proceed in a rational way; but this is not always done.

Rosenfeld. May I interject that I accept this.

Fierz. Another point is the direction of speculation. Bohm speculates in a direction which I think is not the proper one; and if you want me to give reasons for saying this I would point out that the real difficulties of quantum mechanics arise always when we have theories with an infinite number of degrees of freedom—as in field-theory—and in those cases the framework of ordinary quantum mechanics with a finite number of degrees of freedom does not apply because the concept of the Hilbert-space does not exist. Probably the aim of physical theorizing would be to talk about a finite number of degrees of freedom only also in field-theory. Professor Bohm introduces new degrees of freedom—those hidden variables—which means that he multiplies the manifold of the world we want to talk about whereas I want to decrease the manifold of the world we want to talk about, and so we move in different directions. Who is right cannot be made out and the decision is therefore a matter of taste, at least at the moment.

Rosenfeld. It is perhaps more than a question of taste. It seems to me that the processes which we observe in the higher energy domains are of an essentially statistical character, which seems to indicate that the new features that we would like to know in those cases will probably be of an even more statistical character.

Körner. It seems to me that the disagreement between Professor Bohm and Professor Rosenfeld is not so much about the existing quantum theory as about the likely direction of future progress. But the way in which they have formulated their disagreement might be a little misleading. They both speak of von Neumann's proof. Neither of them seems to think that the proof is illogical. Professor Bohm said that it was circular—by which, I think, he meant that it follows from the assumptions. What he should have said was that he does not think that these assumptions are here to stay. Professor Rosenfeld again said that the assumption of hidden variables is logically impossible—by which, I think, he meant it is incompatible with von Neumann's proof. What he should have said is that he does think that the theory will survive. Both the speakers seem to agree that the proof is quite correct, but whereas Professor Bohm wants to change its pre-suppositions, Professor Rosenfeld does not.

Bohm. A comment on what Professor Rosenfeld said; I don't wish to say that we are aiming at a completely deterministic theory. The basic question is whether the limitation of determinism as given by Heisenberg is always and universally valid. Fürth's analogy suggests that over very short times, the limitations of determinism may be less severe than those of Heisenberg, and that if one follows this line, one may even be able to remove the divergences of field-theory. I have given a concrete example showing that such a theory would remove certain basic inconsistencies in the present formulation of quantum electrodynamics. The question whether the number of degrees of freedom should be increased or decreased cannot be decided *a priori* but only by the success of either procedure. There is however an additional argument which I have not had a chance to give here in detail; namely, the fact that in extending this model you obtain an advantage which the present theory does not have. You obtain the symmetry and anti-symmetry as a necessary consequence of the theory and not, as in present-day quantum mechanics, as a further assumption which is added to the theory. So perhaps the theory is not quite as far in the future as it may have been previously. In any case, as Professor Fierz has admitted, the idea that the present quantum mechanics will resolve those difficulties is also *Zukunftsmusik*.

Feyerabend. The discussion and the remarks which Professor Bohm has made in his lecture have greatly clarified the import of von Neumann's proof. He has rightly emphasized that the statement that hidden variables do not exist is a theorem of quantum-mechanics rather than a statement whose truth has been proved absolutely and once for ever. What, then, is the reason which made Bohm's opponents say that his theory is very unlikely to succeed? It is a belief in the truth of some principles of present-day quantum mechanics which is based on an assumption, common to all inductivistic interpretations of science, namely on the assumption (a) that present-day quantum mechanics is a rational summary of facts, (b) that any future theory must also be a rational summary of facts and (c) that, therefore, no future theory can possibly contradict quantum mechanics in its present form. It is true—if challenged, hardly any physicist will subscribe to this view and Professor Rosenfeld obviously does not subscribe to it. But analysis of various more philosophical writings of physicists, such as e.g. of Born's recent book, shows that this view is the implicit reason of the conviction of many physicists, that present-day quantum mechanics, or at least the quantum of action will have to be an essential and unmodified part of any future theory. This, I think, is a very arbitrary view. Another arbitrary view which is part of the Copenhagen-Interpretation is the view that fundamentally the theory is about nothing but classically describable events, experience is to be described in classical terms; quantum theory proper is nothing but a means of predicting classical states of affairs. It is this idea which has led to the famous intrusion of the observer into physical theory. This should show that, far from being 'forced upon us' as Professor Rosenfeld expressed himself (this is again an inductivistic idea) the Copenhagen-Interpretation contains as elements many things which are arbitrary and perhaps even false. I am also not impressed by the fact, mentioned by Professor Rosenfeld, that the law of the quantum of action has always and in all domains been found to be correct. For nothing is easier than preserving a law which one wants to preserve; and I wonder whether in the case of the quantum of action this preservation is not due to the efforts of various physicists to have it preserved rather than to the fact that it is true.—One question to Professor Bohm; he has said that he was able to derive the Bohr-Sommerfeld conditions, the Dirac equation, as well as the symmetry-properties of the wave-function, from his model. This is not sufficient for showing the adequacy of this model on the level of quantum mechanics. For there exist many formal analogies between present-day quantum mechanics and, say the theory of diffusion, analogies which are very seductive but which always break down at one point or another. Hence it is possible that Bohm has done nothing but derive parts of a theory which possesses formal analogies to quantum mechanics rather than quantum mechanics itself. Only the derivation of the *whole* formal apparatus of the present theory *together with its proper interpretation* will show that his model is adequate on the level of quantum mechanics.—A final remark about the relation between present-day quantum mechanics and Bohm's new model. The first thing that comes to one's mind when one hears the objections of Bohm's opponents, are objections which were raised, in the nineteenth century, against the atomic theory. Those objections were much more formidable, as they seemed to reveal a contradiction in the idea of a reduction of thermodynamics to the mechanics of a collection of atoms. There was the reversibility-objection of Loschmidt and the recurrence objection of Zermelo and Poincaré—and nevertheless the atomic theory was finally successful and could even be used for showing that the phenomenological account could not be universally correct. At that time the situation was much clearer, classical mechanics and classical thermodynamics were better understood and less surrounded by a philosophical fog than quantum mechanics is today; and that quantum mechanics, at least in the form in which it is presented by the Copenhagen school is surrounded by a philosophical fog should be clear to anybody who has read, e.g. von Neumann's account which rests upon nothing but the formalism together with the Born-Interpretation, and who compares this account with the orthodox view which contains, apart from elements which follow from the theory in the Born-Interpretation, many other arbitrary assumptions. What we need before any discussion on that matter can be successful is a 'minimum-presentation' of quantum mechanics, a presentation which does not contain anything but what is absolutely necessary. That has not yet been achieved and the Copenhagen-Interpretation is far from having achieved it.

Hutten. I am very glad that the Neumann-proof has been mentioned in this discussion. I think that the misunderstanding in connexion with this proof has been cleared up about two years ago. When reviewing de Broglie's book I pointed out that de Broglie had misunderstood the proof assuming that it was absolute, and that quantum mechanics was the last word in physics. Of course no proof could be of this kind. All that von Neumann could have proved and did prove was that, assuming the basic assumptions were those of quantum mechanics, then no hidden variables could be assumed to exist.

Vigier. I agree with what Professor Fierz has said. I think it is very dangerous to be dogmatic on those questions. The history of science has shown that sometimes assumptions which have no direct experimental basis can have important experimental results. Professor Fierz has quoted the example of de Broglie, but the atomic hypothesists at the beginning of the nineteenth century were in exactly the same position. I have also noticed that Professor Rosenfeld has made a great effort to dissociate himself from what he calls positivism, but he made an utterance which to my opinion is revealing. He said that the presence of an observer is indispensible if one wants to define physical concepts. Now one must be very careful about the meaning of such a word, for the idea of a wave associated with particles has nothing to do with the presence of an observer. Mach condemned the atomic hypothesists exactly on these grounds—nobody had ever seen atoms and one should not introduce into physics ideas which could not be verified on the spot! I think that the relation between theory and experiment is more complex than Mach thought and one should think of it in the following way: although finally everything is decided by experiment, our theories are not always introduced on the basis of experiments. For example the theory proposed by Bohm and myself will succeed or fall depending on whether or not it fits with experiment. But one should not see the relation between theory and experiment in a too dogmatic way. One should wait until the theory develops itself. If I remember correctly, the verification of the ideas of de Broglie came out quite by accident and people were not looking for that effect. The second point I want to discuss is the question of interpretation. Professor Rosenfeld has said that interpretations are uniquely determined by the facts. I think this is also too dogmatic a statement. The gas-laws could be interpretated both ways. On the one hand, you have the interpretation according to which a fluid or a gas is a continuous stuff; and on the other hand you have the atomic hypothesis. Here the same mathematical laws cover very different physical assumptions. Nobody denies the validity of the quantum laws as statistical laws. The question is what is behind those laws. Fierz has said that he thinks that the statistical character of the laws is final, and that nobody will be able to deduce them from a sub-quantum-mechanical level. It is not possible to say at present that this is so. This is a question for practical physics. In that sense I think that Professor Fierz's statement on *Zukunftsmusik* is a bit sweeping. I agree that our interpretation has not yet been completely built but there have been some results. I don't think that even Professor Rosenfeld himself can deny that our theory is logically consistent; what he denies is that it will fit the facts in the high energy domain. Now that is a thing which must be settled by experiment and which one cannot settle by *a priori* dogmatic statements.

Bastin. Professor Rosenfeld has taken a very definite stand with respect to the conceptual basis of quantum theory. He insists that to understand the quantum domain we need to widen our conception of a physical *phenomenon* so that that term includes the experimental techniques which lead to our knowledge of the phenomenon, and that we then need to interpret all the usual quantum formalism in terms of this widened concept. I cannot see that Professor Bohm's criticism succeeds in making contact with this argument. Some physicists, however, attempt to avoid the piece of reasoning Rosenfeld has described by treating the formalism of quantum theory just like that of any other branch of physics except that its laws are statistical in character. To these attempts I think Bohm's criticisms apply, because the attempts do not enable us to understand how it is that in quantum theory but not in macroscopic theory statistical laws come to have their apparently irreducible quality. Whether Bohm himself succeeds in making us understand this is however doubtful, though of course if his methods do enable him to predict new results in the high energy domain, we are more likely to think that he has succeeded.

Süssmann. A remark on Bohm's theory: the symmetry properties of the wave-functions can be derived also from the principles of field theory.

Mackay. I think what worries some of us initially is the feeling that Professor Bohm is introducing a way of deriving these relations analogous to the Ptolemaic way of deriving expressions for the planetary motions by adding epicycles, and we are worried about the question how and when these 'epicycles' could make a difference to our instruments. Does Professor Bohm think that it will be possible to start with an instrument whose quantum of action of perturbation is h, and end up with information about action in units smaller than h? Because if so this would have interesting implications for information theory. This leads me to another point about the quantum of action—I don't know whether it is fair to bring in Professor Bohm's recent book—but I would like to ask whether he still holds his theory of the random motion of a particle under the guidance of a wave in the two-slit diffraction-experiment. In his book he describes the particle as subject to random fluctuations because of fluctuations in the amplitude of Ψ. If one takes the basic uncertainty-relation between frequency and time—($\Delta v \Delta t \geqslant \frac{1}{2}$)—then if you are allowing a fluctuation in amplitude you are predicting an extended spectrum. Would this not imply that in the case of a truly monochromatic electron-wave there would not be any random motion? Finally, on the question whether we describe the world or our interaction with it, Professor Rosenfeld said that we are now resigned to describing only interactions. I would agree with this to the extent that every assertion we make is founded on interaction, so that logically the information-pattern of our assertions is the pattern of interactions. It seems to me however that verbally we still try to push as much as we can on to the far terminal of the interaction—and this is in fact what gives rise to the quantum problem of description. In other words it doesn't seem to me that physics has given up or will ever give up this mode of talking about the world, rather than about interactions with the world. The important thing to realize is that interaction is the basic information-concept. If the basic brick of interaction is the unit h (which is still an empirical question), then all the information patterns which we build to describe the world will also be quantized in bricks of h as far as they are operationally defined.

Hutten. Usually a statistical theory is considered as something wider than a deterministic theory because a deterministic theory is derivable from a statistical theory by leaving out certain variables. It is in this way that it allows for interaction, and we have always suffered in physics from the fact that we can't discuss interaction properly. Therefore, it seems to be doubtful whether an underlying theory can be deterministic rather than statistical.

Bopp. The discussion has so far been unsatisfactory and this for the following reason: we say that Bohm's theory cannot be refuted, adding, however, that we don't believe in it. The reason for this undesirable situation seems to be the following one: the task of physics has been defined by saying that it predicts the possible results of experiment. But what we have done today was predicting the possible development of physics—we were not doing physics but metaphysics. In such a situation it is desirable to formulate concrete problems which may bridge the gulf between the two conflicting opinions in the sense that one obtains a decision in favour of the first opinion or of the second opinion. At the present moment this seems to be impossible, but the remarks made by Feyerabend may be a contribution towards this aim. One would have to start from an analysis of quantum mechanics in its present form; one would have to scrutinize as critically as possible the presuppositions of the present theory. And having done this one could then perhaps ask the question whether it is not possible to formulate the basic principles of quantum mechanics in terms which are well known from classical physics. At the present moment, I can only formulate this question—but I think it is possible to show that it can be answered in the affirmative.

Rosenfeld. It was not my intention to criticize Bohm's theory or to speculate about its prospects of success. What I wanted to do was to vindicate quantum theory against criticisms which I think are unjustified. Of course it is very difficult to separate the two things completely. Now with regard to Dr. Feyerabend's remarks: I think it was not quite fair to quote a single sentence from my paper and not to quote a sentence two or three pages later in which I said explicitly that certainly quantum mechanics as it stands is not sufficient to cope with those new phenomena. Nobody thinks of attributing an absolute validity to the principles of quantum theory. Everybody agrees that something has to be done about it; whether it has to be done in the Bohm way or in any other way remains to be seen; but whatever is done certainly would imply a limitation of the validity of quantum theory in its present form. Now Bohm says that this limitation would be a limitation of the principle of the quantum of action. What I have tried to point out was that hitherto we have not had any indication from experience of such a limitation. On the contrary all the new phenomena have been found to satisfy this principle. Why should one just suspect that it will be this principle which will be at fault? Now Dr. Feyerabend said that there is an arbitrary assumption in quantum theory, namely the assumption that the concepts must be defined in a classical way. Well, it is an assumption, if you like; but isn't that an obvious thing? How could you do it otherwise?

Pryce. Well, you don't do it that way anyway.

Rosenfeld. Of course we do, when we want to be careful. We often forget about it. The only way to define position or momentum is to refer to some operation to which we attribute this property and the reason why we do this in a classical way and by classical means is because classical physics is the kind of physics which is adapted to our scale of observation; the reason why we are forced to do so is that we are after all beings consisting of many atoms and endowed with certain senses, and we see the external world in a certain way. Hence, if we want to describe our experience in a communicable way so that other people like us can understand what we are saying, we must use concepts which refer to these possibilities of observation. Isn't that absolutely obvious to everybody?

Pryce. No. The point behind these interjections, which I did not make explicit, is that we have to reduce our description to 'everyday' concepts, i.e. to what we actually do or can do, and *not* to 'classical mechanical' concepts, which are themselves already abstractions therefrom.

Rosenfeld. That is very surprising.

Feyerabend. As soon as we have a new theory we have to use it throughout, for the description of experience as well as of anything else.

Rosenfeld. Yes, but what does it mean? I am not suggesting that we must refer every single concept to observation. But we must do that ultimately; the way may be a quite roundabout one and in most cases we will not do it explicitly—we can thus forget about it—but ultimately, surely, whatever you do in order to communicate what you think or what you observe to other people, you must use a language which they are capable of understanding; you must put them in such a situation that they can repeat your own observations, so as to understand what you mean. Isn't that a quite obvious thing?

Feyerabend. May I try to explain what I mean by way of an example. Take the special theory of relativity. According to this theory the concept of length is a relative concept in the sense that you cannot attribute length to a given object without at the same time referring to some co-ordinate system. Now before the special theory was introduced, length was regarded as a property of an object. Following the procedure which the Copenhagen school adopts in the case of quantum mechanics—i.e. describing experience not in terms of the best theory available but in terms of some previous theory which has become so intimately connected with our ways of experiencing things that we can hardly imagine things being different—we would be forced, in the case of special relativity, to describe the results of our measurements in a non-relativistic way, i.e. we would be forced to describe them without referring to the co-ordinate system used. Now this would be a very odd procedure and it would also be very artificial to say that the reference to the co-ordinate system comes in only in the theoretical account of the experiment made. The natural procedure is to say that so far our experiences have misled us into believing that length is a property rather than a relation involving a co-ordinate system; and to try and improve the situation by describing even the results of experiments in terms of the new theory of relativity rather than in terms of a previous theory (e.g. Newtonian theory) which did not know anything about the relative character of length.

Rosenfeld. This is a misunderstanding about classical physics.

Hutten. I think that logic can help here quite a lot. We must always have a known language in which to speak about things which are known. If you have a new language and introduce new ideas you must first express them in a language you know—in other words we use classical physics as a metalanguage.

Rosenfeld. But in relativity the situation is exactly the same. Relativity is part of classical physics—by classical physics I mean physics in our scale, including relativity—so, therefore, it is true as you say that as long as we remain within the domain of classical phenomena we attribute the length to the object; that is an approximation we are allowed to make at that level. In connexion with this I would say to Professor Bopp that it seems to me that the kind of analysis he wants has been made by Bohr. He just uses classical language for this kind of experience because classical language is our only tool for describing this kind of experience although its application is limited by laws of nature which are independent of us. This brings me to the question of Vigier who absolutely wants to put the accusation of positivism upon me. I think there is a great difference between the early positivists for whom I have much respect—even for Mach, in spite of his aversion against atomism—and the later positivists. I have not the same respect for the later positivists because I think that where positivism went wrong was when it became a system in which those nice points which I think were made already by Mach, were fossilized into principles of absolute validity; it was maintained that science was only a language and that one could decide about statements only by reducing them to sense data and so on. Mach himself was not very consistent and he made many mistakes which encouraged that direction. However, as far as quantum mechanics is concerned, I would say that it is impossible to understand it without assuming that there is an external world which is independent of what we think and which is the ultimate origin of all our ideas. In that sense I absolutely reject the suggestion of present-day positivists about the subjectivity of our statements. As regards the atoms and the atomic theory which has been invoked by Bohm and also by other people as an example of a theory with hidden parameters which has been successful, I have to say this: of course there are atoms and therefore people who spoke of atoms before it was possible for us to observe them were very lucky; that corresponds also to what Fierz said about the possibility of hitting upon the truth, although one has really no right to do that if one goes the wrong way about it. The latter was certainly the case with Francis Bacon who did not know much about science but who happened to put out certain ideas which proved later to be right, together with many others which turned out to be wrong; so I don't think that argument is very convincing. Now as regards the atomic theory in the nineteenth century it is necessary to go a bit closer into the historical development and to follow up the transformation of this idea from a speculation which might be true or not into a scientific theory. I think that the fact that individual atomic processes were only observed at the end of the nineteenth century is, from our present point of view, more or less an accident. The atomists like Boltzmann were convinced of the reality of atoms for very cogent reasons although they had never seen individual atomic processes. For Maxwell the connexion between the various parameters which are undetermined on the phenomenological level, was a very strong argument in favour of the reality of the underlying mechanism. Another very important point was that it was possible to make predictions, and to find relations between phenomenological parameters without going into details about the structure of atoms; in this way the degree of arbitrariness in the atomic theory was very much reduced. It is true that Maxwell invented his law of distribution but that was not essential. The most beautiful application of atomic theory was the earliest one, namely, Laplace's theory of capillarity. In this theory he only assumed that the forces between molecules are forces of short range and he could deduce all the macroscopic laws of capillarity from that assumption alone. This shows that there was very little arbitrariness in that conception and it is only that feature of early atomic theory which in my view conferred upon it the quality of a scientific theory as opposed to a speculation. When Mach criticized the atomic theory he of course bet upon the wrong horse and he has to bear the blame for it. But apart from that his paper on the *Erhaltung der Arbeit* was just a very sound warning against the danger of introducing arbitrary elements into atomic theory. His whole point was that one has no right to introduce and to apply to atoms the mechanical concepts which have been derived from experiences about macroscopic bodies, unless one has cogent experimental reasons for doing so. I therefore think that it is unfair to criticize Mach just because he happened to draw the wrong conclusion, as his criticisms were completely sound. Now Vigier has presented us with an example where the same physical laws are interpreted in two different ways. I would not describe this example as he does. I would rather say that we have two different theories which are both self-contained—a microscopic description and a phenomenological description: the latter is a definite system of concepts, connected with mathematical symbols; and the former is another system of concepts, namely the properties of systems of a large number of particles assumed to move according to the laws of mechanics; and we define also quantities in that theory which are uniquely connected with the other mode of description and which, of course, satisfy the same relationships.

Vigier. I was talking of the time when the kinetic theory of gases had not yet covered the whole range of macroscopic laws. As soon as it did this—as soon as it covered all the experiments together with things which could not be foreseen on the basis of the macroscopic laws—the situation was different.

Rosenfeld. Now with regard to Dr. Hutten's emphasis on the fact that Bohm made a suggestion how to treat the new processes which require new interactions, I should like perhaps to point out that there are other people who are doing the same thing and have gone a long way already to find, on the basis of quantum theory, descriptions of those couplings and even to reduce the number of independent types of interaction. So there is the same search for simplicity in both cases.

Bohm. I agree with what Dr. Feyerabend has said about using a new theory to modify the definition of older concepts. With regard to the derivation of the Dirac equation, this was meant in the sense of an approximation or a limiting case. I always supposed that at a deeper level there will be a fundamental contradiction between this theory and quantum theory. Also the question was raised as to how we got discontinuity out of continuity. This is all very well known from de Broglie's idea, in which he explained the discrete energy levels as discrete frequencies of vibration of a continuous wave, with the aid of Einstein's relation $E = h\nu$. My next problem would then be to explain Einstein's relation and this is what I have begun to do here. I can show that if there is a continuous distribution of phases, then the requirement of continuity, applied to the integral $\oint p\, dq$, leads precisely to the Bohr-Sommerfeld-relation which implies the Einstein-relation. Such cases are already familiar from classical mechanics where it turns out that non-linear oscillations have stable modes of oscillation with certain energies; and the actual oscillation fluctuates around this stable energy. This one can generalize—it is a very common phenomenon in physics and mathematics that from one conception you can deduce the opposite conception as an approximation, so that in a certain sense one conception implies the other. This is what happens here: from the continuity of the phases of the particles that are coming out of the background of the sub-quantum-mechanical level I deduce precisely the Einstein-relation and the de Broglie-relation for energy and momentum.

I do not wish to say by this that only continuity is a correct concept and that discontinuity is wrong; I want to say that both conceptions are correct but that each one reflects only a certain side of a phenomenon. Each one is reflected into the other, so that you can deduce the one from the other as an approximation.—Next the question was raised about symmetry and anti-symmetry—it is true that by starting with the field-theory you can deduce that the wave-functions are either symmetric or anti-symmetric, but this is done in a rather arbitrary way. In the theory that I am developing, one does not begin by assuming a single field for each kind of particle, with the further stipulation that each field leads either to symmetric or anti-symmetric wave functions. Rather, one begins with a single sub-quantum-mechanical level, out of which come the various kinds of particles with symmetrical or anti-symmetrical wave functions as different sides of one and the same thing. Moreover, the interactions of those particles are implicit in the theory and not postulated. Indeed, two particles are seen to interact, not because they are first assumed in separate existence and then put into interaction, but rather because they are different sides of the same thing. Hence the characteristics of their interaction are deduced from the fundamental theory rather than assumed. This theory therefore opens up the possibility of showing why there are different kinds of particles of different masses, why they interact in the way they do, and why they have such and such properties.—The question of epicycles was raised. I believe our theory is more like the Copernican theory and that the usual quantum mechanics is closer to the epicycle point of view. For at present there are over twenty kinds of particles. To each particle is ascribed a field, and between each two fields a certain interaction is assumed. Nobody can deny the value of that picture; but the situation still remains that you must put in as many fields as there are particles, and that you must assume the corresponding interactions. On the other hand from our point of view there is a deeper level where all this will come out as an approximation. It is explained why there are those particles and why they interact in the way that they do. This raises another point, namely that the basic object of a theory is not just to obtain simplicity. The stress on simplicity is partially right but it is not the best way to say it. The purpose of a theory is to obtain the essence or unity behind the diversity of phenomena. When one has found this essence, then generally one can apply the associated theory in a much broader domain than the original domain of facts. In other words a law which one has discovered holds not only for the facts that one had before; but it also holds for new facts not only in that same domain, but very often in new domains. The world is so built that it has laws of this kind, so that one can extract the essence from a limited number of facts and obtain a theory which contains more than the facts on which it is based. Hence the main point of science is not so much to make a summary of the things one knows, but rather to find those laws which are essential and which therefore hold in new domains and predict new facts. It is an objective fact that the world is so constructed that generally speaking, by finding the unity behind the diversity, one will get laws which contain more than the original facts. And here the infinity of nature comes in: the whole scientific method implies that no theory is final. It is always possible there is something that one has missed. *At least as a working hypothesis* science assumes the infinity of nature; and this assumption fits the facts much better than any other point of view that we know.—The next question was raised by Hutten about the determinate theories which are now obtained as limits of statistical theories. But the opposite is also true. I discussed this point briefly yesterday. If you have a large number of variables undergoing sufficiently complex motions then you can show that most of the essential consequences of a statistical theory, such as randomness and the Gaussian distribution, can be approximated to an arbitrary degree from a determinate theory. Similarly you have the opposite, that any determinate theory can be approximated to an arbitrary degree as the limit of a statistical theory. This again is characteristic of our conceptions. Each particular concept finds its reflection in its opposite and can be approximated to an arbitrary degree in its opposite.—Then I want to bring up this question of the discovery of atoms. Again I believe this was not a question of luck. For the foundation of the atomic theory consisted in the fact that it was necessary to explain certain difficulties of the large scale theory. Demokritos tried to explain the difficulties of Zeno's paradoxes and this is really a fundamental way by which progress in science is made: difficulties of conceptions at a certain level are resolved by suggesting a new conception. We go beyond the phenomena and try to learn more than the phenomena suggest.—Finally I want to raise the question of how we are to define a thing or the conception of a thing, such as position and so on. This was raised by Dr. Feyerabend. I believe that we must define a property such as position in terms of all the concepts that are available. During the Middle Ages or before that time people were not very successful in defining positions accurately; then, when geometry developed, they were better able to define positions. Then with the development of mechanics and wave optics, it was possible to do this still better, for one could use mechanical and optical parameters and so on. And now if we should come to a sub-quantum level then we could define position in terms of the parameters of the sub-quantum level. In other words, the conception of position like all conceptions, may have infinite possibilities as we go deeper and deeper into nature and find out more and more of what is there. We cannot measure position apart from the actual physical properties of the things that we use for measuring. This is one of the lessons of the theory of relativity. In the theory of relativity we use measuring rods and clocks which behave in a certain way, and we must change our conception of position in accordance.

Pryce. Let me comment on one thing in Professor Rosenfeld's initial talk. He said that the purpose of science was to make quantitative statements. Now, I think this has been over-emphasized in the treatment of the philosophy of science. In physics the qualitative statement is often more important than the quantitative statement. You have to know to what concepts you have to attach your quantitative measure before you can set a quantitative measure. Let me give one or two examples. It is very important in the present state of physics to measure accurately the mass of the Π-meson, but before you can measure the mass of the Π-meson, you have to know that there is such a thing as a Π-meson, and to find that out requires a kind of physics which is very important and which is in itself qualitative rather than quantitative. This also is physics. It is science, in fact it is the essence of science. In the links between classical theory, classical mechanics and quantum mechanics and a possible future sub-quantum mechanics, it is the new concepts that have been the important things. We have to know to what we are to attach numerical values. In classical mechanics we attach numerical values to things like position, momentum and energy. In quantum mechanics we introduce new mathematical tools, the Hilbert space, the operators, the vectors in the Hilbert space, to which we give numerical measure, and Bohm is proposing that we should play with different mathematical structures and analyse them. He hasn't got it completely formulated which mathematical structure he wants to relate to reality, but this again seems to me to be a very legitimate form of activity—to be speculative. You may be completely wrong in what you do, then it shouldn't be held against you too much. But you may be right, and then you would be held up as a shining example.

Rosenfeld. The first point of Pryce goes completely in my direction. If I mentioned the importance of magnitudes in physics, it was only to go some way towards Bohm, but personally I quite agree with Pryce that the important thing is the qualities first, and then the quantitative measure for them, because the latter helps us to make more precise predictions. Now with regard to his description of Bohm's. If Bohm only suggested that, then it would just be a gallant effort to go further, and that would be all right; but he implies much more: he implies that his new mathematical concepts would be linked with a deterministic form of causality at that level; and that is saying more, that is making not only a statement of form but a statement of content, of quality if you like, and that is a much more doubtful proposition.

Pryce. I would say that the statement is a hope, and a hope is an expression of a personal taste and one shouldn't hold a personal taste against a person.

Rosenfeld. But one can bet.

Wisdom. Professor Rosenfeld said that it was not the usual procedure, or that he regarded it an impossible procedure to re-interpret formalisms which are already existing. Now there are a number of obvious examples which seem to me to tell against what he had to say. For instance, the interpretation of the wave function itself in terms of probability came long after quantum mechanics was developed as a formal structure, or again the interpretation of negative energy leading to the discovery of the positron; the same applies to the Lorentz-transformations which were re-interpreted in relativity theory. It is possible then to have perfectly a definite formalism to be interpreted. Now Rosenfeld might reply that he's criticizing the re-interpretation of formalism as a whole. But surely there is even an example of that in Einstein's last theory: what I think he was trying to do was to build up an equation around skew-symmetrical tensors and then interpret the tensors as being a bit like an electro-magnetic tensor, a gravitation-tensor, and so on. The interpretation followed the formalism. The other point I wanted to make was about the question of meaninglessness of certain pronouncements. It has become a jargon in quantum mechanics and in various scientific contexts to say that various things that do not hold are meaningless. For instance, some people would say that it's meaningless to talk of the precise momentum and simultaneously the precise position of a particle, and what I wanted to point out was that I think this is obviously false and for the following reason: if you have $\Delta p \,.\, \Delta q \geqslant h/2\pi$ that will be contradicted by $\Delta p \,.\, \Delta q < h/2\pi$. It is contradictory but it is not meaningless to say that $\Delta p \,.\, \Delta q < h/2\pi$.

Pryce. That's just a different usage of language. Philosophers and physicists use 'meaningless' in a different sense. Wedon't disagree with what you are saying there, but we use the word meaningless in a different sense.

Wisdom. Yes, very often, but the reason why it's not quite so unimportant as you suggest is because it has its roots in the Vienna positivism, which did make these things meaningless in the philosophical sense. The contrast is that, if you say one thing and say the contradictory thing, then they would both have sense in the philosophical usage. My point is that they are not meaningless in the philosophical sense but only in the more ordinary colloquial sense; and this connects with the point made by Professor Pryce, that the question of measuring is secondary to the question of establishing something else. You have to be able to say that the electron is in a certain position, and that, though it may be impossible to determine its whereabouts in a range, it is somewhere there—this has to be said before you can start measuring or trying to assess the probability of its being somewhere.

Rosenfeld. With regard to the first point about the interpretation of formalism, I would say that I did not mean the kind of things that you first alluded to. Of course, when one is struggling to find a meaning which one does not know beforehand, then one tries all kinds of constructions. But when you have constructed a good theory, then this theory is an inseparable whole of self-consistent concepts and formulae, and there is nothing to shuffle about; it is a solid block.

Groenewold. It seems to me that in these discussions one has to distinguish rather sharply between the formalism and the way it is applied to observations for prediction and explanation on the one hand, and the interpretation on the other hand. The first thing, the formalism and the way in which it is used, can be discussed and it is possible to come to an agreement if only the theory has been worked out far enough and if we have sufficient experimental data. We cannot really discuss the interpretation, we can only talk about it. That does not mean that there is no connexion between the two things, but the connexion is not a logical connexion. It has been suggested by different speakers that this connexion may be a motive to look for some new developments in the theory. But afterwards this development may turn out to be entirely independent, or it may even contradict the standpoint from which one started, and I think there are many examples for this in the development of physics. For instance the theories of Heisenberg and Schrödinger are both based upon very different interpretations. However, they finally led to the same formalism, with the same consequences. So we all agree about how this has to be applied in this limited domain where quantum mechanics is correct, although we are still fighting about the interpretation. Hence in this formalism, we can distinguish between the limited domain where the theory is more or less closed, and the further development about which we can make speculations. Now, the speculations we make can also be discussed but we cannot come to a conclusion as long as the theory has not been worked out sufficiently far and as long as experimental data are not sufficiently available. I now would like to ask a few questions about the former point. As far as I understood, the formalism in Bohm's first paper was mathematically equivalent with usual quantum mechanics. I am not quite clear how the situation is in the later development, because here one seems to arrive at a different formulation which is not identical with usual quantum mechanics, and which is hoped to enable us to overcome some of the difficulties which the present theory still has. Now, how is it with this formalism which you have written down, is that still meant to be a formalism which is identical with the old one, or is this already a deviation? Another question is about the interpretation of the formalism: in the first papers you assume that this quantum potential which gives rise to the quantum force is an objective quantity and that the wave-function is also an objective quantity. Is that the right interpretation of your opinions?

Bohm. In order to answer this question, I must first make a remark about what I think is an important part of the interpretation. In the original form of this theory, which was quite different, the effort was to re-interpret the wave-function as an objective wave-function, and the particle as an actual particle and to show that you could obtain the same results as in the usual interpretation. Now then, you would say, what is the use of that? The answer is that very often a different interpretation lends itself to changes and generalizations which are not possible in the first interpretation. If I had stopped here it would not have been very interesting. For this interpretation had many features that were unsatisfying; and especially, the quantum potential was rather arbitrary in form. The idea then was to proceed from that point and to change the theory in order to improve it. Here it is important to say that there was no special reason to construct a theory which would give exactly the same results as quantum mechanics. In fact there was every reason to construct a theory that would not give exactly the same results, but only approximately the same results. Hence I began to change the theory until I arrived at the model that I described today in which the quantum potential is an effect of a certain statistical motion. In order to explain this let us take the case of thermo-dynamics. Here the energy of a system at absolute zero is determined just by its internal energy. But as soon as you have fluctuations there appears an additional term, the temperature times the entropy. This term represents an effect of the statistical fluctuations of the motion of the atoms. Indeed it is a kind of statistical potential which must be added to the energy in order to get the effective free energy in any actual transformation of the microscopic system. The present argument is therefore that the quantum potential comes out as an effective statistical term which should be added to the remaining energies to help determine the average motion of the electron. The quantum potential therefore ceases to play an essential role because everything is explained in a deeper way. Now I don't insist that the deeper laws will be purely determinate laws or purely statistical laws. In terms of the infinity of nature we may rather say that every law is at one stage determinate, at another stage statistical; every law leaves out an infinity of factors in lower levels. It is this fact which makes the law an approximation, which makes it statistical. But as you go deeper you see the causes of the fluctuations and thereby the law becomes determinate; but then the deeper level is in its turn subject to factors which have been left out and it will be statistical too. Hence from this point of view, every law must have both a determinate and a statistical side. To say that it must be purely determinate would be metaphysical, just as to say that it must be purely statistical would also be metaphysical.—Now as to the final point which Professor Wisdom raised—the question of whether there must be an electron there in order to measure its position. In both points of view—and I think that here I would agree with Professor Rosenfeld—it is not necessary to assume that an electron is already there, because the apparatus may help to produce the electron. In terms of the model which I propose here there is continual forming and dissolving of the electron in the lower level; and then it may well be that the apparatus helps to precipitate it in a certain place. Even in the phenomenon of critical opalescence, small nuclei would tend to precipitate the particle out in a certain place. Similarly, the very effort to measure a property of the electron may introduce something which would precipitate it out in a certain way. Hence in such a complex situation you are not even sure that what you measure was there before you measured it. Now the difference between Professor Rosenfeld and myself is this: we both agree that present quantum mechanics implies that the apparatus plays a very fundamental role in helping to produce what is there, because there is such a close sensitive coupling between the thing and the apparatus. But I propose a model which aims at the explanation of why this happens. It is a model of the observer and of what he does as well as of the system. This model shows how both the observer and the system exist at a deeper level and how they must both influence each other. In this model the electron may be conceived as an iceberg most of which is not visible above the surface of the sea. The same is true of the observing apparatus. If we make an observation many things are going on underneath; and this is why things are so complicated.

THIRD SESSION

Chairman: Professor L. ROSENFELD

K. R. POPPER: The propensity interpretation of the calculus of probability, and the quantum theory.

J.-P. VIGIER: The concept of probability in the frame of the probabilistic and the causal interpretation of quantum mechanics.

The propensity interpretation of the calculus of probability, and the quantum theory

by

K. R. POPPER

In this paper, I propose briefly to put forth and to explain the following theses, and to indicate the manner of their defence.

(1) The solution of the problem of interpreting probability theory is fundamental for the interpretation of quantum theory; for quantum theory is a probabilistic theory.

(2) The idea of a statistical interpretation is correct, but is lacking in clarity.

(3) As a consequence of this lack of clarity, the usual interpretation of probability in physics *oscillates* between two extremes: an *objective* purely statistical interpretation and a *subjective* interpretation in terms of our incomplete knowledge, or of the available information.

(4) In the orthodox Copenhagen interpretation of quantum theory we find the same oscillation between an objective and a subjective interpretation: *the famous intrusion of the observer into physics.*

(5) As opposed to all this, a revised or reformed statistical interpretation is here proposed. It is called the *propensity interpretation of probability.*

(6) The propensity interpretation is a purely objective interpretation. It eliminates the oscillations between objective and subjective interpretation, and with it the intrusion of the subject into physics.

(7) The idea of propensities is 'metaphysical', in exactly the same sense as forces or fields of forces are metaphysical.

(8) It is also 'metaphysical' in another sense: in the sense of providing a coherent programme for physical research.

These are my theses. I begin by explaining what I call the propensity interpretation of probability theory.[1]

Section 1. *Objective and Subjective Interpretations of Probability.*

Let us assume that we have two dice: one is a *regular* die of homogeneous material, the other is *loaded*, in such a way that in long sequences of throws the side marked '6' comes uppermost in about 1/4 of the throws. We say, in this case, that the probability of throwing a 6 is 1/4.

Now the following line of arguing seems attractive.

We ask what we *mean* by saying that the probability is 1/4; and we may arrive at the answer: What we *mean*, precisely, is that the relative frequency, or the statistical

[1] I have explained the propensity interpretation of probability and of quantum theory very briefly in my paper 'Three Views Concerning Human Knowledge', in *Contemporary British Philosophy*, edited by H. D. Lewis, 1956, p. 388. A full treatment of the propensity interpretation and of its repercussions upon quantum theory will be found in the *Postscript: After Twenty Years* to my *Logic of Scientific Discovery*, 1957.

frequency, of the results in long sequences is 1/4. Thus probability is relative frequency in the long run. This is the statistical interpretation.

The statistical interpretation has been often criticized because of the difficulties of the phrase 'in the long run'. I will *not* discuss this question. Instead I will discuss the question of *the probability of a* SINGLE EVENT. This question is of importance in connexion with quantum theory because the ψ-function determines the probability of a *single electron* to take up a certain state, under certain conditions.

Thus we ask ourselves now what it *means* to say 'The probability of throwing 6 *with the next throw* of this loaded die is 1/4.'

From the point of view of the *statistical interpretation*, this can only mean one thing: 'The next throw is a *member of a sequence* of throws, and the relative frequency within this sequence is 1/4.'

At first sight, this answer seems satisfactory. But we can ask the following awkward question:

What if the sequence consists of throws of a *loaded* die, with one or two throws of a *regular* die occurring in between the others? Clearly, we shall say about the throws with the regular die that their probability is different from 1/4, in spite of the fact that these throws are members of a sequence of throws with the frequency 1/4.

This simple objection is of fundamental importance. It can be answered in various ways. I shall mention two of these answers, one leading to a *subjective interpretation*, the other to the *propensity interpretation*.

The first or subjective answer is this. 'You have assumed in your question', the subjectivist may address me, 'that *we know* that the one die is loaded, the other regular, and also that *we know* whether the one or the other is used at a certain place in the sequence of throws. In view of this information, we shall of course attribute the proper probabilities to the various single throws. For probability, as your own objection shows, is not simply a frequency in a sequence. Admittedly, observed frequencies are important as providing us with valuable *information*. But we must use *all* our information. The probability is our assessment, in the light *of all we know*, of reasonable betting odds. It is a measure which depends essentially upon our incomplete information, and *it is a measure of the incompleteness of our information*: if our information about the conditions under which the die will be thrown were sufficiently precise, then there would be no difficulty in predicting the result with certainty.'

This is the subjectivist's answer, and I shall take it as a characterization of the subjectivist position which I shall not discuss further in this paper, although I shall mention it in various places.[2]

Now what will the defender of an objective interpretation say to our fundamental objection? Most likely he will say (as I myself used to say for a long time) the following:

'To make a statement about probability is to propose a *hypothesis*. It is a hypothesis about frequencies in a sequence of events. In proposing this hypothesis, we can make use of all sorts of things—of past experience, or of inspiration: it does not matter *how we get* it; all that matters is *how we test it*. Now in the case mentioned, we all agree on the frequency hypothesis, and we all agree that the frequency of 1/4

[2] I have discussed and criticized the subjectivist position very fully elsewhere (see the preceding footnote). The subjectivist interpretation of probability is a necessary consequence of determinism. Its retention within the quantum theory is a residue of a not yet fully eliminated determinist position.

will not be affected by having one or two throws with a regular die in between the throws with a loaded die. As to the regular throws, *if* we consider them merely as belonging to this sequence, we have to attribute to them, strange as it may sound, the probability of 1/4, even though they are throws with a regular die. And if, on the other hand, we attribute to them the probability of 1/6, then we do so because of the hypothesis that in *another* sequence—one of throws with the regular die—the frequency will be 1/6.'

This is the objectivist's defence of the purely statistical interpretation, or of the frequency interpretation, and *as far as it goes* I still agree with it.

But I now think it strange that I did not press my question further. For it seems clear to me now that this answer of mine, or of the objectivist's, implies the following. In attributing probabilities to sequences, we consider as decisive the *conditions under which the sequence is produced.* In assuming that a sequence of throws of a loaded die will be different from a sequence of throws of a regular die, we attribute the probability to the *experimental conditions.* But this leads to the following result.

Even though probabilities may be said to be frequencies, we believe that these *frequencies will depend on the experimental arrangement.*

But with this, we come to a new version of the objective interpretation. It is as follows.

Every experimental arrangement is *liable to produce*, if we repeat the experiment very often, a sequence with frequencies which depend upon this particular experimental arrangement. These virtual frequencies may be called probabilities. But since the probabilities turn out to depend upon the experimental arrangement, they may be looked upon as *properties of this arrangement. They characterize the disposition, or the propensity*, of the experimental arrangement to give rise to certain characteristic frequencies *when the experiment is often repeated.*

Section 2. The Propensity Interpretation

We thus arrive at the propensity interpretation of probability.[3] It differs from the

[3] What we interpret is not a word, 'probability', and its 'meaning', but formal systems—the probability calculus (especially in its measure-theoretical form), and the formalism of quantum theory.

A formalized set of axioms for relative (or conditional) probability is the following. (The theory of real numbers is assumed.)

(A) $a, b \in K \rightarrow : p(a, b)$ is a real number, and

(a) $((c)(c \in K \rightarrow p(a, c) = p(b, c))) \rightarrow (d)(d \in K \rightarrow p(d, a) = p(d, b))$

(a′) $p(a, a) = 1$

(B) $a, b \in K \rightarrow : ab \in K$; and $b, c, bc \in K \rightarrow p(a, bc)p(b, c) = p(ab, c) \leqslant p(a, c)$

(C) $a \in K \rightarrow : {'a} \in K$, and $b, c \in K \rightarrow . \, p(b, c) \neq 1 \rightarrow p(a, c) + p({'a}, c) = 1$

(D) $(Ea)(Eb)(a, b \in K$, and $p(a, b) \neq 1)$

(ab is here, of course, the meet or conjunction of a and b, and $'a$ the complement of a.)

This set is equivalent to a more concise set in which no numerical constant such as '1' occurs. It is obtained by retaining (a), omitting (a′), and replacing the second (operational) lines of (B) and (C), as well as (D), respectively, by the following lines ((B) is now made 'organic'):

(b) $d \in K \rightarrow ((p(a, bc)p(b, c) = p(d, c) \rightarrow p(a, c) < p(d, c)) \rightarrow p(ab, c) < p(d, c))$

(c) $d \in K \rightarrow (p(a, a) \neq p(b, c) \rightarrow p(a, c) + p({'a}, c) = p(d, d))$

(d) $(Ea)(Eb)(a, b \in K$, and $p(a, b) = p(b, b))$

This axiom system has the following properties: (1) if we define absolute probability by

$$p(a) = p(a, {'(a' a)}),$$

then we can say that $p(a, b)$ is defined in our system even if $p(b) = 0$. In this respect, the system is a generalization of the systems known so far (except my systems published in *B.J.P.S.*, **6**, 1955, pp. 56f., and in *British Philosophy in the Mid-Century*, ed. C. A. Mace, 1957, p. 191). (2) It is not, as in other systems, tacitly assumed that the elements of K satisfy the postulates of Boolean algebra (this fact, on the contrary, can be proved). This is of advantage in connexion with the problem of interpretation, such as the problem whether propensities satisfy Boolean algebra: it becomes superfluous to postulate that they do.

purely statistical or frequency interpretation only in this—that it considers the probability as a characteristic property of the experimental arrangement rather than as a property of a sequence.

The main point of this change is that we now take as fundamental *the probability of the result of a single experiment*, with respect to its *conditions*, rather than the frequency of results in a sequence of experiments. Admittedly, if we wish to *test* a probability statement, we have to test an experimental sequence. But now the probability statement is not a statement *about* this sequence: it is a statement *about* certain properties of the experimental conditions, of the experimental set-up. (Mathematically, the change corresponds to the transition from the frequency-theory to the measure-theoretical approach.)

A statement about propensities may be compared with a statement about the strength of an electric field. We can test this statement only if we introduce a test body and measure the effect of the field upon this body. But the statement which we test speaks about the field rather than about the body. It speaks about certain *dispositional properties* of the field. And just as we can consider the field as physically real, so we can consider the propensities as physically real. They are *relational* properties of the experimental set-up. For example, the propensity 1/4 *is not a property of our loaded die*. This can be seen at once if we consider that in a very weak gravitational field, the load will have little effect—the propensity of throwing a 6 may decrease from 1/4 to very nearly 1/6. In a strong gravitational field, the load will be more effective and the same die will exhibit a propensity of 1/3 or 1/2. The tendency or disposition or propensity is therefore, as a relational property of the experimental set-up, something more abstract than, say, a Newtonian force with its simple rules of vectorial addition. *The propensity distribution attributes weights to all possible results of the experiment.* Clearly, it can be represented by a vector in the *space of possibilities*.

Section 3. Propensity and Quantum Theory

The main thing about the propensity interpretation is that *it takes the mystery out of quantum theory, while leaving probability and indeterminism in it.* It does so by pointing out that all the apparent mysteries would also involve thrown dice, or tossed pennies—*exactly* as they do electrons. In other words, it shows that quantum theory is a probability theory just as any theory of any other game of chance, such as the bagatelle board (pin board).

In our interpretation, Schrödinger's ψ-function determines the propensities of the states of the electron. We therefore have no 'dualism' of particles and waves. The electron is a particle, but its wave theory is a propensity theory which attributes weights to the electron's possible states. The waves in configuration space are waves of weights, or waves of propensities.

Let us consider Dirac's example of a photon and a polarizer. According to Dirac, we have to say that the photon is in both possible states at once, half in each; even although it is indivisible, and although we can find it, or observe it, in only one of its possible states.

We can translate this as follows. The theory describes, and gives weight to, all the possible states—in our case, two. The photon will be in one state only. The situation is exactly the same as with a tossed penny. Assume that we have tossed the penny, and that we are shortsighted and have to bend down before we can observe which side is upmost. The probability formalism tells us then that each of the possible states has a probability of 1/2. So we can say that the penny is half in one state, and half in the other. And when we bend down to observe it, the Copenhagen spirit will inspire the penny to make a quantum jump into one of its two *Eigen*-states. For nowadays a quantum jump is said by Heisenberg to be the same as a reduction of the wave packet. And by 'observing' the penny, we induce exactly what in Copenhagen is called a 'reduction of the wave packet'.

The famous two-slit experiment allows exactly the same analysis. If we shut one slit, we interfere with the possibilities, and therefore get a different ψ-function, and a different probability distribution of the possible results. *Every change in the experimental arrangement such as the shutting of a slit, will lead to a different distribution of weights to the possibilities* (just as will the shifting of a pin on a pin board). That is, we obtain a different ψ-function, determining a different distribution of the propensities.

There is nothing peculiar about the role of the observer: he does not come in at all. What 'interferes' with the ψ-function are only changes of experimental arrangements.

The opposite impression is due to an oscillation between an objective and a subjective interpretation of probability. It is the subjective interpretation which drags in our knowledge, and its changes, while we ought to speak only of experimental arrangements, and the results of experiments.

Section 4. Metaphysical Considerations

I have stressed that the propensities are not only as objective as the experimental arrangements but also *physically real*—in the sense in which forces, and fields of forces, are *physically real*. Nevertheless they are *not* pilot-waves in ordinary space, but weight functions of possibilities, that is to say, vectors in possibility space. (Bohm's 'quantum-mechanical potential' would become here a propensity to accelerate, rather than an accelerating force. This would give full weight to the Pauli-Einstein criticism of the pilot-wave theory of de Broglie and Bohm.) We are quite used to the fact that such abstract things as, for example, degrees of freedom, have a very real influence on our results, and are in so far something physically real. Or consider the fact that, compared with the mass of the sun, the masses of the planets are negligible, and that, compared with the masses of the planets, those of their moons are also negligible. This is an abstract, a relational fact, not attributable to any planet or to any point in space, but a relational property of the whole solar system. Nevertheless, there is every reason to believe that it is one of the 'causes' of the stability of the solar system. Thus abstract relational facts can be 'causes', and in that sense physically real.

It seems to me that by stressing that the ψ-function describes physical realities, we may be able to bridge the gap between those who rightly stress the statistical character of modern physics and those who, like Einstein and Schrödinger, insist that physics has to describe an objective physical reality. The two points of view are incompatible on the subjectivist assumption that statistical laws describe our own imperfect state of knowledge. They become compatible if only we realize that these statistical laws describe propensities, that is to say, objective relational properties of the physical world.

Beyond this, the propensity interpretation seems to offer a new metaphysical interpretation of physics (and incidentally also of biology and psychology). For we can say that all physical (and psychological) properties are dispositional. That a surface is coloured red means that it has the disposition to reflect light of a certain wave length. That a beam of light has a certain wave length means that it is disposed to behave in a certain manner if surfaces of various colours, or prisms, or spectographs, or slotted screens, etc., are put in its way.

Aristotle put the propensities as potentialities *into* the things. Newton's was the first *relational* theory of physical dispositions and his gravitational theory led, almost inevitably, to a theory of fields of forces. I believe that the propensity interpretation of probability may take this development one step further.

The concept of probability in the frame of the probabilistic and the causal interpretation of quantum mechanics

by

J.-P. VIGIER

BEFORE entering the specific object of this paper I would like to come back on one point which has been treated partially in this morning's discussion: namely the antagonism, which to my mind is irreducible, between the subjective and objective conceptions of probability. I shall try to present these two points of view in the sharpest way possible to encourage the discussion. Naturally in doing so I may simplify things a bit but this is a minor inconvenience if it helps clarifying ideas.

First a few words on the classical theory of probability.

If you analyse this theory you see that it attempts to and, as experience shows, really does describe the real effect on a given phenomenon of 'chance' effect or 'chance contingencies' that is, phenomena not connected or rather loosely connected with the phenomenon we examine, that is lying outside the causal contexts we use to predict its behaviour.

Let us analyse for example the rate of traffic accidents in a city like Paris. You realize immediately that any given individual accident depends on an enormous number of causal factors which, though they can be analysed causally, make the precise prediction of what has happened to the individual cars concerned practically impossible; for whatever number of factors you take you always neglect causes which could also influence their fate. Nevertheless experience shows that if you consider an ensemble of cars, you can detect general statistical laws which are more and more precise as your ensemble increases. You can even act on the rate of traffic accidents by playing on given factors (traffic regulations, red light at cross-roads, and so forth).

The same type of consideration applies to all phenomena. The shooting of a given shell by a gun can be predicted only with a certain degree of accuracy because of the innumerable chance contingencies (strength and direction of the wind, temperature etc.) acting on it. If, however, you consider an ensemble of shells shot with the same known initial conditions you can predict a certain statistical behaviour and verify that the real impacts are distributed in a regular way (inside an ellipse) around the theoretical point of impact calculated by the laws of classical mechanics.

This illustrates two points I wanted to make, namely (1) that even in classical mechanics you cannot separate causal and chance laws from the analysis of any phenomena. (2) That when you consider ensembles of phenomena you see general regular statistical trends appearing above the detailed fluctuations.

These are the statistical laws. In fact we can say that the tendency for contingencies lying outside a given context to fluctuate approximately independently of happenings inside that context has demonstrated itself to be so widespread that one may enunciate it as a principle, namely the principle of randomness. By randomness we mean just that this independence leads to a fluctuation of these contingencies in a very complicated way over a wide range of possibilities; but in such a manner that statistical averages have a regular and approximately predictable behaviour.

In a sense one can say that the statistical laws are the causal laws of 'ensembles'.

Now we can raise the question: how do these laws connect with the usual theory of probability? To attempt an answer let us recall the example of the game of dice.

If you throw dice many times as we all know the results fluctuate independently of each other.

Then you see that corresponding to each combination there are 'fair odds' such that in the long run a player betting on them will neither win nor lose.

As everybody knows you can calculate these odds by supposing that each face is 'equally likely'. Thus the probability of obtaining any given result with a die (such as the number 3) is $1/6$, the probability of having a double 3 is $1/6 \cdot 1/6 = 1/36$ (since the two dice are 'independent'), and the total probability is the product of the separate probabilities. Now already on that simple example you see the two conceptions mentioned before appearing.

First the 'subjective' interpretation. We know nothing about the detailed behaviour of the dice, so if nothing suggests a special tendency favouring one face all faces are equally probable. In that sense probability is something that measures or reflects a degree of our information and would cease to have a meaning if we could obtain more precise knowledge concerning the initial conditions and causes influencing the motions of the dice in each throw.

This is not satisfactory since our personal ignorance does not explain *why* the *experimental* relative frequency is correctly predicted by the theory of probability. (Evidently our ignorance applies not only to one throw but to all throws.)

We are then led to the idea that the probability of a given result is an objective property associated with the dice that are being used and the process by which they are thrown; that is a property which is quite independent of whether we know or not what will happen in each individual throw, but which results objectively and necessarily from the uncorrelated action of many complex causes. This could be called the 'objective' interpretation of probability.

Let us say immediately that this explanation of the nature of statistical laws as consequences of the action of a very complex ensemble of uncorrelated causal factors is not generally accepted.

First, because it has not been possible to prove that it is so in all cases (there is no general demonstration of the ergodic theorem though it has been possible to prove in a certain number of particular cases that such causal ensembles do lead to statistical laws) and second for philosophical reasons. Indeed the success of the probabilistic interpretation of quantum mechanics has led more and more people to take the standpoint that statistical laws cannot be explained in terms of causal laws at all and that they constitute an ultimate limit for our knowledge.

Thus the classical framework contains two basic ideas.

(a) First, that the validity of the application of the calculus of probability can be eventually deduced from general properties of the application of causal laws outside or underneath the context you consider.

(b) The conception of von Mises that it cannot be so and that in a genuinely random distribution to which we apply the theory of probability there are no causal relationships at all; the distribution is 'lawless'.

In this second conception we recognize one of the basic points of the probabilistic interpretation of quantum mechanics, namely, the idea that probability laws represent an ultimate state of knowledge and that they can never be understood as an approximation of some deeper set of more nearly determinate laws.

Notice that in a sense this position is just as mechanistic as the position of Laplace. For Laplace there existed a unique set of causal laws (the laws of classical mechanics) which represent an ultimate limit of our knowledge and out of which one can deduce completely the behaviour of Nature. It is true that in that frame there is still room for statistical laws such as those of the kinetic theory of gases but it must be possible in principle to deduce them from the complex causal behaviour of the ensembles studied; so that all nature is comparable to a machine whose behaviour is completely determined by its initial conditions.

In a sense the position of von Mises is just the reverse. For him also there is an ultimate limit to knowledge (namely the statistical laws describing 'lawlessness') and causal laws are just averages of statistical behaviour. The world is then comparable to an immense unanalysable 'roulette wheel'; which is just another type of machine.

Let us say immediately that Professor Bohm and I myself do not agree with these two points of views which seem to us too narrow and one sided; we think that the real connexion between causal and statistical laws must be sought in a broader context (which synthetizes some aspects of both these points of view) which is suggested in our opinion by the development of quantum mechanics.

Before I come to that let us discuss the meaning of probability in the frame of the present probabilistic interpretation of quantum mechanics.

To study this question let us recall a very well known example, the Young diffraction experiment, which has now been realized not only with photons but also very recently with electrons (in Toulouse) and which could in principle be realized with all known types of particles.

If you take a source *S* of particles so weak that there is never more than one particle at a time in the apparatus and send these particles in the direction of a screen II

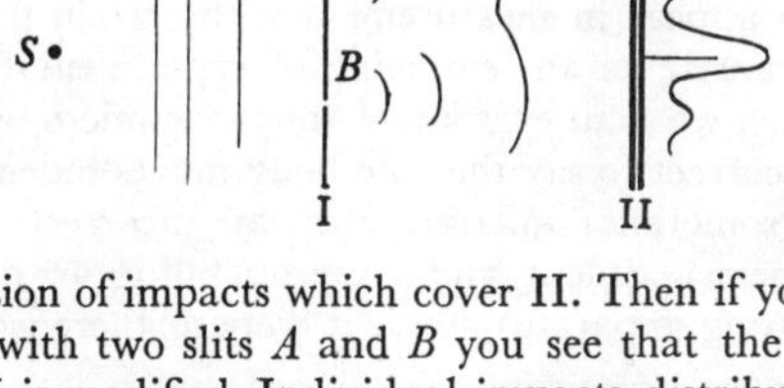

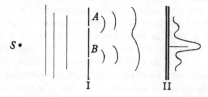

you observe a succession of impacts which cover II. Then if you interpose between *S* and II a screen I with two slits *A* and *B* you see that the distribution of individual impacts on II is modified. Individual impacts distribute themselves on an interference pattern (that is, they concentrate on certain regions and avoid other regions) and the form and breadth of these regions depends on the form and breadth of the slits A and B.

It is clear that this experiment implies that individual particles[1] have properties very different from the classical model. At the level of II they manifest a particle-like character and we must notice that this is always the case in all known experiments (the things which we finally observe are always the particle-like aspect of matter or can be reduced to it). But at the level of screen I the micro-object has wave like properties since the distribution of the ensemble of impacts is influenced by the presence of the two slits A and B.

Everything happens as if each individual micro-object interfered with itself on I to be finally absorbed with a preference for the regions where the diffraction pattern presents a maximum wave amplitude.

Experiment then establishes an essential property. The particle-like aspects of the micro-objects are distributed with a density $P = |\psi|^2$ where ψ denotes a continuous wave satisfying one of the equations of wave mechanics, such as the Schrödinger equation for non-relativistic electrons.

The usual interpretation of this experiment is well known. At the left of I the micro-object has no position and no trajectory: it is represented by a plane wave ψ which determines its probability of presence $P = |\psi|^2$ at each point. On I ψ transforms into two cylindrical waves centred on the two slits. After I these waves interfere and create on II an interference pattern which determines the distribution of the eventual impacts of the particle-like aspect of the micro-object. Finally the micro-object materializes on II. Hence if you observe an ensemble of micro-objects you obtain the experimental distribution $P = |\psi|^2$ with a high degree of accuracy.

In that experiment there is then a wave ψ and a particle but the particle has no velocity or position except when one makes an experiment which determines them. ψ represents an ensemble of experimental potentialities with their respective probabilities and determines all we shall ever know of the micro-objects we study. This analysis has the advantage to put into full light the main features of the probabilistic interpretation. We can summarize them as follows:

(a) The object of the theory is not to describe the behaviour of things but to build a formalism which gives the results of experiments (in the present case the distribution $|\psi|^2$).

(b) Outside measurement no knowledge is possible since these micro-objects cannot be described within space-time (as can be seen in this experiment where on I the body has no motion but has at the same time an infinity of possible positions and velocities (which can appear in measurement with certain probabilities).

The ψ wave just represents an 'ensemble of experimental potentialities' which cover everything which we shall ever know about the micro-object.

(c) Thus it is not correct to say that the body moves independently and outside the observer (as is sometimes inferred from an incorrect interpretation of the Heisenberg microscope experiment) and that probabilities are due to the perturbation caused by the measuring apparatus, for if it were so there would be a reality (the

[1] We will call them micro-objects henceforward to avoid confusion.

motion through one slit) not described by ψ so that the description would be incomplete.

The only knowledge you can have is of statistical nature but this probability does not result from our ignorance of some more detailed behaviour, or from the complexity of causes acting on microphenomena, but it represents an ultimate knowledge. Thus it is different from the classical notion of probability and reduces to pure contingency. It is then clear that this interpretation coincides with von Mises's point of view.

Now recent work has shown that there are other ways to explain this experiment in the frame of a different conception of probability.

The one I will explain has been developed by de Broglie, Bohm, and others.

It rests essentially on the following ideas emphasized by Professor Blockinzev namely:

(1) The micro-objects exist independently of all observation.

(2) It is possible to describe them causally and individually taking into account their individual behaviour and their 'ensemble behaviour'. This individual description will have to take into account the particle-like and wave-like aspects presented by the microphenomena.

(3) As a consequence quantum mechanics is not a description of individual micro-objects but a real statistical theory in the sense that it describes correctly the statistical distributions of the physical quantities defining an ensemble of micro-objects submitted to certain physical conditions. Thus it cannot pretend to give a complete description of the individual behaviour of the individual micro-objects which belong to the 'ensembles' considered in actual experiments.

Our problem is then to indicate a model of individual micro-objects which implies as statistical mechanics for its particle-like aspect precisely the statistics of quantum mechanics.

Now the model I am going to present is evidently not the only one possible which satisfies those conditions. It has been developed by de Broglie, Bohm, myself and others as an attempt to understand quantum mechanics in terms of a deeper behaviour of matter. But though it has progressed in that direction and covers the greater part of known results its new consequences have not yet been tested by experiment. So it should not be taken dogmatically but considered as a possible step. The basic idea is the following. Instead of saying that the micro-object is either a wave or a particle, we assume it is objectively a wave and a particle at the same time; or rather that it has simultaneously wave- and particle-like aspects.

In the first approximation you can assume that ψ is a real wave field (representing something very similar to a real spin wave) propagating in a chaotic sub-quantum level of matter. This wave has also a singular non-linear region in its amplitude which represents the particle-like aspect. This region propagates in the sense of Einstein (that is there is a localized concentration of the field which remains in a time-like tube of space-time) in such a way that it follows one of the lines of flow of the hydrodynamical representation of the wave field (that is for example with a flow velocity

$$v_\mu = \frac{\psi^{+}\gamma_\mu\psi}{(\psi^{+}\psi)^2+(\psi^{+}\gamma_5\psi)^2}$$

in the Dirac case or with a velocity $\mathbf{v} = -\nabla S/M$ if $\psi = R \exp iS/\hbar$ in the Schrödinger case).

A particle is thus considered as an average organized excitation of a chaotic subquantum-mechanical level of matter; similar in a sense to a sound wave propagating in the chaos of molecular agitation. It has at the same time both a wave-like and a particle-like aspect.

The Young diffraction experiment is thus explained in the following way for an isolated micro-object. The particle-like aspect moves along a line of flow and passes through one slit. But the wave-like aspect being extended passes through both slits. So that after I the motion of the particle-like concentration is influenced by the wave perturbed by the two slits and finishes its career on certain regions of II only.

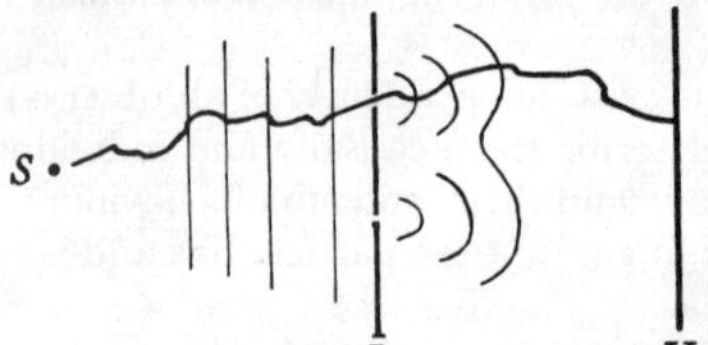

But now you can ask why is the density distribution of an ensemble of micro-objects all of which have the same real ψ field just $P = |\psi|^2$?

As Professor Pauli has pointed out it is not enough to say that if this relation is established initially it holds for all time because of the continuity equation, since any distribution could in principle hold initially.

The answer is that the preceding causal description of the micro-object is not sufficient and that you have to take into account systematically chaotic fluctuations at that level of the description of Nature. These fluctuations could come from phenomena outside the context (such as boundary fluctuations etc.) and also from deeper levels not considered so far so that the particle-like aspect instead of following one line of flow really undergoes a random walk in the ψ field which also oscillates around average values which satisfy the known wave equations. To assume these fluctuations is reasonable since all known physical fields, such as real electromagnetic fields always have complicated and irregular fluctuations. In the electromagnetic case they came from thermal radiation and from the walls of containers, and similarly hydrodynamic fields representing velocity and density distribution of real fluids also have turbulent fluctuations about an average satisfying simplified equations. Hence it is reasonable to assume that ψ undergoes random fluctuations about an average that satisfies Schrödinger's equations.

The details of these fluctuations are not relevant here, since they belong to a finer description of Nature. All that is necessary is to make some reasonable assumption of their average effect and see the result on the distribution of the density P of the particle-like aspect.

Now if you make the most simple assumptions namely:

(1) That on the average ψ satisfies the usual wave equations;

(2) That particle-like aspects follow the lines of flow of ψ real;

(3) That the fluctuations are independent of ψ, and of time and that they provoke jumps from one average-line of flow to any other line;

(4) That they are acyclic in the sense of Markoff; that is that no region around any point is forbidden in such a jump and that in a finite time there is a finite probability of passing from any line of flow to another;

then you can demonstrate as Professor Bohm and myself have done that you are dealing with a particular case of a time-dependent Markoff process and that the density P of the particle-like aspects associated with the same average ψ necessarily goes towards an equilibrium distribution which is just $P = |\psi|^2$. Moreover you can show that this equilibrium distribution is reached exponentially (according to a law $|P-|\psi|^2| < ke^{-\lambda t}$ with k and λ constant) in a very short relaxation time which should be of the order of 10^{-23} seconds. In other words the statistical distributions of quantum mechanics are to be considered as equilibrium distributions reached after very short times by ensembles of micro-objects submitted to the same average physical conditions.

This shows how Professor Bohm and myself propose to go beyond the present limitation of knowledge implied by the present interpretation. Instead of starting from Born's probability distribution we attempt to show how it can be understood as an equilibrium statistical law (analogous to Maxwell's distribution in the kinetic theory of gases) coming from fluctuations at a deeper level. We do not wish to return to Laplacian determinism and to reduce all laws to causal laws. In fact we think that it is one of the greatest achievements of Bohr and his school to have stressed the importance of statistical behaviour in the microscopic domain and established their mathematical form. All future theory must take that into account but we don't agree that such laws represent an ultimate limit to knowledge. We would prefer to say that at all levels of Nature you have a mixture of causal and statistical laws (which come from deeper or external processes). As you progress from one level to another you get new qualitative laws. Causal laws at one level can result from averages of statistical behaviour at a deeper level, which in turn can be explained by deeper causal behaviour and so on *ad infinitum*. If you then admit that Nature is infinitely complex and that in consequence no final state of scientific knowledge can ever be reached you see that at any stage of scientific knowledge causal and probability laws are necessary to describe the behaviour of any phenomenon and that any phenomenon is a combination of causal and random properties inextricably interwoven with one another. All things in Nature then appear as a dialectical synthesis of the infinitely complex motion of the matter out of which they surge and grow and into which they finally are bound to disappear.

Discussion[1]

Braithwaite. I haven't much to say because I so much approve of what Professor Popper has said. I should merely like to make a historical point: the language Popper used resembles what will be found in some notes which C. S. Peirce wrote in 1910, where he says that to state that a die has a certain probability of falling, for instance, with six uppermost is to state that it has a certain 'would-be' which is analogous to a habit; and that this 'would-be', like other habits, though testable by experiment, cannot be reduced to results of experiment. Popper expresses the frequency theory in the same admirable way by using the term 'propensity' to emphasize the similarity of a probability to a habit. At one place he seemed to me to be making a distinction which doubtfully exists. He spoke as if his 'propensity' interpretation was superior to the theory which he had held before, in that a propensity is a property of an experimental arrangement rather than of a set of events. But the set of events has to be specified by reference to the experimental situation; so I think this is a distinction without a difference. Professor Popper is perfectly right, however, in emphasizing that a probability (e.g. of falling with heads uppermost) is not a property of a coin in itself, but is a property of a coin with respect to a particular sort of coin-throwing situation.

Hutten. I don't agree at all with what Professor Popper said. I cannot see that his propensity interpretation is in any way better than the straightforward frequency interpretation, for example, of Reichenbach. There is a slight improvement, it is true, on the frequency interpretation; the probability of a die to show a certain face uppermost when thrown being one-sixth is characterized as a physical property of a physical die. This is now slightly improved by saying that it includes not only the die but the way of throwing and the whole set of conditions. But there is still the gross mistake that he takes the relative frequency as a probability. This is inadmissible as it involves something like induction or the regularity of nature which says that what was the relative frequency of yesterday will also be the relevant frequency of tomorrow; in this way what is going to happen in reality is prescribed by rules, and this is inadmissible. There is also another difficulty. Popper talks of a subjective and an objective interpretation; but this dichotomy is by no means as simple as he seems to think it is in quantum mechanics and I am sure that hardly any physicist would agree with what he said about this.

Bastin: Professor Popper's *propensity* interpretation of the probability of a quantum event taking place depends upon the assumption that such a probability is a quantity analogous to the probability of a die falling with a certain face uppermost. Now I want to question this assumption. In the case of a die which exhibits unexpected behaviour there are an indefinitely large number of ways in which we can examine

[1] Professor Popper was not able to attend the meeting. His written reply will be found at the end of this discussion.

the die so as to find more about why it behaves as it does. For example, we can cut it open to see if its density is non uniform, and so on, indefinitely. An elementary particle is however quite different. The number of independent ways we have of discovering and assigning attributes to an elementary particle is strictly limited and the existence of this limit is a profound indication of the difference between an elementary particle and a macroscopic object. Therefore it is the difference between the two rather than what they have in common, from the point of view of statistics, that we need to see explained.

Ayer. It is not at all clear to me what propensities are to be ascribed to. In the case of a die the situation is clear; but this is not so in the case of the horse-race and I don't see how one is going to evaluate the probabilities here in terms of propensities.

Braithwaite. I certainly shouldn't try to apply propensities to the horse-race situation. I should use it as an explanation of probability only as applied to what Popper calls 'experimental situations'.

Mackay. The case of the die is too easy an example because it is static, the horse-race on the other side is too difficult. But there are practical situations in which Popper's distinction is helpful. For example, consider a nerve cell. The 'probability' that a nerve cell will be excited depends on the chemical concentrations and electric fields in the neighbourhood; but the difficulty of the concept of probability as frequency-in-a-sequence is that conditions are not stable enough for you to observe a sequence. You want a concept such that you can say meaningfully and rigorously that the 'probability' is changing rapidly,—more rapidly, maybe, than the impulses are coming out. Therefore it seems to me that to use some other term, such as propensity, is helpful. But now I want to ask Professor Popper whether his 'propensity' is not very similar to the idea of frequency in an ensemble of identical situations, rather than in a sequence. In order to determine the composition of your imaginary ensemble, you have to know the physical parameters, (e.g. temperature, concentration, and so on) of the nerve cell. In this sense, 'propensity' is a physical property of the situation. If this is so, I am not sure how Dr. Hutten's objection applies.

Bohm. I think that in some cases there is some advantage in talking about propensities. An example is the case of statistical mechanics, where probability may have a number of possible definitions. In one definition, it is a certain volume of phase space that is accessible to the representative point of the system concerned. You could say that this volume in some way represents a kind of propensity of the system to act in a certain way. That must be combined with some idea that the system has a tendency to fluctuate over its possible states, such that, in the long run, the propensities of many single systems would come out close to their relative frequencies. In this sense there seems to be a contribution to distinguish between propensity and relative frequency. Still, I don't think it solves any problems of quantum mechanics. The wave-particle duality is just as difficult when you regard it through propensities as when you regard it in any other way.

Kneale. Professor Popper is quite right, I think, to draw a distinction between the subjective and the objective and to say that subjective probability has no place in the formation of physical theory. The subjective comes in when one is dealing with probability as a property of opinion, when one is commending opinions to people. But there is another context in which one talks simply of the probability of an A-thing's being B, and, in this latter context a subjective interpretation is quite inappropriate. Now, in the past, the frequency theory, as presented, for example, by von Mises and Reichenbach, has enjoyed an improper advantage among physicists and scientists in general because it has been the only theory in the field which seems to be clearly objective. More recently the difficulties of the frequency interpretation, i.e. the muddles, if not the plain contradictions, which can be found in von Mises, have become well known, and I suppose that these are the considerations which have led Professor Popper to abandon that interpretation of probability. But in suggesting a 'propensity' interpretation, he seems to be doing no more than provide a new name for objective probability. What we really want is an objectivist analysis of the probability of an A-thing's being B which is yet not a frequency theory. I should like to conclude by asking M. Vigier if he could go a little farther in his account of an objective probability, as distinct from a frequency. Does he believe that his account involves the notion of equal possibility?

Darwin. As I understand Professor Popper's paper this is not on the quantum theory but on the basis of probability theory. We have all been physicists and we tend to think about probability on the basis of relative frequency. We have, frankly, from the point of view of probability, a very easy problem, as we can regard it as frequency in all the things we do. But there has got to be a theory of probability which is not a frequency-theory, as I can show by citing the case of the horse-race. When I bet and take the odds as four to one on the horse winning the race I do not mean that I know that this horse is going to run the race 100 times and to win 20 times; I am absolutely certain that it is not going to run 100 times; therefore I have got to have an independent, separate idea of probability. Now, whether four to one is the propensity of the horse to win one in four—I think it is—but I don't think that it does anything but use the word propensity instead of probability. I would also like to raise a question which I feel is very important, and that is the question of inverse probability. It is a most important question for the theory of probability, but fortunately in quantum mechanics you are practically free of it—what prior probabilities you have is either Dirac or Einstein.

Vigier. I think the case of the horse race and the case where you have relative frequencies are two separate questions. The word 'probability' has just introduced confusion. The word has a meaning only in the second case where you have an ensemble and calculate relative frequencies. In the other case, the word is just confusing the issue and the word 'probability' there is not a good word at all.

Darwin. You don't believe in betting.

Vigier. I don't think betting is probability theory—it is amusing in itself. The second question raises a very important point. It raises the question of chaos and randomness. Now it is true that there is no general demonstration of the ergodic theorem, but in a series of particular cases you can show that uncorrelated causes or causes which are correlated in a very complex way do lead to distributions given by the theory of probability, and that in my opinion is the way in which the theory of probability should be tackled. Even in the case of classical mechanics you would be able to show that if you throw an unbiased die, it would eventually produce a distribution which is described by the calculus of probability—but I do not want to reduce probability to such a causal analysis, as the two must always be taken as intercorrelated and we must always push the analysis to a deeper and deeper level.

Gallie. I agree with Mr. Kneale that Popper has not explained the notion of probability by the word 'propensity', but he may have done something sound, namely he may have given us the beginning of a philosophical exposition of the notion of probability: he is trying to emphasize that probabilities are *bona fide* elements in reality—they just do occur and they are as real properties of processes as are ordinary properties, although they are only displayed through a long sequence of events. It must of course be admitted that this is a beginning and not an explanation—it still remains to be shown how and why propensities arise in these peculiar circumstances—and perhaps a different kind of explanation would have to be given in different cases.

Scriven. The suggestion that by calling it a 'propensity' one does no more than rechristen it seems to me an error very much like saying that when calling a substance 'soluble' one does no more than say that when it is put into water it will dissolve. Now, it has been very commonly said that these two things are exactly identical, but one can argue and suggest that in fact there is a difference here, although it is not a difference which would affect one in a practical situation; it is a difference in the language that is being used: one commits oneself to a standard experimental procedure for deciding whether the succession of being put into water and subsequently dissolving is in fact due to the substance being soluble or is alternatively due to something else. In the same way, it seems to me to be logically incorrect to identify a probability with frequency, although for practical purposes this is a useful equivalent and in certain circumstances it is never going to cause trouble.

Hutten. Professor Vigier said that already in classical physics he had a mixture of deterministic and statistical laws. Now, what exactly do we mean by a statistical law? In the classical case we say that the individual effect is rigidly determined by the equations of motion, whereas the phenomena *en masse* are described by statistics. But then we must never forget that we uphold the deterministic laws in a very strange way as a fiction, as in many cases we are not able to determine the initial conditions. We have to take an average and in this way produce statistics. But this case, I think, is quite a different case from the one Bohm seems to have had in mind this morning, which is much more profound. And it is also different from the way in which Einstein originally introduced the fluctuations in connexion with the needle radiation in his derivation of the blackbody radiation, where he started out by saying that the average energy was in one case given by the Rayleigh-Jeans law and in the other case by the distribution law. He so obtained a sum in which one part must be due to photons with the characteristic of particles and the other one due to something with the characteristic of waves. Here we have a mixture of two different kinds of laws, or rather two different kinds of processes, which makes this case essentially different from the rather trivial case of classical statistical mechanics which rests on an idealization anyway and which uses also some rather metaphysical ideas.

Süssmann. Yesterday I said that it is not possible to derive the probabilistic principles of a statistical theory, such as of quantum mechanics, or of classical statistical mechanics, from purely mechanical principles even if the ergodic theorem had been proved. I think that this objection has not been refuted, neither by Professor Bohm nor by Professor Vigier. In order to underline this I would like to add that probability is a non-mechanical concept which therefore needs non-mechanical axioms. If it were possible to derive probabilistic principles from purely mechanical laws then the second law of thermo-dynamics would not hold. We should then be able to draw conclusions about the past just as we draw conclusions about the future. Hence I think a thermo-dynamical principle is needed, a principle about the distribution of initial conditions—I call it a thermo-dynamical principle because it essentially transcends mechanics—and only then the second law of thermo-dynamics can be derived.

Bohm. I think there is a relation between the axiomatic school of mathematicians such as Kolmogoroff and the propensity-theory. It is the point of view of these mathematicians that you must not identify relative frequency and probability, that probability depends on the things that we are talking about and possibly the environment and the whole process which determines the result. In the case of throwing a die the probability would be a property of the die and the person who threw it in a certain way. Now, I would like to know in what way the propensity theory differs from this view of Kolmogoroff and the mathematicians. I think that I agree with the idea that relative frequency should not be identified with probability, but whether the propensity is the right way to solve the problem I am not quite sure.

Mackay. I think we keep missing Professor Popper's point because of Professor Braithwaite's analogy between propensities and habits. Habit is a backward-looking word; propensity is a forward-looking word. I think Popper means us not to think of something with a past, like a habit, but he means rather a structural property here and now. My second question concerns the interpretation of Schrödinger waves. When I teach wave mechanics I use the analogy of a wave of influenza moving over the country. This does not mean that influenza victims move over the country, it means that when the wave hits a given town there is a greater probability of the incidence of particular events, namely, the impact-of-influenza on members of the population. Now, although this does not entail speaking about *influenza victims* anywhere between the source and the sink, it does entail the notion that there is something on the move between the two.

Vigier. Yes, germs!

Mackay. My question is whether this theory of Professor Bohm is not analogous in some sense to a theory of the infection process behind waves of influenza?

Fierz. I would like to object against the claim that in statistical mechanics you have to introduce a probability notion, and especially that such a notion is necessary for the derivation of the second theorem. This was settled in the old discussion of Boltzmann with Zermelo and others about the H theorem and the ergodic theorem. It is of course true that you cannot give a general proof of the ergodic theorem, but at least this theorem is in itself a purely mechanical theorem. Moreover there is a special case where we can prove the ergodic theorem, namely the case of the movement of a mass point on a plane of constant negative curvature. And if you have the theorem then all of statistical mechanics follows.

Rosenfeld. No. You need to introduce a coarse-grained density.

Fierz. This has nothing to do with probability theory; this has only to do with the notion of a macroscopic observer. But I do not want to enter into the discussion too long—I only wanted to say that there are other people who have a different opinion and who would vote as I have done. Another point arises from the theorem of inverse probabilities, for I think that the degree of our belief in a theory is judged by that theorem. Now, usually one isn't aware of this, because one simply puts the degree of belief equal to unity for all possible hypotheses, a procedure for which there exists no logical reason.

Pryce. I want to criticize a straight mistake by Popper. He says that the quantum theory is a probability theory just as any other game of chance and this he illustrates by taking a quantum example which is one from Dirac's book about a photon going through a polarizer. The other example is of the tossing of a coin—one tosses it, one is short-sighted and one can't see whether it is heads or tails. In the quantum-situation he says the photon can be in one of two states and if one makes the observation then one forces it into being either in the one or in the other eigen state and when one looks at the penny then the Copenhagen spirit—a beautiful sneer—enters into one and forces the penny into one of its eigenstates. There is, I think, a very fundamental difference between the quantum situation and the penny. When you say 'one of its eigenstates' for the penny you are quite right—it is either heads or tails and that is independent of the observation—when you are talking of the photon it has not only two, it has any linear combination made out of two linearly-independent states and that is an infinite number.[1]

Ayer. A question to Professor Vigier and to Professor Bohm: what do they mean by causal law? In Hume's analysis, to state a causal law is to state what uniformly happens and if one accepts this analysis it doesn't seem to me that the difference between causal laws and statistical laws is a very great one; but there is an enormous difference between saying what happens in a hundred per cent of cases and what happens in eighty per cent of cases. Now, as I understand them, Professor Vigier's and Professor Bohm's programme is to explain statistical phenomena on the basis of

[1] Having now read at leisure Professor Popper's text I find I had misjudged him, and I am quite satisfied that his point is valid and correct. [M. H. L. Pryce.]

what Bohm called 'deeper theories'. This is extremely exciting and extremely important if it comes off. What I don't see is whether it is necessary from their point of view that the elements in this deeper theory should obey causal laws.

Bohm. As I said before, there are many causal laws which can give good approximations to the laws of probability in the sense of relative frequency. Nevertheless this is not a perfect representation of a law of probability; there is always some difference between the predictions of this causal law and the—let me call it the 'determinate law'. I think we should make a definition of terms at this point. By a uniquely determinate law we mean a law that aims to determine completely and precisely what is going to happen in every detail. Now a statistical law is any law which holds for a large collection of objects, events or any such things independently of certain kinds of details. We can even get precisely determinate statistical laws, such as, for example, the law of the uniform motion of the centre of mass of a collection of atoms. It is just the fact that there exist laws which can be expressed without knowing everything about everything which enables us to formulate laws of nature. As I have explained before there is no case where those laws are completely satisfied—there will always be some discrepancy between the predictions of an underlying determinate law and any set of laws of probability. This discrepancy, I think, is an advantage rather than a disadvantage. First of all we do not know that any set of laws of probability is absolutely and universally true—we only know that it is true in some approximation and in some domain. From the point of view which I am proposing this is hardly surprising as single events are always dependent on an enormous number of factors which fluctuate in a very complicated way. As a result, the laws of probability are nearly right. Now these factors are not always as disconnected as we thought, some hidden connexion may exist which we discover by more frequent experimenting. There has been a general tendency to stress the fact that laws of probability contain causal laws as a limiting case, but it goes the other way as well. If you take a causal law as a limiting case of a law of probability it will not be a perfect causal law but only an approximate case; and if you take a law of probability as a limiting case of a causal law it will also be only an approximate law of probability. So if you suppose the infinity of nature then—no matter how far you carry the laws—there will always be something outside, something that gives rise to fluctuations. Hence no causal law can be perfectly exact. On the other hand, however, every fluctuation comes from some causes and therefore no law of probability can be perfectly exact. Whereas a law of probability states that certain events are absolutely random and have no systematic relation to each other, they may in fact have a relation which can only be revealed at a deeper level. So in reality events are related by causal laws and by laws of probability as well as by still other kinds of laws which have not yet been developed. I do not wish to stress that we are looking only for a causal law, but I wish to stress that to try to reduce nature to either of these two extremes is metaphysical. As regards the question of reversibility—I do not think that this question is yet fully understood. I think that the notion of infinity of nature will explain it on the basis of the notion that every reversible law always leaves out an infinity of factors, which could render it irreversible. I think that if you work it out it could probably be shown that with an infinity of variables there could be no reversal. In fact, Schrödinger has already done this for a special case. Finally the question of Hume: I think that one should say that causality is some abstraction—some approximation—from reality: because of the infinity of nature you cannot have any finite perfect causality. No law is ever perfectly correct and therefore one must finally find a contradiction. Then by studying the details of the contradiction one will be able to abstract another law which is more general and contains the former one as a special case. This is the general method of science. Now at first sight it looks like a tautology because it seems to say that law works because it works. But the very existence of science shows that it isn't a tautology. If you follow such a procedure systematically you actually will learn about the world. Of course there is no perfectly universal law which holds in all cases. For every law is abstracted out of a certain domain of cases. Nevertheless, it generally holds in a still broader domain of cases. One must keep on using it until one comes to a contradiction; and by studying all the details of the contradiction, one comes to a still broader law.

Polanyi. I would like to warn against Professor Vigier's and Professor Bohm's attempt to use the notion of complexity instead of the notion of randomness—I do not think those notions are synonymous. A painting, for instance, is very complex and has very complex relations of its various parts but those parts are not arranged at random.

Bopp. Is it correct that Professor Vigier wants to interpret this distance of 10^{-13} cm or the corresponding time of 10^{-23} secs. as an upper limit which doesn't follow from the theory but which is derived from the assumption that no deterministic interpretation should contradict the uncertainty relation?

Vigier. Your question contains two points which must be considered separately. The first point is: if you make the assumptions we have made—the Markoff process—then you can prove that the law has this form. Naturally the factors will depend on the nature of the fluctuations themselves; the choice of the constants amounts to a physical hypothesis on the nature of the fluctuations themselves, and this is a point that should be decided experimentally. Of course, the limit you have given has been chosen in order not to come into contradiction with Heisenberg's uncertainty principle; but what we know is that the law has this form.—Now if in the controversy about the derivability of statistics from mechanics I were supposed to vote, I would vote with Professor Fierz, because I think that the statistical laws are also limiting cases. The fact that the ergodic theorem can be proved in a particular case shows that you can understand the probability law as a limit of very complex procedures—I also think that using the word complexity instead of chaos is a step forward and not a step backwards because chaos cannot be defined mathematically. But complexity and non-correlation of causes which provokes the distribution can be attacked by mathematical devices, which has a definite advantage.

Finally I would agree with Dr. Mackay that the wave may be regarded as something like an influenza wave. It is in a way comparable with a spin wave in a chaos of rotating structures.

Bopp. My next question is a consequence of what M. Vigier has just been saying. If Vigier's considerations are not refuted by detailed tests, then his results are of the greatest interest because they contain a point which enables us to subject to experimental tests the things we have been discussing this afternoon. But now the following paradoxical situation may arise. Assume that Vigier's theory can be established satisfactorily on a mathematical basis, and that it leads to the statement that 10^{-13} is a lower limit admissible for lengths. Assume that on the other hand, it is completely impossible to scrutinize this domain experimentally. How would you judge such a situation?

Vigier. I think there would be a way of testing the theory, even if not by direct experimentation in that particular field. We could develop the consequences of this theory. The theory considers the particles as excitations of that fundamental field, and if it predicts the mass spectrum and the way in which particles decay into each other, then we get an indirect way of showing the validity of the theory; and in fact that is the way certain parts of the theory can be tested. If I remember correctly, the atomic theory was tested in this way. The first verification was not the discovery of the atoms themselves but it was an indirect verification on the basis of Brownian motion of the existence of atoms which you could not see.

Rosenfeld. I only want to interject a pedantic remark about the question of thermodynamics. I don't think really that this is a question for voting. I am sure that Dr. Süssmann thought that his remark was quite innocuous in the sense that it would be accepted by everybody, that you cannot expect to derive an irreversible behaviour of phenomena from laws which are essentially reversible.

Groenewold. I have a question for Professor Vigier. On the one hand there is his mathematical description of quantum phenomena and we can calculate from it things which can be observed, namely the spots on a certain screen. On the other hand there is the matter of interpretation, namely the question which language has to be used when we are talking about what happens in between the source and the sink. Now I would like to see how he would deal, on the basis of the formalism and of his kind of interpretation, with another well-known experiment which originally was used as an argument in favour of such a deterministic description, namely the experiment discussed by Einstein, Rosen and Podolsky and commented upon by Bohr. Now here in the two cases discussed (measurement of position or measurement of momentum) we have two different waves. From your point of view, these waves are some real waves propagating in three dimensional space. Now assume that we first decide to measure the position but at the last moment we change our mind and we measure the momentum, does then the wave we first used—the plane wave—hurry back in order to start anew in a different form—or how do you explain this case in your realistic picture?

Bohm. There are various ways to deal with this problem. In one way we may accept the notion of infinite velocity. If you don't like to do this there are other ways. Consider the sub-quantum-mechanical level and remember the analogy that the electron and the observing apparatus are like icebergs, most of them are not directly visible at our level. They are in intimate and complex connexion at the lower level. Now, an apparatus is also made of electrons which also exists partially on the lower level. Under normal conditions the apparatus and the electron have no close relationship between them, as the fluctuations which are going on on the lower level do not produce any systematic coordination between the apparatus and the electron. But under special conditions it is possible that there are co-ordinated fluctuations arising at the lower level which will simultaneously affect the electron and the apparatus, so that under those conditions the electron and the apparatus will work together. For example, even in classical mechanics, two resonant oscillators may fall into a coordinated motion, although they may be very far from each other, and therefore only in very weak interaction. Two experimental methods exist for testing such an idea. One is the observation of two photons which have been created in a positron-electron annihilation; their directions of polarization are co-ordinated in a way which resembles this paradox. In this case the actual experiment demonstrates that the quantum-mechanical prediction is verified. This is the nearest that there is to a proof of the paradox. But you must remember that this experiment is done with an apparatus which has been sitting around for quite a while. There has been plenty of time for it to come to a thorough equilibrium in the sub-quantum-mechanical level. As a result, one could argue that the very process by which the positron-electron pair decays need not be independent of the process by which it will be scattered in the next part of the apparatus that measures its polarization. Rather, the motion of the apparatus could be coordinated to that of the photons by small but hidden sub-quantum connexions. To avoid this possibility, we could do the experiment more rapidly. While the photons are still in flight, we could change the orientation of the apparatus. This has not been, however, actually done, and we do not know what the result would be if it were done. The apparatus would have to be re-oriented very rapidly, because the velocity of light is so very large. Hence, if you want to make a sensible experiment you would perhaps have to have the apparatus a few hundred thousand miles away from the source of the photons in order to give time to re-orient the apparatus. It is quite possible that the predictions of the quantum mechanics would turn out to be wrong for that case.—Regarding the question of randomness, it has been said that randomness should not be defined. Well, that's a good way out of the question. Nevertheless if we refrained from defining everything that was puzzling we might avoid very many interesting questions. What I'm trying to propose is that between randomness and complete regularity there are all kinds of intermediate situations. In most cases distant things have no regular relation to each other and they are random. In some cases, however, distant things do have a co-ordination, as I tried to show when discussing experiments to test the paradox of Einstein, Rosen and Podolsky.

Ryle. I want to back one point which Professor Polanyi made and to attack another. One point I want to protest with him against is the identification of the complex with the chaotic. The inside of my car is clearly very complex but only sometimes is it chaotic. Professor Vigier and Professor Bohm define the chaotic, I think, in terms of the factors being caused independently of one another. I think in calling things complex we do not imply that they are independent but merely that they are intricate.

So I do suggest that a confusion is brought in by trying to explain randomness just in terms of complexity. Again Professor Polanyi seemed to fall into the trap of saying that randomness has got something mysterious about it, and at one point he even spoke as if randomness accounted for the behaviour of the cards and of the shuffler of the pack. As if randomness was a sort of fairy who does things to the cards. But in this case the notion of randomness is quite simple, namely, the reactions of the cards to the shuffler's fingers are not determined by the pictures on the faces of those cards. But of course, if the cards are painted badly with sticky paint, then they are. It's the business of the card maker to see that the reactions of the cards to the shufflers' fingers are not determined by the paint on the front, and consequently, the position of the card in the pack after the shuffle is independent of the pictures on their faces, and this is the main point of what randomness means in the case of shuffled cards.

Prof. Popper's Reply.

I wish to thank the organizers of this conference for enabling me to reply to a most interesting discussion which, unfortunately, I was prevented from attending. And I wish to thank Dr. Feyerabend in particular for reading my paper at the conference, and for keeping me informed about the discussion.

As to the discussion, I can only say that I am extremely pleased about the various reactions, critical as well as affirmative, to my paper.

First, there is a general remark I wish to make.

I have been working on these problems for 29 years; and it is now 29 years since I convinced myself that the quantum riddles are likely to be closely connected with problems inherent in the interpretation of probability. An early result which I still consider correct was the clarification of the problem of the 'reduction of the wave packet'. It can be shown that this problem arises in *all* probability contexts. (Lately I have shown that it also arises in *all* indeterministic theories.) This result misled me by making me underrate the difficulties of the problem; and although I found this out in 1935, it was only four years ago that I turned to the propensity interpretation. I soon saw that with its help, all those elements of subjectivity which some physicists—Einstein, for example, and Schrödinger and Bohm—were reluctant to accept, disappeared from the interpretation of quantum theory without creating any new difficulties.

This new interpretation of quantum theory has now stood up to four years' endeavours to find a flaw in it. I have presented it at some length in a book that is now in the press. The paper submitted to this conference was merely a very brief outline of one of its chapters. You may remember that it was confined in length to twenty minutes.

I am saying these things because they contain my answer to various speakers in the discussion who rightly felt that my paper was only a beginning, and that it did not contain all the answers to the highly pertinent questions which they raised.

One of the speakers (Dr. Mackay) asked me a straightforward question. My answer is: yes. The main difference between the propensity interpretation and a purely statistical frequency interpretation can be put thus. According to the propensity interpretation, probability statements *may* be said to make assertions about *virtual* frequencies; but they may also be said to make assertions about the experimental situation and the 'tendencies' (something like 'forces') inherent in it: the propensity interpretation extends the idea of 'forces' to mere open possibilities—weighted possibilities, of course.

Professor Darwin said that my paper, if he understood it, was not on quantum theory but on the basis of probability theory; and a somewhat similar opinion was expressed in effect by Dr. Bastin. But my central thesis is that a re-examination of the basis of probability theory is capable of solving some of the riddles of quantum theory —riddles which I and others have found disconcerting; and therefore my paper concerns both, probability theory *and* quantum theory.

I was very pleased to see that Professor Bohm endorsed the point (made very briefly in my paper) that the transition from the frequency to the propensity interpretation corresponds to that from a mathematical formalism like that of von Mises to a measure theoretical formalism like that of the French school, Kolmogoroff, and Doob.

But there is a point in Professor Bohm's later intervention with which I cannot agree. It is his very interesting suggestion that we may not only interpret a causal law as a limiting case of a probabilistic law (as we generally do) but also a probability as a limiting case of a causal law. This view seems to me to lead with necessity to the subjectivist interpretation of probability. (In a causal system, probability can enter only with *our lack of knowledge* of the initial conditions.) But I wholeheartedly agree with his later remark that causality is an abstraction from reality, and therefore an approximation. (I have tried, in the book mentioned, to develop this view into a coherent though sketchy picture of the physical world.)

I do not think that Professor Pryce is right about the 'straight mistake' which he believes I made in a very elementary point. No doubt he was misled by the brevity of my wording, and a second reading might convince him that my words were not meant in the way in which he interpreted them. Of course, the photon has, *prior* to its interaction with the polarizer, an infinite number of (virtual) states—as has the penny *prior* to its interaction with the table. But the whole system—the photon plus the given, orientated polarizer—singles out precisely *two* of these virtual states; just as does a smooth table (as opposed to one with a few cracks or slots—of different directions, perhaps—which may catch the penny upright).

Professor Pryce also described what, I hope, was just a little harmless joke of mine, as 'a beautiful sneer'. His remark is understandable if he thought I was trying to belittle Niels Bohr. Nothing was further from my mind. Although I feel unable to accept Bohr's idea of complementarity, my admiration for both the physicist and the man is boundless. If we think of Bohr himself as 'the spirit of Copenhagen' then, indeed, my joke was out of place, and Professor Pryce's remark was a fitting reply to it. But I can only assure him that I did not mean Bohr when I used this phrase, the 'Copenhagen spirit'. What I tried, rather, was to poke fun at those sometimes uncritical admirers of Bohr who coined this phrase, and who linked it, more especially, to the idea of complementarity. Rightly or wrongly, I believe that this idea is lacking in clarity—a value which we should never surrender—and that some of those who speak about complementarity are making a fetish of it. This belief of mine formed the background of my remark.

FOURTH SESSION

Chairman: Professor A. J. AYER

M. Fierz: Does a physical theory comprehend an 'objective, real, single process'?

S. Körner: On philosophical arguments in physics.

M. Polanyi: Beauty, elegance, and reality in science.

Does a physical theory comprehend an 'objective, real, single process'?

by

M. FIERZ

THE so-called 'orthodox' interpretation of quantum theory has been criticized in recent years from different sides, by Einstein, Schrödinger, and de Broglie. These critics think that the ideas about quantum theory put forward by Bohr and others are much too far away from those points of view that have been successful and productive in the development of our science for the last three hundred years.[1] They claim, against the 'orthodox' or 'Copenhagen' school, that wave-mechanics is an incomplete theory, even inside its field of application, because this theory does not comprehend really an 'objective and real single physical process'.[2]

Now everybody acknowledges the great success of wave-mechanics in explaining quantitatively a multitude of physical phenomena. And nobody denies that our theory, as it stands, is incomplete, as there is no mathematically irreproachable relativistic generalization. Just because of this the question arises, in what direction we should search for a better relativistic theory. It seems to us that our 'heterodox' colleagues think it might be helpful to look for a theory which can be interpreted more akin to classical mechanics or field theory. Surely it is not their aim to translate only the physical contents of quantum theory as it stands, into a language different from the one of Bohr.

I think, indeed, that the ideas developed by Bohr during the growth of quantum theory will not lose their leading character. I further expect that the new features characterizing Bohr's way of thinking, will even be more dominant in a new and better relativistic quantum theory. Such a theory will lead to physical ideas even more different from those of old.

Only the future can decide if I am right or wrong. At the moment there is no possibility of proof, as no such a theory has been discovered. But we can try to justify our point of view by plausible arguments. To do so, we may ask: does classical theory describe really an 'objective and real single process'? Our critics would answer this question in the positive—at least I think so, as they are in quest of a 'realistic' theory.

If one takes 'real' as opposed to 'ideal'—against this one could argue with good reasons indeed—one might say: a physical theory never describes real events. It treats always idealized systems, as only these are capable of mathematical treatment.

[1] E. Schrödinger, *Act. phys., Austr.* **1**, (1948) p. 216.

[2] A. Einstein, B. Podolsky, N. Rosen, *Phys. Rev.*, **47** (1935) 777, L. de Broglie, *La Physique quantique restera-t-elle indeterministe?* (Paris 1953). See also the literature quoted in P. Fevrier, *L'interpretation physique de la mécanique ondulatoire* (Paris, 1956).

One may however, claim the idealization to be a simplification only, not referring to any essential features of the system under consideration. But the distinction between the essential and the inessential already contains a theoretical element; and theory itself seems to me something ideal. I don't want to pursue further the questions following from this consideration. This would lead us to rather general problems, not directly linked to our special question. This question is: does classical physics describe or comprehend single physical events? It does indeed, but only in so far as these can be looked at as an example, contained in a class or ensemble of similar events. The judgement that such events are similar and form a class is naturally always a theoretical one. And by this judgement some features of a given event must be taken as inessential. To these so-called inessential features now belong those which make our event a single and unique one, showing up here and now. So, in some sense, physical theory never comprehends a real single process.

To make this statement clearer, I refer to Kepler's theory of the solar system, a theory belonging to a pre-physical state of science. Kepler was convinced that the sun is the centre of the universe. He held the universe to be a singular harmonic structure, a cosmos, contained in the sphere of the fixed stars. The infinite space of Giordano Bruno, containing an infinity of worlds, seemed to him to be a horrible exile. His own theory was meant to explain the one harmonic universe. He wanted to understand why there are just 6 planets, circling at well defined distances around the sun. By constructing, in a most ingenious way, the spheres of the planets with the help of the 5 regular or 'platonic' bodies, he thought he had reached his goal. The order in which he had to arrange the bodies seemed to him to be mathematically unique, and as there are just five of them, he claimed to have explained the uniqueness of our world. This still remarkable theory is very beautiful, but we no longer believe in it.

In Newton's theory, which we think to be right, the solar system is just one example taken from the innumerable systems of planets created by God in infinite space. Newton had no ability, nor did he feel any need, to explain the number 6 of our planets—and there are really more than 6.

So Newton's theory just does not achieve what Kepler held to be of utmost importance for a theory of the solar system. It foretells neither the number of the planets nor their distances from the sun. There is also no longer any essential difference between planets and comets, a difference which was very marked in all old theories of the solar system.

The strength of Newton's theory is not to explain the unique structure of this system, but to comprehend in general terms the movement of any system of planets, independently of the number and the bulk of the celestial bodies contained in it.

Classical mechanics does not give equations for a definite movement of the masses in a system, but for all their possible movements. The real movement taking place depends on initial conditions, corresponding to the constants of integration of differential equations. These initial conditions have to be known experimentally. From the theoretical point of view they are arbitrary. If there were a law stating only one initial condition to be possible, the theory would lose much of its sense, as 'almost all' of its statements would refer to something impossible. There would be no reason either to assume the only path possible to be embedded in a family of curves, fulfilling certain differential equations of second order. I think the theoretical arbitrariness of the initial conditions, the fact that they have to be given experimentally, is an essential feature of classical mechanics. It shows this theory to be one belonging to an experimental science, where the experimenter has the freedom to interfere with a system and may form an initial state corresponding to his aims.

Against this, one may point out that there are systems, as the system of planets, where we cannot change the initial state. That's true. But the laws ruling over the movements of the planets are the same as those ruling over the fall of a stone on earth. These we can explore experimentally, and we can verify them with different examples. One is the solar system, in which Jupiter with his moons can be looked at as a second small and independent one. Similarly we are able to understand the processes in the interior of the sun, where we can't do any experiments. They can be explored with the help of terrestrial experiments, because these processes are not peculiar to the sun. By this again the sun becomes but an example of a system, where such processes take place. It seems to me, that all this was clear to Newton, when he wrote his second *regula philosophandi:*

> Ideoque effectuum naturalium eiusdem generis eaedem sunt causae: descensus lapidum in Europa et America, lucis in igne culinari et in Sole, reflexionis lucis in terra et in planetis.

From our point of view, the idea of Laplace that the whole world is nothing but a huge mechanical machine seems rather queer. In this picture there is no room for an experimenter as all initial conditions are given for ever. This is quite contrary to Newton's outlook, who even in his cosmological speculations assumed God to be the great experimenter, who changes from time to time, according to his purpose, the state of the world. In Laplace's view, we cannot take the whole world as an example of a possible world, as by definition there doesn't exist any other one. The situation becomes quite different indeed if we base our cosmology on the assumption that the world is homogeneous in the large scale. If this is done, every region big enough can be looked at as representative of the whole world. A given region, for example the one we are able to survey, can be taken as an example for any region. In such a theory everything distinguishing one region from another must be looked at as accidental, and so in some sense as inessential. Thus such a theory needs to be a statistical one.

We may sum up all this with the statement that physical laws refer to reproducible phenomena only. Correspondingly, an experiment is meaningful only if it is reproducible. Although physics is not bound to experimentally reproducible events, it can only treat phenomena where every single event can be taken as representative of an ensemble or class of similar events.

Now in some sense every real event is something single and unique and happens never again. But this feature of reality is outside physical theories. As this is true for classical theory, we should not be astonished, if it is more so in quantum theory. This is a statistical theory, and as such very well fitted to treat reality, in so far it consists of reproducible phenomena. Therefore it is a logical and natural development. The dominant role the experimenter or observer plays here, if we interpret the theory as Bohr does, clarifies the general feature of physical theories. To me this seems definite progress.

If somebody wants to construct a theory, comprehending the unreproducible reality of a single event, and this seems to me the only other consequent alternative, he should not only discard Bohr's ideas on what a physical theory can be, but even those of Newton. He should look for a theory which in its whole character is more akin to Kepler's ideas—and even Kepler's theory, as he himself understood it, is highly platonic!

I do not believe that in such a way the actual problems of relativistic quantum theory come nearer to a solution.

On philosophical arguments in physics

by

S. KÖRNER

WHEN the task in hand is not the solution of problems within some established conceptual framework, but rather the construction of the framework, physicists tend to use philosophical arguments. The creators of quantum mechanics, for instance, now and then interrupt their physical and mathematical reasoning by appealing to certain general philosophical principles in order to support positions which they are defending as physicists.

The present paper is an attempt to clarify the relation between these philosophical principles and the physical theories which they are alleged to support; and thus to clarify to some extent the relation between philosophy and physics.

(1) *Physical formalisms and physical explanations.* Although the invention of a particular physical formalism may require rare intellectual gifts and its efficient manipulation long training, the general structure of such formalisms is clear enough and on the whole uncontroversial.[1] A physical formalism consists on the one hand of a mathematical part or calculus. It gives rules for the formation of formulae from given signs and for turning well-formed formulae into new ones which are again well-formed; and it selects some well-formed formulae as postulates. On the other hand it consists of an interpretation, i.e. rules of reference which relate the signs and formulae to possible observations, in such a manner that some of the interpreted formulae express empirical laws of nature. These latter are either causal or statistical correspondences between empirical predicates. Once the general structure of physical formalisms is exhibited, their function in the achievement of conceptual economy, in prediction, and in the technical control of events is easily seen.

The notion of a physical formalism is narrower than the notion of a physical explanation: for a formalism may be reasonably criticized for lacking certain characteristics which it must possess, in addition to those mentioned, if it is to be a satisfactory explanation. Similarly, two physical formalisms which cover the same ground or, more precisely, which imply the same empirical laws of nature, may be reasonably compared with respect to their explanatory power. The distinction between a physical formalism as such, and one which by conforming to additional requirements is qualified to function as an explanation, has also been expressed, among other ways, by saying that only the latter makes the phenomena intelligible. Examples of the distinction being made by physicists come easily to mind and will be given below.

[1] For accounts by physicists see e.g. Hertz, *Die Prinzipien der Mechanik* etc., Leipzig 1894, Introduction; and Dirac, *Quantum Mechanics*, 3rd edition, Oxford 1947, p. 15; for accounts by philosophers e.g. Duhem, *La Théorie Physique: Son Objet, Sa Structure*, 2nd edition, Paris, 1914; Popper, *Logik der Forschung*, Vienna 1935; Braithwaite, *Scientific Explanation*, Cambridge 1953.

Whereas the notion of a physical formalism is unambiguous, the notion of a physical explanation (of physical intelligibility, etc.) changes from one group of physicists to another. A physicist's statement to the effect that a certain formalism is or is not an explanation, or that it is a better explanation than another, expresses the fact that he has adopted a normative or regulative principle to which he requires physical formalisms to conform. The importance which he attaches to the principle may, of course, vary from individual to individual. But, if it carries any weight at all, its acceptor will, if confronted with the choice between two physical formalisms both of which imply the same empirical laws of nature and of which only one conforms to the principle, prefer that which does so conform.

The regulative principles which express what various physicists require of an explanatory or intelligible formalism are closely related to, if not identical with, propositions of speculative philosophy or metaphysics. The classic instance is the principle of causality—say in its Kantian formulation as the second analogy of experience.[2] Whatever other meaning or function this principle may have for the theoretical physicist who has adopted it, it will function as a principle of conduct—a principle regulating, more or less strictly, his construction of physical formalisms and his choice between them.

The adoption or rejection of any rule by a person is a contingent fact. It is always conceivable, however unlikely it may be, that a physicist should have no adopted regulative principles by which to distinguish intelligible from unintelligible, or more from less intelligible, formalisms. If, however, a physicist has adopted a regulative principle it will have a role to play in his reasonings.

(2) *Arguments which operate by confronting physical formalisms with regulative principles.* Among arguments involving regulative principles we can distinguish roughly two types: those which simply confront a physical formalism with a regulative principle which is assumed to be generally adopted or whose adoption is, at least, not called into question; and those which are intended to influence the adoption or rejection of some regulative principle.

Some of Schrödinger's arguments in favour of his version of wave mechanics are good examples of the simple confrontation of a formalism with regulative principles. In his first paper on *Quantisation as an Eigenvalue-problem*[3] he considers as 'more congenial' (*sympathischer*) the idea that 'in a quantum process energy makes a transition from one form of vibration to another' than the 'idea of jumping electrons'. In his second paper on the subject he declares the suggestion to the effect that 'the events in the atom cannot be subsumed under the spatio-temporal mode of thinking' as being 'from the philosophical point of view . . . an unconditional surrender' (*loc. cit.* p. 36).

These and similar remarks are remarks concerning the explanatory power or intelligibility of formalisms which from the point of view of logic and experimental confirmation are unobjectionable. One therefore at once looks out for some formulation of regulative principles. A very clear statement of such is found in a paper by the same author written twenty years later. 'The *intelligibility* of the picture (namely the world-view of natural science) permits no deviation from the necessity with

[2] *Kritik der reinen Vernunft*, Akademie edition III, p. 166.

[3] *Gesammelte Abhandlungen zur Wellenmechanik*, Leipzig, 1928, p. 15.

which in a spatio-temporal process (*im raumzeitlichen Ablauf*) every subsequent stage is determined by the preceding'.[4] The regulative character of this statement is made unmistakeable by the occurrence in it of the term 'permits'.

Again Einstein's dissatisfaction with contemporary quantum mechanics is based quite expressly on his having adopted a regulative principle to which he thinks any wholly intelligible physical formalism must conform. What he finds unsatisfactory in the quantum theory 'is its attitude towards that which appears to be the *programmatic* aim of all physics: the complete description of any (individual) real situation (as it supposedly exists irrespective of any act of observation or substantiation)'.[5]

Those who disagree with Einstein and Schrödinger show that they are well aware how largely the dispute is due to the disputing parties having adopted incompatible regulative principles. Their choice of words, one would almost say their tone of voice, suggest disagreements about rules of conduct. Thus Pauli, in a letter quoted by Born, not only predicts that 'the statistical character of the function, and thus of the laws of nature . . . will determine the style of the laws for at least some centuries' but also declares that 'to dream of a way back, back to the classical style of Newton-Maxwell' seems to him 'hopeless, off the way, bad taste'.[6]

(3) *Arguments supporting the adoption or rejection of regulative principles.* Whereas the correctness or otherwise of a logically consistent physical formalism is shown bv comparing its empirical laws, statistical or causal, with observation, no such comparison is available in the case of regulative principles. These can be related to observation only indirectly, *via* physical formalisms which conform to them. As examples we may consider the regulative principle of causality, i.e. the rule to the effect that no physical formalism *should* (= no *intelligible* physical formalism *does*) imply irreducibly statistical correspondences; and the contradictory regulative principle of irreducibly statistical correspondences according to which some formalisms, e.g. those relating to atomic events, should imply irreducibly statistical correspondences.

In favour of any one of these principles, the following indirectly empirical, or quasi-inductive, argument may be and has been put forward: since all or most formalisms which have stood up well to experimental tests conform to the regulative principle in question, it is prudent to expect that new successful formalisms will also conform and to act accordingly in one's search for such. Those who argue for the retention of the principle of causality point to all the successful formalisms since Galileo and those who argue for its rejection either consider as alone relevant formalisms relating to atomic phenomena or else they attempt to show that, despite *prima facie* appearance, even the classical formalisms imply irreducibly statistical correspondences.[7]

Logical arguments for adopting any particular regulative principle presuppose some measure of agreement either about other such principles or about the need to preserve some given formalism. An example of a logical argument of the former kind is that put forward by Dirac[8] in favour of the principle that a formalism which

[4] *Die Besonderheit des Weltbildes der Naturwissenschaft, Acta Physica Austriaca*, vol. I, p. 233.

[5] *Albert Einstein: Philosopher-Scientist*, ed. by P. A. Schilpp, Evanston 1949, p. 667, my *italics*.

[6] *British Journal for the Philosophy of Science*, vol. IV, p. 106.

[7] See e.g. the paper by M. Fierz in the present volume.

[8] *Quantum Mechanics*, 3rd edition, Oxford, 1947, p. 3.

explains the constitution of matter would, unlike the classical systems, have to give an absolute meaning to size. His reason is that any classical explanation of the constitution of matter would assume it to be made up of a large number of relatively small parts behaving according to some postulated laws and would thus leave untouched the structure and stability of the constituent parts. The cogency of the argument depends on the assumption that those to whom it is addressed have adopted a further principle, to the effect that any explanation of the constitution of matter must derive the behaviour of it in bulk from laws governing—absolutely or relatively—its small parts. This regulative principle is by no means generally adopted or 'necessary'. It has been rejected e.g. by Leibniz. Indeed Leibniz, as does Dirac, regarded explanation in terms of relatively small parts as incomplete and unsatisfactory. But he considered the adoption of the notion of absolute size as more objectionable than the replacement of atoms by monads.[9]

An example of a logical argument which presupposes the need for preserving the physical formalism of quantum mechanics and which is put forward in favour of the adoption of the principle of irreducibly statistical correspondences is outlined by Heisenberg. He summarizes it by saying that 'the *determinate* propositions (die bestimmten Aussagen) of quantum mechanics . . . imply that a supplementation of the statistical propositions of quantum mechanics is impossible'.[10] In other words, according to Heisenberg it is logically impossible that the *physical* formalism, which as it stands violates the principle of causality, should be embedded in a wider formalism which conforms to it. The question whether this assertion has been formally demonstrated, especially by von Neumann, is still a controversial one. Moreover the demonstration would not show that a causal supplementation of the mathematical formalism only—with changes in its interpretation—is also logically impossible. It is the search for this latter sort of causal supplementation which, for example, Einstein is recommending.[11]

(4) *On the relation between physics and metaphysics.* If the principle of causality and similar metaphysical principles are regulative, then we must reject some widely held doctrines about the relation between physics and metaphysics. These are, first, the positivistic doctrine, held in various forms by Carnap and others, that metaphysical propositions are irrelevant to physics because they are meaningless; second, the doctrine, held e.g., by Duhem[12] that metaphysical propositions are irrelevant to physics because they are about a different subject-matter which is inaccessible to physics; lastly the view, held in particular by Kant, that those metaphysical propositions which are relevant to physics are true indicative propositions and that their relevance lies in the fact that their denial, though not self-contradictory, would make the construction of any physical formalism, and indeed of any scientific theory, impossible.

The view defended here may be summarized as follows: Some metaphysical propositions are, or function as, regulative principles governing more or less strictly the search for physical formalisms and the choice between them. Like other normative

[9] Leibnitz, *Nouveau Système* etc., e.g. §§ 3, 11.

[10] Heisenberg, *Prinzipielle Fragen der Modernen Physik*, Stuttgart, 1948; p. 45.

[11] *Loc. cit.*, pp. 666 ff.

[12] See e.g. *loc. cit.*, p. 431.

propositions they admit of alternatives in the sense that of two mutually incompatible regulative principles both may be satisfiable. (Of two incompatible indicative propositions one, at least, must be false.) They define, again like other normative propositions, standards of excellence, in the present case standards of the intelligibility or explanatory power of physical formalisms. Lastly they share with other normative propositions the capacity of becoming the subject of rational argument.[13]

[13] For a fuller statement see my *Conceptual Thinking*, Cambridge, 1955, chapters XXX—XXXIII.

Beauty, elegance, and reality in science

by

MICHAEL POLANYI

I SHALL start from the inarticulate ways of acquiring knowledge, which can be most reliably observed in animals, since they cannot speak. I find that their modes of learning fall readily into three classes, two of which are more primitive and are rooted respectively (1) in the *motility* and (2) the *sentience* of the animal, while the third handles both these functions in (3) an *implicit operation of intelligence*. I shall give examples of these three types.

Type A is *Trick learning*. A hungry rat which has two or three times accidentally depressed a lever which releases a pellet of food, will tend to depress the lever again, intentionally. Such a rat has learned to *contrive* a useful result; it has discovered a useful means-ends relationship.

Type B is *Sign learning*. It is demonstrated by experiments in the discrimination box. The animal (usually a rat) is faced with two compartments, bearing different markings which can be shifted from one door to the other. To start the experiment, we must make the animal aware that there is food hidden in some compartment and that it can be got at by pushing open the door. Attempts at guessing the food-laden compartment will follow, and after some experimenting, the animal will identify the marking which is a sign of food. To learn this is to make an *observation*: it is to discover a *sign-event* relation.

Type C. Learning of this type occurs not by any particular act of contriving and observing, but by achieving a *true understanding of a situation given almost entirely from the start*. A rat achieves such an understanding by learning to run a maze. Type C has been described as *latent learning*, in order to suggest that in such cases the animal learns something that it can intelligently apply in more numerous and less predictable ways than it can apply the lessons of trick and sign learning.

The gap which separates these small feats of animal intelligence from the achievement of scientific thought is enormous. Yet the towering superiority of man over the animals is due, paradoxically, to an almost imperceptible advantage in his inarticulate faculties. The situation can be summed up in three points. (1) Man's intellectual superiority is almost entirely due to the use of language. But (2) man's gift of speech must be due to pre-linguistic advantages. Yet (3) if linguistic clues are excluded, men are only slightly better at solving the kind of problems we set to animals. From these premises we may conclude that the inarticulate faculties by which man surpasses the animals and which—by producing speech—account for the entire intellectual superiority of man, are in themselves almost imperceptible.

Therefore, if scientific discovery is—as I believe it to be—the work of our inarticulate faculties, the ways in which animals acquire knowledge may well recur in the human pursuit of knowledge and even in the pursuit of science.

We may begin to move in this direction by acknowledging that our three types of animal learning are primordial forms of three faculties more highly developed in man. Trick learning may be regarded as an act of invention; sign learning as an act of observation; latent learning as an act of interpretation. From these faculties we can then pass on to the respective sciences. The science of practical inventions is *technology*; the sciences of observation comprise the whole of the *natural sciences*; while the sciences of pure interpretation—that is of the systematic elucidation of implications—are the *deductive sciences*. Admittedly, no single faculty can develop into a science; yet each of the three major domains of science is dominated by one faculty, with the support of the other two.

The learning of animals consists in reorganizing the clues of a problem for the purpose of finding its solution. The gift of language increases our power of acquiring knowledge by offering us symbols which can be more easily stored and reorganized than our direct experience of the things for which our symbols stand. The reorganization of symbols can itself be conducted either informally or according to explicit rules; but in either case the reorganization is taking place within a fixed articulate framework.

Such symbolic operations represent the distinctive powers of the human mind; and the more strictly they follow precise logical rules, the more will they approximate to the ideal of objective and publicly demonstrable thought. Such strict processes of inference are—to use Piaget's term—*reversible*, which is indeed their glory; it renders them reproducible and capable of being critically re-examined at will. But the reversibility of logical operations implies the persistence of the existing articulate framework, and this sets a limit to the process of reorganization.

The learning of animals and the act of scientific discovery both *break through* this limit. The animal has no articulate framework, so that when it reorganizes the field which it intellectually controls, it does so always irreversibly; and scientific originality works likewise informally and irreversibly, whether it operates on symbols or on immediate experiences. This will be our clue to the understanding of beauty as a token of reality in science, by contrast to mere elegance which has no such significance.

The kind of beauty I want to talk about here is intellectual—it is something intellectually exhilarating. There is clear evidence to show that animals can appreciate such beauty. Köhler's chimpanzees who had invented a trick for hauling in bananas, eagerly repeated it to haul in useless pebbles. There is indirect evidence of this exhilaration in the tense quietness of posture assumed by a chimpanzee facing a knotty problem. The striving which fills the animal in this condition imposes a heavy strain on it, so that, if the animal is made to intensify its efforts at solving a problem, it may suffer a mental breakdown. It will go frantic or turn listless—or else succumb to compulsive behaviour. The frustration inflicted in the animal here goes far deeper than a mere failure to get hold of a banana: it inflicts a shattering defeat on its efforts to keep its surroundings under intellectual control. The severity of the intellectual strain to which the animal thus proves liable is a measure of the intellectual joy of which it is capable.

The originality of scientists can likewise be assessed by its exhilarating effects. Patents are granted only for inventions of sufficient originality; and if—as may happen—the courts have to establish whether a particular improvement involves a feat of originality, they decide this by assessing the degree of pleasant surprise which the improvement in question may have caused among experts in the art. This emotional shock measures jointly the unpredictability of the invention and the advantage afforded by it; it assesses both the discontinuity between two states of knowledge —the old and the new—and the profit of the new over the old. We may call the discontinuity in question the logical gap—or the heuristic gap—traversed by the act of invention. This gap measures the degree of irreversibility, or, if you like, the change of mind, involved in the invention.

In the natural sciences or in mathematics the originality of a discovery can also be assessed by the pleasant surprise which it may legitimately evoke. Its surprising effect distinguishes a discovery from a mere surveying of manifestly open avenues.

By crossing a logical gap, discovery creates a new understanding. A problem once solved can never puzzle me again. Having gained a foothold on the far side of a heuristic gap, I shall never again see the world quite as it appeared before: I have modified my framework and converted myself, however slightly, to new, more satisfying assumptions. This creativity is present even in the thrill of identifying a new species of worms, and in it lies the beauty of the greatest discoveries of science.

Psychologists have noted the necessity of this passionate coefficient for the solving of a problem; Kurt Lewin has called it ego-involvement. He observed that we do not become deeply involved either in a task that is too easy or that is too difficult, but only in tasks that we can just master at our best.

But we can say more than this about the logic of these passionate self-transforming operations. If discovery is a process of inference that cannot be carried out according to any precise rules, we must expect its logic to be somewhat paradoxical. Plato has given one formulation of this paradox in the *Meno*, by asking how we can seek something we do not know, since in that case we do not know what we are looking for. In his book, *How to Solve It*, G. Polya evokes this paradox by emphatically admonishing the student of mathematics in the words: 'Look at the unknown. Look at the conclusion . . . Look at the end. Remember your aim'. Since these injunctions are used by the author in a sober, practical sense, we may conclude that we must distinguish here between two kinds of knowing. We are not asked to look at what we cannot yet see, but are only told to look at the given elements of the problem in a particular way, namely as putative clues to the unknown solution. By concentrating our attention on an unknown end in terms of the clues by which it may be achieved, we may succeed in reorganizing these clues into a satisfactory solution of our problem; and we may add that if we looked at the clues themselves, without any purpose in mind, they would mean nothing to us. A skilful act can in fact be paralysed by focusing attention on its particulars, and consequently we may never know such particulars *focally*, though we do know them well in practice, *subsidiarily*. These particulars may thus prove altogether unspecifiable.

To see a problem, to pursue it persistently and to make a discovery by solving it—these are acts of skilfully acquiring knowledge, by the reorganizing of focally unknown, unspecifiable, particulars. Hence we can both focus our attention on a prospective discovery and be unable to tell what we are attending to. And this logical structure explains also why problems, intimations, or discoveries, all deeply involve the person having them, or making them. For any new subsidiary awareness of a thing is acquired in the way we learn to use a tool: namely, by assimilating the thing to our own body. When we ponder a problem by reorganizing our experiences, we learn to use these experiences as pointers to discovery, and in doing so we assimilate them to our own person. This pouring out of ourselves into these particulars constitutes the irreversible self-modifying commitment involved in all heuristic acts.

Our heuristic passions have it in common with our bodily passions that by following them we imply the existence of something that can satisfy them. But the satisfier of a heuristic craving has no bodily existence. It is not a hidden object, but an idea not yet conceived. And yet only by assuming its potential pre-existence can we go on passionately searching for it. Only this conviction can evoke in ourselves the bright ideas leading to its discovery.

Herein lies a paradoxical qualification of all intellectual creativity: we can exercise originality only while assuming that we originate nothing but merely reveal what is there already. And yet this throws a new light on the nature of what it is that we discover. It presents it as something possessing reality. Originality appears now as a groping for a foothold on the far side of a heuristic gap: a foothold to be gained by a new contact with reality.

This reality is external to us. Though it satisfies our intensely personal intellectual passions, it satisfies them impersonally, with universal intent. Only if we submit to the demands of something real, as being there whether we like it or not, can we gain a measure of intellectual control over that real thing.

Owing to its contact with reality, the structure of a discovery is akin to that of a real problem. Both hold a true promise of things still hidden in them. A problem has a hidden solution; a discovery has both manifest implications in form of definite predictions, and other implications, often much wider, that are yet unknown. Explicit scientific predictions which, by a process of induction, patently go beyond established experience, have attracted much attention in philosophy. But not all scientific discoveries predict future experiences, and indeed those in mathematics and technology never do. The characteristic quality of all true discovery lies in the indeterminate range of its hidden implications. We have recognized this quality already in a primordial form when a rat which has learned a maze was said to have acquired a *latent* knowledge that it can manifest in many unpredictable ways.

The exhilaration caused by a scientific discovery ascribes to it a beauty which is distinct from mere elegance, and the difference lies precisely in the fact that we attribute an indeterminate range of veridical implications to a discovery possessing real beauty, but not to an innovation possessing mere elegance. This difference was brought out in the discussion of the heliocentric system, following its announcement by Copernicus in 1543. A zealous Lutheran minister, Andreas Osiander of Nuremberg, had urged for some years on Copernicus to declare that his system was merely a formal advance on Ptolemy. Osiander did actually succeed in getting this view stated in a preface to Copernicus' book. In his letters to Copernicus, Osiander had argued that 'hypotheses are not articles of faith', so that 'it does not matter whether they are true or false, provided that they reproduce exactly the phenomena of motion'. This conventionalist theory of science, current in the late Middle Ages, was meant to deny science access to reality; consequenctly its wording coincides with the positivist analysis of science which seeks to purify it from metaphysics by avoiding any reference to reality.

However, Osiander's view of science was violently rejected by the Copernicans. Giordano Bruno called it the work of an ignorant and presumptuous ass. Kepler went to the heart of the matter by declaring: 'It is indeed a most absurd fiction to explain natural phenomena by false causes'. The controversy went on bitterly for 150 years. The participants were divided on the question whether science could establish the truth in such matters; and this was not due to any disagreement as to what constituted truth and what merely convenience, in a scientific theory.

Eventually, the Copernican System bore fruits which decided in its favour. Thus the Copernicans proved right in having anticipated that surprising true consequences might one day emerge from the heliocentric view, and in regarding it therefore as not merely convenient, but true.

There are many other examples to show the significance of beauty in science as distinct from elegance—and the difficulty of deciding between the two.

Discussion

Rosenfeld. I am in general agreement with Professor Körner's remarks about the regulative and normative character of the general views of the physicists. I am not quite sure how strongly he felt that these normative principles were more or less a matter of taste or choice for the physicists. What I should like to say is that we are guided in the choice of normative principles by considerations of *Zweckmässigkeit* which are of an epistemological character: that is very strongly the case in quantum mechanics. The fact that we refer to the observations in terms of classical concepts is not just a normative principle which we adopt arbitrarily, but it is imposed upon us by our position in nature and by the very function of science. After having heard Professor Bohm's talk yesterday morning I was overcome by a kind of meekness because I was impressed by the fact that Bohm is after all an earnest seeker after truth; but after hearing Vigier's talk in the afternoon I was hardened again because it struck me that he was going in such a direction which seems to me to lead to logical or epistemological contradictions of a very serious character. I was reminded of this by Groenewold's question about the Einstein-paradox, which was invented by Einstein as a teaser for quantum theory, and which now turns out to be a teaser for our friends here. This case is a striking illustration of the fact that we are here not faced with a matter of choice between two possible languages or two possible interpretations, but with a rational language intimately connected with the formalism and adapted to it, on the one hand, and with rather wild, metaphysical speculations about an infinite number of levels on the other. So now I would no longer like to agree that by any method, by hook or crook, one might hit upon the truth. Of course, the chance is always there and I have no more sincere wish than that would happen to our friends, but it seems to me extremely unlikely.

Körner. I was very glad to see that Professor Rosenfeld agrees with me in general, and I think that the answer which I give to his question will not disturb this concord.

The choice of normative principles, is not, I believe, a mere matter of convention. Although we can sometimes choose to accept normative principles, we cannot also choose to make them satisfiable. Two incompatible normative propositions may both be satisfiable in the world. (For instance, the two incompatible normative propositions that I should now drink coffee, and that I should not drink coffee now, are both fulfillable.) But their satisfiability does not depend only on my choice but also on features of the world. Which normative principles are really useful to a physicist will be decided by hunches presupposing great familiarity with physics. If a physicist says to me that after many years of doing physics, he feels that a certain line of approach is profitable, I, who am not a physicist, can hardly dispute this. What I am interested in is a logical point: I am trying to exhibit the difference in logical status and function between, on the one hand, principles for the construction of theories and, on the other, the theories themselves. This difference is important and to neglect it is to invite confusion.

Polanyi. I agree with the uneasiness expressed by Professor Rosenfeld that Professor Körner did not give sufficient emotional weight to these principles which he calls regulative. Such heuristic visions which appeal to different conceptions of reality must be passionately opposed to each other and yesterday everybody was so peaceful that I was feeling very uneasy.

Hutten. Professor Fierz said that in classical mechanics we can never measure anything exactly and that this is the reason why probability considerations come in. But this is of course purely accidental and has nothing to do with the logic of the theory. For in classical theory we are always allowed to idealize and to assume that we know the initial conditions without any limitation in precision. On the other hand, in quantum mechanics there exists a law, namely the uncertainty principle, which prevents us from ever knowing the simultaneous values of p and q with accuracy. It would be fatal to overlook this distinction. The second remark concerns Professor Körner. I must say that I always feel very sad when people follow the post-war fashion of intellectual reaction and speak as if logical positivism had been defeated. No one denies that the original positivists were very exuberant and made highly provocative pronouncements; but at the time the pronouncements were made they were not taken very seriously by the positivists themselves.

Ayer. Yes, they were.

Hutten. This is really unfair. Logical positivism today is a fighting word, but the discussion of meaninglessness was a perfectly honourable attempt to understand the use of certain expressions, and to draw attention to the fact that meaning always depends on the context. In particular, I think that Körner himself when speaking about empirical laws became the victim of certain misunderstandings which the people who have invented this particular kind of word have tried to avoid. It's highly doubtful that what we call in physics a law is an empirical statement. It is even possible to argue that the word 'law' as used in physics or in science in general has very many different senses. To say, for example, that the second law of thermodynamics or the second law of Newton is an empirical statement is sometimes true and sometimes not. In any case it does not completely explain the role of those statements. They certainly are not empirical statements in the sense that they are confirmed or verified in a straightforward manner, just as the statement that the table is brown is confirmed or verified.

Fierz. I have never explicitly said that in classical mechanics the initial conditions are statistically given and that this should be an essential point. The initial conditions are arbitrary with respect to the formalism. But we may even say that they are also practically arbitrary, so that we can handle the world. Statistics is used only insofar as there are phenomena which we cannot handle—for example stars. But that has naturally nothing to do with probability theory proper. My main point is that the statistical character of quantum theory seems to me to be in line, because it is a fact that physics only deals with reproducible phenomena; and for those phenomena statistics is quite a proper tool.

Körner. Concerning Professor Polanyi's remark that I don't give emotional weight to regulative principles: I don't deny that they can have this, and that for most people they do have it, but I was trying to be rather unemotionally logical about their function. Concerning Dr. Hutten's remarks: I am not trying 'to bring back metaphysics'. No old-fashioned metaphysican would be happy about an analysis of metaphysical propositions as normative, rather than as indicative propositions.

Bohm. I agree with a lot of what Professor Fierz said—his analysis of what is essential and inessential in a given problem is very important. However, I would not ascribe to the observer such an important position in this problem. I would rather look at it in another way: every law must be to some degree a universal law, that is it must apply in many cases. If it would only apply to one case we would hardly call it a law. Now this raises the question '. . . Am I not forced to admit like Professor Fierz that the individual or singular is outside the scope of law, that it simply cannot be treated by universal laws, and that each event and each thing must have something about it which is beyond law?' To answer this question, I return again to the infinity of nature. If nature is infinite, then of course, there is no law which covers the whole universe; there can only be a law covering some domains. There is, therefore, room for every law to be universal because it applies in many cases; nevertheless because of the infinity of nature each individual can be defined by an infinity of particulars and properties. Hence, if you go deep enough you will find what makes a particular individual different from some other similar individuals. Let us take the case of quantum mechanics of two electrons which are said to be identical at the level of quantum mechanics. From this point of view, if you go more deeply you would eventually reach a point where they are different. This would make no significant effect on the level of quantum mechanics but it would have a significant effect somewhere else. This also raises the question of what is statistical, for a law can only be a law if it applies to various cases; but the various cases which actually exist will cover some distribution and this suggests something statistical. Statistics is, therefore, closely connected with the particularity of things. For if you take any law, it aims at first to be a universal law. But it cannot cover any given thing completely because of the infinity of nature; and the differences are then further particulars.

Fierz. When Professor Bohm says that there is a possibility of looking at the problem of individuality and of law in a different way, then he is not referring to the situation from which I started, namely, physics as it is now. At least classical mechanics does not take into account this infinity of nature. Classical mechanics, I would guess, is in the sense of Professor Bohm a theory which just only treats a finity of nature.

Bohm. For it abstracts from the infinity of nature.

Fierz. What Professor Bohm says seems to me to have a very strong similarity to ideas of Leibniz, where the individual is characterized by an infinity of predicates whereas the finite can be characterized by a law and therefore by a finite number of terms. This can be elucidated by the picture Leibniz uses himself: a curve which is given by a law such as e.g. a parabola, is finite in the sense that the human mind can grasp it. But a curve which I am drawing on paper cannot thus be grasped by a finite mind. Now Leibniz's outlook was not successful in making physics whereas Newton's outlook was—though from the purely logical point of view, you cannot say that Leibniz was wrong.

Bohm. Also you cannot say that Newton's method may not apply in a certain domain of problems from which we have now changed to a different domain. Now a question to Professor Körner. He seems to have raised the question that certain physicists finally seem to be guided by causality, and others by the hypothesis of a statistical theory, while there is no very definite way of knowing which of these hypotheses is really correct. I would rather suggest although it may be inevitable that there is always some metaphysics in our thinking, physics always involves an effort to try to avoid such metaphysics. I think one can try to avoid it by going to a more general way of thinking, which shows why the previous ways of thinking were metaphysical. Of course in doing this we may also be doing something else metaphysical, but we are nevertheless trying to reduce the element of metaphysics in our thinking, to reduce the importance of metaphysics. Suppose e.g. that for a long time, guided by general experience, we discover that certain causal laws hold and that then other physicists discover that statistical laws hold and contain these causal laws as limiting cases. The first physicists will have the point of view of causality as a necessary way of thinking, and the others will hold the statistical or probabilistic point of view as a necessary way of thinking. To avoid metaphysical hypotheses, however, I think that we should try to understand when and why we should have probability, and when and why we should have causality. This could not be done by adopting one or the other of these modes of thinking as basic, but it could be done by trying to adopt a still broader mode of thinking which would explain the limitations of causality as well as the limitations of statistics. I think that this has been the characteristic of the progress of science in general: i.e. one discovers that two different limiting cases have to be applied, then the best way to make progress is to see what it is that determines which way is correct in a given case. This carries us to a more general way of thinking. Therefore, I would like to propose the point of view that you have neither rigid causality nor rigid probability laws. In some cases the first kind of law applies and in some cases the other kind, and there may be even some cases in between, some new form of law which we have not yet fully defined. Causality is then not defined as a regulative principle but it is defined by the actual existing physical conditions which we have found later. Of course, in doing so we may, as before, have adopted something else which is metaphysical; somewhere in our science we always make a hypothesis and whenever you make a hypothesis there is always something there which is not fully given by the facts.

Körner. I think the name 'metaphysics' is what really causes you the trouble. In your recent book you put forward a whole set of guiding principles which you think will help you in the construction of a physical theory implying empirical laws of nature. Now all I wanted to do was to show that and how these two sets of statements —the guiding principles and the laws of nature—are different. I don't deny—as I said to Professor Rosenfeld—that normative principles are not entirely a matter of choice. I do think however there is a real danger in confusing the status of principles for the construction of theories and propositions within theories. What you do, most interestingly and excitingly in your book, is to put forward some general principles about desirable theories rather than such theories themselves.

Groenewold. Concerning the role of 'metaphysics' I should like to add a few remarks to those I made yesterday. Both Schrödinger and Heisenberg were starting from more or less vague philosophical principles. Heisenberg from the principle which said that one has to eliminate from the theory any element which is not directly connected with experiment. On the other hand Schrödinger started from the idea that there must be some harmony in nature, a continuity; and in a certain way one can say that his standpoint was more or less opposite to that of Heisenberg. And the theories which corresponded to these ideas, namely the matrix theory and the wave theory, looked also very opposite to each other. But in spite of that they soon turned out to be formally equivalent. This case shows very clearly how the theory which comes out in the end has become pretty independent of the initial vague ideas. The distinction between the theories and those ideas is not absolutely sharp and may also change with the development of science. But the point I want to make is that to a large extent these two things are logically independent of each other. Now I would not go so far as in a certain stage the positivists went, declaring all the other metaphysical things as meaningless, because already the fact that people are so much engaged in it shows that they are not meaningless anyhow. Also I think it would be rather a disaster for the development of science if one went so far as to prohibit metaphysical statements because this would curtail the development of science very severely. But the price one has to pay for using them is that for every idea which has led to fruitful development there are a thousand others which have led astray. There are also other functions of philosophy for instance analysis of the way in which theories are used. But the role of metaphysics in physics is more or less a transitory role; it is of great importance as it can lead to new theories. But when these theories have been found metaphysics is wholly eliminated from them.

Körner. I would also like to draw Professor Groenewold's attention to a historical fact. When the isomorphism between matrix mechanics and wave mechanics was discovered by Schrödinger the philosophical controversies about quantum mechanics did not cease. They are still going on.—I agree with Professor Groenewold about the *logical* independence between metaphysical principles and physical theories. They are independent because the metaphysical statements I am considering are rules and because empirical laws of nature are indicative statements. Yet in spite of this lack of logical dependence there is a connexion between metaphysical propositions *qua* rules for the contruction of theories and the construction of the theories: for the construction of theories is an activity which satisfies or violates the rules. It is this dependence which seems to me important, and which must not be confused with logical dependence between indicative propositions.—One last point. When you say, again I believe quite rightly, that what philosophers should do is analysis, I should say that this is just what I was trying to do in exhibiting the difference between physical formalisms and physical explanations.

Vigier. One should stress the fact that Laplace for example, did not try to make an analysis of the role of the observer in classical physics and he even points out that in the classical domain an observer can study a system without disturbing it too much. I think that with respect to quantum mechanics the most important contribution of Bohr was that he tried to make us understand the physical effect of the apparatus upon the observed object. Naturally we do not agree with Bohr and the Copenhagen School in the interpretation of this effect. We think it is possible to describe and to understand the interaction between the observing apparatus and the observed object, but it must be kept in mind that in that respect things are fundamentally different in the classical domain and in the quantum-mechanical domain. Now as to what Professor Körner has said. He has shown that metaphysical principles play a very great role in the development of physical theories, they indicate complete lines of research. This gives me the occasion to emphasize, just as Professor Rosenfeld has done, that the two outlooks which have been presented yesterday are completely and fundamentally different, and that there can be no compromise between them. The first difference is the fact that we believe that the micro-objects exist independently of any observer, and that the quantum-mechanical laws are objective laws which apply to these objects whether there is an observer or not. The second point of disagreement is the position towards the nature of different laws in different domains: when you go into other domains then the laws undergo qualitative changes. We don't think that we can solve the crisis of present-day physics just by going in the same direction. That is not a matter of taste but it is really a matter of experiment, of physical results; whether one point of view is correct or not that will be settled by the physical results of the theory. Questions of taste do not play any role in such a problem.

Süssmann. Modern physics implies the following fundamental distinction. On the one side, there is the *general*, the laws of nature, and on the other side there is the *contingent* or singular, the properties of things which are not implied by the laws. More especially, within classical mechanics we meet the following scheme: if a certain body is here today, then it follows from the laws that it will be there and there tomorrow; and that it has been at a certain point yesterday. But whether it is here today—this does not follow from the laws, that fact must be taken as something given. Here we are faced with a historical feature which is taken into account by physics. Now the principles of which I was talking yesterday—those non-mechanical principles about the probability-distribution of the initial conditions—are closely related with this character of contingency. In this way, the second theorem of thermodynamics, too, mirrors historical features of the world. In quantum mechanics this realm of contingency has been largely increased, because here probabilities are being introduced into pure mechanics.

Fierz. You could formulate it in this way but I do not like it too much. I prefer as I did in my talk to stress the experimental side of physics.

Feyerabend. Professor Fierz has said that people like Einstein and others want to give a description of an individual single process, and he has tried to point out that the attempt to give such a description would lead to difficulties already in classical mechanics. In trying to show this, he has argued (1) that we always make idealizations and (2) that any assertion about an individual can be tested only by comparing it with other objects. I think that in saying this he has forgotten that in different situations these two methods may lead to different results. Take classical physics and quantum mechanics. In both cases we make idealizations. In both cases we base our assertions or our theory on comparisons between different objects. But in the first case the idealization made is of a completely different kind than the second case, and what Einstein wants to arrive at is the classical kind of idealization rather than a complete description in Professor Fierz's sense. As to the controversy, between Professor Körner and Professor Rosenfeld—Professor Körner has said that we can argue about the regulative principles we introduce and that there is a certain freedom. Professor Rosenfeld has objected; he said there is not very much freedom, at least not in the case of quantum mechanics, and he has given two arguments which I think are both invalid. The first argument is: if we try to use a different 'meta-' interpretation we arrive at epistemological contradictions. My point is we arrive at epistemological contradictions with a presupposition which the orthodox hold and which I think must be attacked—it is the presupposition that experience is to be described in terms of classical mechanics rather than in terms of the best theory available. This presupposition, Professor Rosenfeld has said yesterday, is a triviality, a matter of course. I do not think it is a triviality as so far physicists have never yet adopted this principle, they have always described experience in terms of the best theory available, and I think it is this principle which leads to the epistemological contradictions. The second argument used by Professor Rosenfeld is the argument of Einstein–Podolsky–Rosen. But this is not really an argument as long as there is no experimental evidence showing that the result predicted by quantum mechanics is in fact correct. A final brief remark about Professor Bohm's infinity of nature. He seems to oscillate between two interpretations which should be kept separated; in one interpretation the principle of infinity of nature would be a methodological principle saying that every statement of physical theory is not final, but may turn out to be false at some time. In the other interpretation, this principle may be called an empirical statement, a statement describing the world and saying that there are infinitely many individuals in the world, and that each individual has infinitely many properties.

Fierz. I never said that there is not a real difference between quantum mechanics and classical mechanics, simply I couldn't talk about it because you can't talk about everything you mention.

Hush. What Professor Körner has shown in his paper is the enormous importance of what he has called regulative principles in formulating scientific theories and interpreting them. But then, in making them principles, he seems to evaluate them along such statements as 'keep on the left' and the like. Now if they are as important as all this, it is possible that an argument could be put forward for this. I should have thought that some statements which we think are trivial and indicative in some sense, for example, statements about identity, or a statement that one has no theory in which one doesn't have the notion of a thing having a certain property over a finite stretch of time, or the like, should be considered in this connexion, as in focusing attention on causality, one is taking rather the easy way out, because in the case of causality it is not obvious what is involved—one may not be involved in contradictions in denying causality.

Körner. What I was trying to show, really, was something quite modest. I wanted to exhibit the relation between physical and 'metaphysical' statements in the writings of creative physicists. Apart from the regulative function which metaphysical statements have, they may also have an indicative function. Indeed if one accepts any rule of conduct—whether from the activity of theory-construction or any other activity—one usually assumes that the prescribed conduct can be realized, and this assumption is itself not a rule but an indicative proposition.

Öpik. My first remark concerns mainly a certain point raised by Professor Polanyi. The word 'reality' occurs in the title of his lecture and was discussed in the lecture to some extent. Suppose we have two theories with two ways of describing a certain class of phenomena and suppose that they are such that they give exactly or approximately the same results when they are verified by observation. Which of these two theories is to be regarded as more real? The example mentioned was the description of the solar system by the old Ptolemaic theory and by the new Copernican theory. The Ptolemaic theory looks very artificial, is very complicated and requires assumptions to be made such as, for example, that the whole universe makes a revolution in 24 hours, so all the laws like Newton's laws would have to be modified accordingly to get the right results. Now as this is extremely complicated and also extremely unnatural, we abandon it and say that although this theory is in principle capable of getting the correct description of what is observed, obviously we are misreading things, we are misinterpreting the real meaning, the real significance of Nature. Now in this particular case it is easy enough to decide—it is an extreme case. But I think you can easily have intermediate cases where one theory may be slightly more natural than another theory, and where people's judgements about this may differ. So I would like to make the suggestion that as in many other matters, the question of reality is not one to which we should always expect a definite and clear-cut yes or no, but we should also be prepared to have intermediate cases. Furthermore, even where a theory gives an approximate description of nature and of what is actually observed, such as Newton's law of gravitation (as against Einstein's general theory of relativity), even then I would not like to say that the theory is false. I would still like to be able to say that in a certain restricted sense Newton's theory is true, in spite of the fact that we need a *qualitatively* different theory to make it exact. If we insist on calling Newton's theory entirely false, then I think we are faced with a situation of never being able to trust any of our theories to give a true or real description of reality.

Polanyi. I essentially agree to this. I have spoken about the degree of contact with reality, or about a theory revealing an aspect of reality, and that is a matter of degree. But the point I was trying to make is that Newton's theory was true, precisely because it had an indeterminate range of implications; and that the Copernican theory was true—and was rightly defended as true by its adherents—because it affirmed an indeterminate range of implications. The presence of such an indeterminate range of implications is what I mean by having contact with reality.

Öpik. I would like to derive a regulative principle not from metaphysics but from past experience, which has shown that we are so liable to be wrong, that the principle would be to try and to trust our thinking as little as is possible, and to be influenced as little as possible by past ways of thinking, and always to be prepared to find something unexpected and try and base one's assertions on experience as closely as possible.

Frank. My first point is perhaps addressed mainly to Professor Polanyi because I thought that his paper was nearer than most to the subject defined in the title. When a scientist says that he makes a choice on philosophic grounds then he only means on grounds of prejudice. Take an example; we have before us Professor Bohm's theory and we must say that this theory is a model of a not quickly refutable alternative theory to the orthodox one; it's had a two-fold status there, we have had grounds to reconsider the logical basis of the view that the orthodox theory is absolute. We have also had an example of scientists differing on grounds which they call philosophic. We have had expressions of opinion as to whether it is a good theory, based on the question whether it is in the current spirit of science. Now I believe that the direction of the current of science is somehow created by the simpler-minded historians of science. It is only necessary to look at, say, Whittaker's account of the history of the theories of the aether and electricity, or Duhem's account of the theory of gravitation, to see that the current changes direction many times, that when the river of learning enters a delta and is about to open into a wider sea, there are many different courses of the river which one must follow, most of which end in weeds. The reasons for the scientist's choice are to be sought rather in the field of psychology than in the fields of philosophy or pure science. Now which choice you make, whether it is profitable or not, which particular psychological bias is the profitable way at a certain time is not the same as at another time. In the middle of the nineteenth century when anti-atomism was, I think, the orthodox view, it was a very powerful incentive to the further development of thermo-dynamics and anti-atomism cost Faraday very little, it merely cost him the credit of being the discoverer of the electron; but by 1900 the retention of the old orthodox view of anti-atomism cost Duhem very much. I think the present situation is analogous—we cannot tell from the spirit of science, from what we think is the present direction of the current, which choice of bias is the best, and I think that all choices based on principles said to be philosophic are indeed choices based on psychological bias.

Polanyi. This kind of bias sometimes leads to great discoveries. If we consider that such assumptions are frequently the sources of discovery then I think it is justified to consider them in this light, rather than classing them all as bias. That is why I would include them in epistemology rather than regard them as purely psychological. Only the mental processes involved in holding these assumptions irrespective of their truth-value belong to psychology.

Körner. I have no objection to Professor Frank's calling metaphysical propositions or philosophical grounds 'prejudices'. Their function in thinking, especially the thinking of physicists, does not become thereby less interesting or important.

Mackay. I would like to make two remarks briefly about 'meaninglessness', because I think there is a danger in the reaction against the overuse of this stick of forgetting what we ought to learn from the positivist emphasis. First of all, meaningfulness does not want to be attributed to a statement in isolation, but to a statement against the background of a given receiver. I think, therefore, it is important for us to ask under what circumstances statements can be meaningful for a scientist, and to distinguish two different ways in which they can be meaningless. In order that a statement should be meaningful to me, I would suggest that it has to make a difference to my *state of readiness for activity* in the relevant domain; and in order that a statement should be scientifically meaningful, it should make a difference to my state of readiness to act either intellectually or physically in a certain scientific context. One can say then, using perhaps a jargon term of information theory, that a meaningful statement has to exercise a *selective* operation on the 'ensemble of states of readiness' of the receiver.

This implies that there are two different kinds of meaninglessness. The first is typified by making such a noise as 'the gups are plean' where the individual entities have no *defined* selective function. The second one is typified by saying 'this colour is isosceles' where individual selective functions are defined, but taken together are *incompatible*. In science we have examples of meaninglesssness in both senses. I think that statements about the aether were regarded, and still are regarded by many scientists, as meaningless for the first reason, that in the end no operation or way of affecting one's state of readiness by the use of the word aether became available. Statements about the energy of an electron at an instant, or its momentum at a point, were called meaningless for the second reason, that the conditions under which the term 'energy' acquired selective function were believed to be incompatible with the conditions under which the term 'instant' acquired selective function. This rests on the logical indeterminacy between the concepts 'frequency' and 'time.' It is a logical fact that the conditions under which 'frequency' is sharply defined are incompatible with the conditions under which the 'position of the wave packet' can be sharply defined; (the fact that it becomes difficult to determine the pitch of a note when the note is made shorter and shorter isn't a physical fact but a logical one in the end.) If now we say that from this it is equally 'meaningless' to define the energy of a particle at an instant, it is important to realize that we are importing here an additional empirical condition, identifying energy and frequency by the factor h, $E = h\nu$. Whenever we say in quantum theory that certain questions are meaningless, we ought then to say under what conditions of definition. If a man says he thinks he could localize energy at an instant of time, he ought to be made to realize that what he is querying is the relation $E = h\nu$. One further remark about Professor Polanyi's paper which I confess I found most illuminating. I think he put his finger on something which one feels particularly within the behavioural sciences, where mathematical laws are often produced which do not give us any sensation of 'pleasant surprise'. Although they fit the facts perfectly, we have the unhappy feeling that their implications are all *summaries.* I would like however to ask Professor Polanyi whether it is not the *unpredictability* rather than the *indeterminacy* of the range of implications, which makes a theory significant?

Gallie. A remark on the discussion between Dr. Feyerabend and Professor Rosenfeld on this question about the use of the most recent theory. We seem to have come very close to the heart of the discussion of yesterday. Now it seems to me that this is just a special case of a more general problem which arises in connexion with the use of any new language. Any new language or symbolism must be introduced, to start with, as a correction of the previous one, and therefore, when it is first applied the introducer must use the old symbolism to start with to describe the things which he is about to redescribe. Now in this process, the introducer of the new symbolism is bound to be accused of speaking either nonsense or contradictorily. This has happened again and again in the history of thought. I am going to give a few example of successful innovations in philosophy because I am not equipped to say whether the new innovations which have been suggested in this meeting are successful or not. A very obvious example is Locke's attempt to create an empiricist language. He had to do this by correcting all sorts of previous usages and any clever fool could always say how contradictory and stupid John Locke was.

Other examples would be the way in which philosophers like Ryle have encouraged us to talk in a rather more bodily manner about the mind. It is an excellent thing, it seems to me, but of course, the way proposed by Ryle has appeared to some people to be absolutely absurd. Hence while it is true that physicists always try to apply the most recent theory, they are obviously bound in point of fact to use the language of the theory they are replacing.

Cohen. I want to take up the general line of the suggestion that Professor Körner has made with regard to principles. I would suggest that out of what Professors Bohm and Vigier were saying yesterday there emerges not only the need to talk about regulative principles but also about higher order regulative principles. According to a regulative interpretation of the 'infinity of nature' idea one would be invited to replace a causal theory that seems to be unsuccessful by an underlying theory in statistical terms and where you have an unsuccessful statistical theory you are to look for a causal theory. Now this would be a regulative principle of the same logical order as the ordinary one—'look for a causal theory', or 'look for a statistical theory'. But there is something more to what Professors Bohm and Vigier say and it seems to me that this is a Hegelian idea: whenever you get two regulative principles which seem to be in conflict then assume that one applies at one physical level and the other at another. This will apparently apply not only to the statistical-causal dichotomy, but it will apply also to other dichotomies such as the dichotomy continuous-discrete, and in principle this could apply to all regulative principles determining the major formative concepts of our theories. This is an extremely interesting idea then; but one does feel this about Hegelian ideas that it is often easy to apply the notions of dialectic—thesis, antithesis and synthesis—after someone has already thought of the thesis, someone else has thought of the antithesis, and you have thought of the synthesis, but it is much more difficult to use it predictively, as it were. In order to bring out this point, I want to ask now, as a question of still higher order, what one would say of this second-order regulative principle, namely, wherever you get these conflicting first-order principles, you should say one applies to one physical level and the other to another. This is itself a *thesis* at the second-order of regulative principles. Now I want to know what would be the antithesis; and if someone suggests the antitheses is the ordinary idea 'Be dogmatic, just take the causal, or statistical line, and stick to it', then what would be the synthesis here? If someone answers 'In the nature of this dialectical theory one cannot predict: it doesn't enable one to go forward inevitably but only gives one kind of explanation of a step one has already taken', then has this second-order regulative principle a solid foundation behind it, and should we be perhaps content with the first-order principles? This is a question partly to Professor Körner but also indirectly to Professors Bohm and Vigier.

Fierz. I would like to ask Professor Polanyi a question. He said that the discovery of a new foothold on the other side of the river gives the scientist the feeling of a shock; the shock is a shock of exhilarating beauty. Secondly, he quoted Plato in this connexion. In the Platonic theory of science beauty has just this quality that if you learn something you have the impression that you see a little of this exhilarating beauty. I would like to ask if Professor Polanyi would agree that in his description of making science the Platonic element is contained.

Körner. There is no time to answer Mr. Cohen's very interesting question about the relations between different regulative principles. His question about the Hegelian set of regulative principles is one which Professor Vigier and Professor Bohm will perhaps find opportunity to answer from their own point of view.

Polanyi. There is an element of the Platonic view included, but with the intention of avoiding the possibility of having Platonic ideas laid up somewhere and looking at them in a detached manner. For these 'Platonic ideas' of mine exist only in our acceptance of them. But this problem actually lies outside the framework of my paper.

FIFTH SESSION

Chairman: Professor M. H. L. PRYCE

P. K. FEYERABEND: On the quantum-theory of measurement.

G. SÜSSMANN: An analysis of measurement.

On the quantum-theory of measurement

by

P. K. FEYERABEND

(1) *The Problem.* Within classical physics the relation between physical theory and ordinary experience was conceived in the following way: ordinary experience is something that can be described and understood in terms of physics. Such a description involves, apart from physical theory, certain approximations. But the conditions under which those approximations apply (they correspond to the initial conditions of, say, celestial mechanics), taken together with the theory, are supposed to be sufficient for giving a full account of ordinary experience. Consequently, classical theory of measurement (which, like any other theory of measurement, links together terms of ordinary experience and theoretical terms), is a piece of applied physics and all processes which happen during measurement can be analysed on the basis of the equations of motion only.

When we enter quantum mechanics (QM for short), we are apparently presented with a completely different picture. For according to the current interpretation of elementary quantum mechanics, ordinary experience—and this now means classical physics—and physical theory (and this now means QM), belong to two completely different levels and it is impossible to give an account of the first in terms of the second.[1] Any transition from the quantum level to the level of classical physics must be taken, not as a transition *within* QM from the general to the particular, but as an essentially new element which is incapable of further analysis. Consequently, the quantum theory of measurement, as it has been developed by Bohr, Heisenberg ((**10**), (**11**)), and in its most elaborate form by von Neumann, involves, apart from the equations of motion, such independent and unanalysable processes as 'quantum-jumps', 'reduction of the wave-packet' and the like.

It is the purpose of this paper to show the inadequacy of this theory of measurement. I shall try to show that it is possible to give an account of the process of measurement which involves nothing but the equations of motion and statements about the special properties of the systems involved, especially statements about the properties of the measuring-device; and according to which the theory of measurement is a piece of applied physics, just as it was in classical theory. As a satisfactory account of the classical level in terms of QM is still missing, my suggestions will have to be somewhat sketchy—but they may still be useful, at least as an indication of how a more satisfactory theory of measurement may be built up. The last section of the paper will also develop some more general consequences of the possibility of such a theory.

(2) *Von Neumann's Theory of Measurement.* My point of departure is von Neumann's theory of measurement ((**16**), Chs. IV, VI). The essential point of this theory is

1. Cf. e.g. (**1**), Ch. 23.

that it is about the behaviour of *individual systems*, although only a probabilistic account is given of this behaviour. Probability is introduced in two steps. First, in the usual way, viz. as the limit of relative frequencies within large ensembles.[2] This procedure which has greatly clarified the role of probability within QM, is suggested (a) by the fact that the Born-interpretation, 'the only consistently enforceable interpretation of quantum mechanics today'[3] is a statistical interpretation in a straightforward and classical sense,[4], and (b) by the fact that the statistical properties of large ensembles can be studied by experiments upon small samples, whatever happens during those experiments.[5] The statistical properties of the ensembles are completely characterized by their statistical operators. In the second step which is usually overlooked by those who interpret QM as a variety of classical statistical mechanics,[6] it is proved (a) that every ensemble of quantum-mechanical systems is either a pure ensemble, or a mixture of pure ensembles, and (b) that the pure ensembles (1) do not contain subsensembles with statistical properties different from their own, (2) are not dispersion-free. This proof[7] allows for the application, to individual systems, of probabilities in the sense of relative frequencies. Hence, any operation with an *ensemble* which leads from a statistical operator W to another statistical operator, W', can also be interpreted as an operation with an *individual system* (which may, or may not be completely known), leading from the state W to the state W' and vice versa, a procedure which would not be possible in the classical case.[8]

[2] Von Neumann adopts the Mises-Interpretation of probability. Cf. (**16**), 289 fn. There is no objection against this procedure as within physics the Mises-approach does not lead to any of the difficulties which have made it untenable for mathematicians and philosophers.

[3] (**16**), 210. Most of von Neumann's results are based only upon the formalism of QM together with the Born-Interpretation. This is true especially of the 'Neumann-Proof' which involves none of the more or less arbitrary philosophical assumptions characteristic for the Bohr-Heisenberg-approach.

[4] Cf. also (5).

[5] (**16**), 301.

[6] Cf. e.g. (5), (**25**), (**21**), (**13**), p. 55 as well as (**17**) Ch. VII. In my note in *Zs. Phys.* 145 (1956), 421 I committed a similar mistake.

[7] This is the 'Neumann-Proof'.

[8] Attempts have been made (cf. e.g. (**8**)) to justify such a procedure on the basis of a slightly modified interpretation of the concept of probability. In this modified interpretation it is possible to apply probabilities also to individual systems. This is done e.g. by ascribing to a single die the *propensity* to exhibit a certain distribution (e.g. 1/6, 1/6, 1/6, 1/6, 1/6, 1/6) when suitably thrown (i.e. when thrown in such a way that the conditions of equiprobability are fulfilled). In this interpretation the statement 'die X has the probability of showing six in 20% of all cases' is no longer equivalent to the statement '20% of all throws with die X are 6'—for conditions may have been realized which led to a different distribution, in spite of the fact that the probability (in the sense of propensity) was as indicated. This interpretation is still not sufficient for the purpose of QM where we want to use ensembles in order to get information about the *actual state* of a system rather than about its *ability*, or *disposition* to produce such a state with a certain relative frequency, when handled in a suitable way. For within the propensity-interpretation we can still assume that a system which possesses a propensity $0 < x < 1$ to be in state A is, in fact, in state A whereas the same probability-statement, made with respect to a pure state, *excludes* such an assumption (or its negation, viz. that the system is *not* in state A). Hence, turning frequencies into propensities does not strengthen the connexion between statistical assertions and assertions about the individual system, it leaves it unchanged. This change of interpretation of probability has therefore no influence upon the problems of quantum mechanics. Nor is it possible to compare the quantum mechanical 'reduction of the wave-packet' with the sudden change of probabilities which occurs whenever the evidence is changed.

It should also be noted that the peculiar property of the ensembles of quantum-mechanical systems which was mentioned in the text does not necessitate a revision of the concept of probability in the sense of relative frequency (or propensity). For the property of being not dispersion-free and yet irreducible is not at variance with the property of being a collective (in von Mises' sense or in Wald's sense). It is an additional property which is satisfied by special collectives.

The theory of measurement proper rests upon the assumption that the state of a system may undergo two different kinds of changes, viz. changes which are continuous, reversible, and in accordance with the equations of motion—those changes happen as long as the system is not observed, however strong its interaction with other systems may be; and changes which are discontinuous, irreversible, not in accordance with the equations of motion and which happen as the result of a measurement. Two arguments are presented for this assumption, an inductive argument, trying to relate the existence of the discontinuous jumps to experience, and a consistency-argument which shows how they can be fitted into the theory without leading to contradictions. The inductive argument is invalid and will not be discussed here.[9] The consistency-argument which may be said to contain von Neumann's theory of measurement, may be stated thus: assume that the observable R (eigenfunctions $|\phi_1\rangle$, $|\phi_2\rangle$, ... , eigenvalues λ_1, λ_2, ... —we shall assume that the spectrum is discrete and non-degenerate) is measured in S (initial state $|\Phi\rangle$) with the help of the measuring-device M (initial state $|\Psi\rangle$). If the result of the measurement is taken into account, or, as we shall express ourselves, if a *complete measurement* is performed, then the statistical operator of S will change from P_ϕ to $P_{\phi i}$, λ_i being the eigenvalue found (we assume that all measurements are well designed). If we make a measurement without taking notice of the result, i.e. if we make what we shall call an *incomplete measurement*, then we can only say that λ_i will appear with the probability $|\langle\phi|\phi_i\rangle|^2$ which means that an incomplete measurement induces the transition

$$P_\phi \rightarrow \Sigma_i \,|\langle\phi|\phi_i\rangle|^2 P_{\phi i} = \Sigma_i \, P_{\phi i} P_\phi P_{\phi i} \tag{1}$$

This process contains only part of what is happening during the measurement. For (1) compares the initial state of S with its state immediately after the end of the interaction, without considering this interaction itself. We shall therefore call the account of measurement which consists in asserting that transition (1) has happened the *direct account*. In order to show the consistency of this direct account with the equations of motion it must now be demonstrated that the interaction between M and S, taken together with a direct account of a measurement of the apparatus-variable R' (performed immediately after the interaction) produces, with respect to S, the same result, as the direct application of (1) to S. It can be shown that for well designed measurements this problem is equivalent to the problem whether it is possible to choose an H (of $\{S+M\}$) and a T such that

$$\exp[-i/\hbar \, . \, HT]|\Phi\Psi\rangle = |\Phi\Psi\rangle' = \Sigma_i \langle\phi|\phi_i\rangle|\phi_i\rangle|\psi_i\rangle \tag{2}$$

and this problem is easily solved—at least theoretically. This completes von Neumann's theory of measurement.

It should be kept in mind that this theory does not lead to the elimination of process (1). It is not shown that the mixture in (1) emerges from P_ϕ on the basis of nothing but the initial states of M and S together with the equations of motion for the combined system $\{S+M\}$. It is only shown that the direct account of a *further* measurement, viz. of R', leads, with respect to S, to the same result as if one gave a direct account of the measurement of R in S from the very beginning. Hence the

[9] The argument is based upon an analysis of the Compton-effect. It is invalid as it takes into account only the classical features of this effect and completely neglects its finer, quantum-mechanical properties.

jumps (1) are still an irreducible element of the theory. Are they a necessary element? This question must be answered by a more detailed analysis of the current theory. In order to carry out such an analysis we first present this theory in a suitable form. This will be done in the next section.

(3) *Stages of Measurement.* We start with the following two assumptions: (A) R has only two eigenstates, $|\phi_1\rangle$ and $|\phi_2\rangle$, and

$$|\langle\phi|\phi_1\rangle|^2 \neq |\langle\phi|\phi_2\rangle|^2 \quad (3)$$

This assumption is introduced in order to simplify the argument, but (3) will be dropped in sec. 5; (B) the states of M which correspond to $|\phi_1\rangle$ and $|\phi_2\rangle$ (the eigenstates of R') are macroscopically distinguishable. In order to fix our ideas we may assume that M contains a pointer which is capable of only two positions, A and B (e.g. up and down) and that A and B can be easily registered by some means as taking a photograph, asking somebody else to look, looking oneself, etc.

Using these simplifications and taking into account the interaction between S and M, we may now distinguish three stages of a measurement of R in S.

Stage 1: Interaction between S and M until the combined state of $\{S+M\}$ is of the form (2).

In classical physics this stage is the only interesting one. For according to the classical point of view, S as well as M are now in a well defined, though unknown state. The remaining processes (looking at M, etc.), although of importance for the observer (they inform him about the state of M and thereby about the state of S) cannot have any decisive influence upon what is already fixed in M: The pointer is already pointing up, or down, and we need only to look in order to discover what is already there in nature, i.e. in M.

Within QM this classical point of view leads into difficulties as is easily seen from the following considerations: According to (2) the state of $\{S+M\}$ at the end of *stage* 1 is given by $P_{|\Phi\Psi'\rangle} = P'$ (for short). On the other hand the assumption that M is already in a well defined, though unknown, state means, within the formalism of QM, that $\{S+M\}$ is the mixture $P_M = |\langle\phi|\phi_1\rangle|^2 P_{\phi 1} P_A + |\langle\phi|\phi_2\rangle|^2 P_{\phi 2} P_B$. And as in general

$$P_M \neq P' \quad (4)$$

this latter assumption must be given up: we must not say that at the end of the interaction M (or S) is in a well defined, though unknown state.

This fact has sometimes been used as an argument in favour of the assumption that quantum mechanics is an incomplete theory which must be supplemented by additional parameters in order to become a complete theory.[10] This is the argument: at the end of *stage* 1 the pointer is already in a well-defined position; P' does not allow us to draw this conclusion. Hence, the description on the basis of P' is incomplete; and as in the situation described QM cannot provide us with a better description, QM is itself incomplete. In this argument it is overlooked that P' is not 'too poor' to provide us with such a description since it explicitly *excludes* such a description. It is therefore not possible to interpret transition (1) or the transition

$$P' \rightarrow P_M \quad (5)$$

[10] The argument is Einstein's (Cf. *Science News* 17 (1948)). It is frequently used by the more recent opponents of present-day quantum mechanics.

as a substitution of an incomplete description by a more complete description which does not correspond to any change in reality. Transition (5) must be interpreted as a real process. This is the most decisive argument in favour of the existence of 'quant-tum-jumps'.

Stage 2: involves two elements, namely (a) the incomplete measurement of R' and (b) the direct account of this incomplete measurement.

Since R' is a macroscopic variable (a) does not create any technical difficulties. Making an incomplete measurement of R' means measuring R' without taking the result into account; e.g. making a photograph of M and destroying it; asking an observer to watch M and not listening to his report; looking oneself at M without thinking. Such a measurement is a physical (or biological) process which does not involve any element of consciousness. If we treat this measurement as a further interaction between, say, $\{S+M\}$ on the one side, and light striking a photographic plate on the other, we have, on account of the above argument, to assume that the plate, even if developed, will not contain a definite picture of M. This indefiniteness will spread, the more objects interact with M, and it may even reach the mind of the conscious observer, making it impossible to say that he has received definite information, however certain he himself may feel about it.[11] It is not before we give a direct account of one of the stages described that we can return to attributing definite properties (positions, perceptions) to well defined objects (measuring instruments, observers). Hence, this step, i.e. transition (5) is necessary for connecting the quantum level with the classical level (the theory with experience—in Heisenberg's discussion of measurement).

Stage 3: Completion of the measurement of R' in M. Result: S (as well as M) is left in a well defined (and known) pure state.

(4) *Difficulties*: This theory of measurement is unsatisfactory for the following reasons.

(I) R' is a macroscopic observable. The values of macroscopic observables are fixed independently of any account which is given of their observation. The theory does not yield this result, not even as a first approximation.[12]

(II) Assume that this first difficulty has been solved, i.e. assume that it is possible to characterize the state of $\{S+M\}$ by P_M already at the end of *stage* 1. Assume, furthermore, that equation (3) does not hold. Then we are still unable to say the pointer is either pointing up or pointing down as now every linear combination of A and B is compatible with P_M. This shows that *stage* 3 which looks quite innocuous and which is usually not separated from the other stages, is not always unproblematic.[13]

(III) Any measurement leads to irreversible changes. For a wide class of changes, including incomplete measurements, the H-theorem can be proved without involving anything but (1) the equations of motion; (2) the specific properties of M;

[11] It is frequently assumed that M and S both jump into one of the eigenstates of R' and R respectively as soon as the observer *looks* at M (*esse est percipi*). The above considerations show that this is too simple a picture of the situation with which we are faced when trying to give a rational account of the process of measurement.

[12] This difficulty was first discussed by Schrödinger (**19**), § 5. (Schrödinger's cat).

[13] This difficulty has hardly ever been discussed in connexion with the process of measurement. Jordan (**12**) was the first physicist who explicitly drew attention to it; but his treatment is impaired by the fact that he does not distinguish it from difficulty (I).

(3) the specific properties of the observer B who registers the state of M. Yet, within von Neumann's theory, irreversibility appears only if we apply the direct account, whereas any process which is in accordance with the equations of motion leaves the entropy unchanged.

A careful analysis of these three difficulties, especially of the last one, leads to the following suggestion: the theory of measurement which was developed in sec. 2 and 3 is correct, but incomplete. What is omitted is the fact that M is a macroscopic system and that B cannot discern the finer properties of M. In other words, what is omitted is the fact that stage 2 and stage 3 occur at the macroscopic level. Now the transition from the level of QM to the level of classical mechanics involves certain approximations.[14] Within a theory of measurement which omits reference to the macroscopic character of both M and B those approximations cannot be justified. Hence, within such an incomplete theory the transition to the classical level will have to be treated as an independent element which cannot be further analysed and which cannot be explained in terms of the equation of motion. We suggest that a complete theory which contains a reference to the macroscopic character of both B and M will allow for such an explanation. And we now proceed to discuss the outlines of such a complete theory.

(5) *The Classical Level.* A simple calculation shows that immediately after the interaction is over, $|\psi_1\rangle$ and $|\psi_2\rangle$, the eigenfunctions of R', may be written in the form

$$|\psi_1\rangle' = |c_1\psi_1\rangle e^{-i\alpha} \qquad |\psi_2\rangle' = |c_2\psi_2\rangle e^{-i\alpha 2} \tag{6}$$

where $\alpha_1 = \alpha_1(\lambda_1 H)$; $\alpha_2 = \alpha_2(\lambda_2 H)$ (H being the Hamiltonian of interaction, supposed to be large as compared with H_S and H_M and commuting with R). The demand that $|\psi_1\rangle$ and $|\psi_2\rangle$ should be classically distinguishable implies that the real parts of the exponentials in (6) will have to differ by a great many nodes, i.e. it implies that

$$\alpha_1 - \alpha_2 \gg \pi \tag{7}$$

Now consider the following two assertions:[15] (a) Interaction satisfying (7) destroys all interference between the eigenfunctions of the observable measured and hence also between the corresponding eigenfunctions of the apparatus variable; (b) immediately after the interaction is over, i.e. already at the end of *stage* 1, the statistical operator P' can be substituted by P_M.

Assertion (a) follows from equation (7) only if we assume that all values of α_1 and α_2 which are compatible with (7) are equally probable. We shall call this assumption the *principle of equiprobability*. This assumption, which so far has only been used in connexion with quantum statistics, is an indispensable part of any complete theory of measurement. As opposed to classical theory of measurement the quantum theory of measurement is essentially a statistical theory, i.e. it is a theory which uses, apart from the equations of motion, also further statistical assumptions. (7), i.e. the assertion that A and B are macroscopically distinguishable, implies, together with the principle of equiprobability, that, for all practical purposes, P' and P_M yield the same results with respect to the properties of S (we omit the simple calculation).

[14] There is still no satisfactory account available of those approximations.
[15] Cf. (1) Ch. 22.

This is the first step towards the solution of difficulty (I), section (4): P' can be substituted by P_M not because the jump (5) happened in nature, but because under the conditions mentioned the difference between P' and P_M is negligible, i.e. because it is highly improbable that there is a measurement (in S) of a magnitude compatible with R whose result in P' differs appreciably from its result in P_M.

In the second step we make use of the fact that B is not able to discern the finer details of M. More especially, B cannot discern anything like complementarity;[16] or, to be more precise: if R is observable for B then S is observable for B if and only if S commutes with R. This we call the *observer-principle*. With respect to the theory of measurement this observer-principle has the following consequences:

First: Equation (4) implies that there are observables whose expectation is different in P' and in P_M. It can be shown that this does not apply to any observable which commutes with either R or R'.[17] But according to the observer-principle an observable which does not commute with either R or R' will not be accessible to a macro-observer. Hence, *for a macro-observer*, systems in the state P' will be indistinguishable from systems in the state P_M. This goes beyond our above result, where it was shown that (on the basis of (7) and the principle of equiprobability) P' coincides with P_M—with respect to the properties of S which are compatible with R. Our present result is that $P' = P_M$ for a macroscopic observer—with respect to any property of P' or P_M. But there is a still more important application of the observer-principle which does not follow from (7) and the principle of equiprobability. It is

(*Secondly*) connected with the solution of difficulty (II): if equation (3) does not hold then any linear combination of A and B will be compatible with P_M. In a state (of M) which is a linear combination of A and B neither A nor B will be diagonal. Such a state is the eigenstate of an observable which is not accessible to a macro-observer. Hence, the observer-principle guarantees the consistency, with the formalism, of our third assumption: classical properties are always diagonal (the *diagonality-principle*). This solves the second difficulty.

Example: An especially striking example where (3) does not hold has been discussed by Einstein:[18] a macroscopic particle is elastically reflected between the side-walls of a cubical container of length l. The wave-function corresponding to the stationary process is $C\,.\,\sin[n\pi/l\,.\,x]\,.\,\exp[-i/\hbar\,.\,E_n t]$ (E_n being the nth eigenvalue of the energy). The macroscopic character of the process implies that $n\pi/l = \sqrt{2mE_n}/\hbar \gg 1$. Therefore $\sin^2[n\pi/l\,.\,x]$ will oscillate rapidly within any classically definable interval Δx and $W(\Delta x)$ (the probability to find the particle within Δx) will be constant. Now, although this is a macroscopic process we are, on the basis

[16] From the fact that the classical level does not show the feature of complementarity, it has been concluded that classical objects cannot be described in terms of QM, that QM must be restricted at the classical level, and that this restriction must be regulated by a new axiom (for such a suggestion cf. Jordan (**12**)). But in such an argument it is overlooked that the absence of complementarity at the classical level is due to the superposition of *two* causes viz. (1) the special properties of macroscopic objects which justify the introduction, into the formalism, of the principle of equiprobability and (2) the special properties of the macroscopic observer who is unable to determine all the properties of those objects: we may, without fear of contradiction, admit that macroscopic systems can be described in terms of wave-functions if we assume at the same time that a macroscopic observer has never enough information at his disposal in order to set up such a wave-function.

[17] For this cf. (**8**) and (**9**).

[18] (**6**), 32, Cf. also the discussion by Bohm in the same volume. This discussion is unsatisfactory as it consists in nothing but a detailed exposition of the transition from what we called *stage* 1 to what we called *stage* 2. But this amounts to *discussing* the difficulty, not to *solving* it.

of QM, apparently still unable to say that the particle has a definite, though perhaps unknown, position within the container, e.g. we cannot say that it is in the right part, or that it is in the left part of the container. This difficulty can now be solved by pointing out that an account of the classical level is an account of classical objects *as observed by classical observers*. Such an account is compatible with the diagonality-principle and hence, also with the assumption that the particle is at a definite, though unknown place within the container. And such an account also disposes of the objections which Einstein derived from his example.

Thirdly: the introduction of a macroscopic observer is of decisive importance for the investigations in connexion with the quantum-mechanical ergodic theorem and H-theorem (it corresponds to the introduction of coarse-grained densities).[19] But it was not before quite recently that those investigations were connected with the quantum theory of measurement.[20] The result of those more recent investigations is that the observer-principle is valid under conditions which are nearly always fulfilled in reality[21]; and that it may be possible to give a proof of the diagonality-principle. This result amounts to a consistency-proof of the extended theory of measurement as it has been developed in this paper, as well as to a reduction of the diagonality-principle to some deeper assumptions. It also amounts to a solution of our third difficulty.[22]

(6) *Conclusion.* A theory of measurement can be developed which depends, just as its classical counterpart, on nothing but the equations of motion and the special conditions (macroscopically distinguishable states; macro-observers) under which those equations are applied. This has the following consequences:

(1) All the processes which happen during measurement can be understood on the basis of the equations of motion only; hence, it is incorrect to say (as e.g. Dirac does, thereby expressing what is believed to be true by numerous physicists) that a mere interaction between a system *S* and its surrounding 'is to be distinguished from a disturbance, caused by a process of observation, as the former is compatible with the . . . equations of motion while the latter is not.'[23]

(2) As von Neumann has pointed out[24], the transitions (5) are the way in which the old idea of 'quantum-jumps' is expressed within the formalism. Hence, our result can also be stated by saying (a) that there are no quantum-jumps and (b) that the idea that there are quantum-jumps has its origin in an incomplete theory of measurement. In this respect we agree with Schrödinger's recent attack against the orthodox interpretation of elementary quantum mechanics.[25]

(3) The theory of section (5) has been criticized; it has been objected that it is not 'exact' as it omits, by a process of approximation, interference-terms which

[19] Cf. (**7**) and the literature given there. For a less recent but more detailed discussion cf. (**24**). (**23**) contains all the literature in the field.

[20] This was mainly done by Ludwig (**15**) and his pupil Kümmel (**14**).

[21] Those conditions are stated very clearly in (**14**).

[22] In fact this third difficulty was first attacked in von Neumann's attempt at a proof of a macroscopic H-theorem in 1929.

[23] (**4**), p. 110.

[24] (**16**), p. 218, footnote.

[25] Schrödinger (**20**). Cf. also my note in *Zs. Phys.* 148 (1957).

are postulated by QM.[26] Now those interference-terms are omitted also within the 'exact' theory. But the 'exact' theory omits them, not on the basis of a rational account, which does not deny their existence and which tries to *explain* why they can be neglected; it just omits them, gives a name to this procedure ('reduction of the wave-packet"; 'cut'; 'decision'; 'quantum-jump') and assumes that this amounts to having discovered a new kind of physical process (process (1) or process (5)).

(4) If we want to understand why this is done we must remember that the current interpretation of quantum-mechanics contains the following philosophical thesis: QM is a tool for producing predictions rather than a theory for describing the world, whereas classical terms have direct factual reference.[27] This thesis implies, of course, that the classical level and the quantum level are entirely distinct and that the transition from the one to the other cannot be further analysed.

(5) Now our analysis, if it is correct, shows that the classical level cannot be regarded as something which is totally distinct from the quantum level; it is rather a (particular) part of that level. Hence, the philosophical thesis, referred to in the last paragraph, must be revised and replaced by a realistic interpretation of the formalism of QM.

(6) Apart from leading to the rejection of part of the current *interpretation* of QM the result of our analysis can also be used for showing the inadequacy of various attacks against the *theory itself*. More especially, it can be used as an argument against all those attacks, which proceed from the difficulties we mentioned in section (4), and which interpret them as in indication that the present theory is incomplete[28] or subjectivistic. For we have suggested that, and how, those difficulties can be solved *within* the present theory.

(7) Within certain schools of philosophy it was, and still is, fashionable to distinguish the level of every-day experience (or the 'observation-language'[29], or the 'everyday-language') from the theoretical level, and to assume that the transition from the first level to the second level is totally different from transitions between parts of either the first, or the second level. This view is a generalization of the 'orthodox' view about the relation between classical mechanics and QM and it may therefore be called 'scientific'. But this only shows that nowadays scientists are committing a mistake which so far philosophers (notably positivistic, or 'scientific' ones) had the privilege to commit alone. On the other hand par. (5) of this section suggests that, quite in general, the everyday level is part of the theoretical level rather than something completely self-contained and independent; and this suggestion can be worked out in detail and leads to a more satisfactory account of the relation between theory and experience than is the account given by Carnap, Hempel and their followers on the one side, and some contemporary British philosophers on the other.

[26] For this objection cf. e.g. (**22**).

[27] 'The entire formalism is to be considered as a tool for deriving predictions, of definite or statistical character, as regards information obtainable under experimental conditions described in classical terms and specified by means of parameters entering into the algebraic or differential equations. . . . These symbols themselves are not susceptible to pictorial' (i.e. classical) 'interpretation'. (Bohr, *Dialectica* II (1947), 314). The general philosophical background of this 'instrumentalist' view has been discussed by K. R. Popper in his *Three Views of Human Knowledge*.

[28] For this point cf. footnote 10 of the present paper as well as the corresponding passages in the text.

[29] Cf. e.g. (**2**) as well as (**3**), p. 38 ff, especially p. 40 f.

REFERENCES

(1) Bohm, D., *Quantum Mechanics*, Princeton, 1951.
(2) Carnap, R., Foundations of Logic and Mathematics in *International Encyclopedia of Unified Science*, Chicago, 1939 I/3, sec. 23.
(3) Carnap, R., The Methodological Character of Theoretical Concepts; *Minnesota Studies in the Philosophy of Science*, Vol. I, Minnesota, 1956.
(4) Dirac, P. A. M., *The Principles of Quantum Mechanics*, Oxford, 1947.
(5) Einstein, A., *Journal Franklin Inst.* **221** (1936) Nr. 3.
(6) Einstein, A. in *Scientific Papers Presented to Max Born*, Edinburgh, 1953.
(7) Farquhar-Landsberg, P. T., *Prod. Roy. Soc.*, Ser. A, Vol. 239 (1957), 134.
(8) Furry, R., *Phys. Rev.* **49** (1936), 393.
(9) Groenewold, H. J., *Physica* **12** (1946), 405.
(10) Heisenberg, W., *Physikalische Principen der Quantentheorie*, Leipzig, 1944.
(11) Heisenberg, W., in *Niels Bohr and the Development of Physics*, London, 1955, pp. 12–29.
(12) Jordan, P., *Phil. Sc.* **16** (1949), 269.
(13) Kemble, E. C., *Fundamental Principles of Quantum Mechanics*, New York, 1937.
(14) Kümmel, L., *Nuovo Cimento* I/6 (1955), 1057.
(15) Ludwig, G., *Zs. Physik* **135** (1953), 483.
(16) von Neumann, J., *Mathematical Foundations of Quantum-Mechanics*, Princeton, 1955.
(17) Popper, K. R., *Logik der Forschung*, Vienna, 1935.
(18) Popper, K. R., The Propensity-Interpretation of the Calculus of Probability and the Quantum-Theory; *This Volume.*
(19) Schrödinger, E., *Naturwissenschaften* **23** (1935), 483.
(20) Schrödinger, E., *British Journal for the Philosophy of Science*, Vol. 3 (1952), 109 ff.
(21) Slater, R., *Journal Franklin Inst.* **207** (1929) 449.
(22) Süssmann, G., A Quantum-Mechanical Analysis of the Measuring-Process; *This Volume.*
(23) ter Haar, D., *Rev. Mod. Phys.* **27** (1955), 289 ff.
(24) Tolman, R. C., *The Principles of Statistical Mechanics*, Oxford 1938.
(25) van Vleck, J., *Journal Franklin Inst.* **207** (1929) 475.

An analysis of measurement

by

G. SÜSSMANN

THE whole information we have on the present state of motion of a closed system is briefly called the *state* of the system. The state thus defined can change in two different ways: 1. *dynamically*, according to the equations of motion, and 2. *by observation*. The dynamical changes are *continuous* and uniquely determined. The changes by observation on the other hand contain, in general, *discontinuities* and can be predicted only with a certain probability. Keeping in mind that a so-called state does not express the motion of a system but our knowledge of the motion these discontinuities are quite natural.

This epistomological situation is by no means characteristic for quantum mechanics; it is well known from classical thermodynamics[1] since Boltzmann and Gibbs. Within classical thermodynamics the state is described by the distribution function $\rho(q, p)$ for the probability in phase space. Being a macrostate, it represents an imaginary statistical ensemble of microstates which are denoted by the phase points q, p. By measurement the thermodynamical states will be changed discontinuously. This change, of course, has nothing to do with Liouville's canonical equation of motion, but it has to do with the change of our knowledge. Accordingly we can find uncertainties and some sort of complementarity, especially between energy and temperature. These *thermodynamical uncertainties* are of the order of magnitude of Boltzmann's constant k.

In quantum mechanics the situation is quite similar. The state is described by Schrödinger's configuration function $\psi(q)$, which represents a complex probability amplitude of indefinite phase. Besides Schrödinger's equation of motion, we have the discontinuous *reduction of the state*, $\psi \rightarrow \psi'$, caused by a measuring process. The *quantum mechanical uncertainties* are of the order of magnitude of Planck's constant h.

There is only one, yet fundamental, difference between classical and quantum mechanics. In classical theory it is always possible to assume that there is a complete mathematical picture of the object itself, which is exactly equivalent with the best possible knowledge of the object. From the physical point of view these two interpretations of the mathematical formalism are equivalent; the difference becomes important only in epistemology. Hence, the thermodynamical uncertainties can be understood in terms of our ignorance only.

In quantum theory, on the other hand, there exists no mathematical formalism describing the object itself. There is a possibility of introducing hidden parameters, but so far we are not able to observe them. Bohm's first deterministic interpretation cannot be disproved; though it is important for the discussion of quantum

[1] By thermodynamics I understand that extension of mechanics which has to be used if the knowledge of the object is not the best possible. I avoid the expression 'statistical mechanics' because in quantum theory pure mechanics already contain statistical elements.

theory, I think that it does not agree with the principle of simplicity. (*Simplex sigillum veri.*) Compared with the similar case of Einstein's gravitation theory, the deterministic interpretations of quantum theory would correspond to interpretations in Euclidian space. As I am not dealing with these questions here, I shall base my discussions on the usual statistical interpretation of Born, Jordan, and Dirac, according to which quantum mechanics contains uncertainties even in the best possible state. Though ψ is a statistical quantity, it describes a *microstate*. The discontinuity of the state reduction is therefore an essential feature of the theory.

We are now in a position to answer Schrödinger's question: 'Are there quantum-jumps?' The Schrödinger equation described a continuous change of the state in a deterministic way and hence does not involve quantum-jumps. By a measurement, however, a discontinuous statistical element is introduced into the theory, and this is the reason for all the so-called quantum-jumps. The discontinuity of the quantum-jumps is based on the discontinuity in obtaining information. The jumps show clearly[2] that the wave function cannot be considered to be a mathematical equivalent of the object system.

Only recently, the question appeared whether ψ can be interpreted as nothing but a jumping 'information wave' or whether there is any possibility of understanding it as a real quantity which is continuous in time, even though one rejects the idea of hidden parameters. Let us compare ψ with the two state concepts of the classical theory. Just as the probability distribution ρ, ψ is a statistical quantity which will be changed discontinuously by measurements. But like the phase point q, p, it is an *elementary* state-quantity, a microstate, our knowledge being the best possible; in other words: ψ is not a thermodynamical but a mechanical state. Hence Schrödinger's equation has a relationship to both Hamilton's and Liouville's equations. Since the Schrödinger equation is an *elementary equation of motion* we may try to avoid the discontinuity of the state reduction, because an interruption of the equation of motion is easier to understand in thermodynamics than in mechanics. For easier discussion let us assume two physicists A and B, A stating that Schrödinger's equation is valid under all circumstances, and B stating that it is interrupted by a measurement. A and B now have the following dialogue.[3]

A says: When we discuss the measuring process in classical thermodynamics, we may disregard the disturbance caused by the observer; but in quantum mechanics it is not allowed to neglect the interaction with the apparatus. This is a fundamental difference. The reduction of ψ is a consequence of this interaction. Considering the whole system 'object+apparatus', the discontinuity of the Schrödinger function disappears. The apparent discontinuity $\psi \rightarrow \psi'$ follows from the artificial restriction to the object-system alone.

B answers: By coupling the apparatus to the object system, the discontinuity in Schrödinger's equation cannot be removed but is only shifted to another point, which can be shown by a detailed analysis of the process of measurement. Let us distinguish the following parts of the procedure:

1. decomposition

[2] A drastic example is given in the famous paper by Einstein, Podolski, and Rosen (1935).

[3] For a more detailed treatment see G. Süssmann: *Bayer. Akad. d. Wiss., math.-nat. Kl.* (1957), in press.

2. division
   (a) extension
   (b) recording
   (c) abstraction
3. reading

They are of quite different character: decomposition perhaps may be called a 'mathematical' act, extension and abstraction may be called 'logical' ones, the recording a 'material' one, the division a 'physical' and the reading a 'mental' one. These steps will be discussed now one by one.

1. *Decomposition.* The mathematical analysis on which the measurement is based follows from the statistical transformation theory. More especially, it tells us the possible measuring values and the probabilities of the occurrence of a special value in the act of measurement. This theory is based upon Dirac's quantum mechanical superposition principle, according to which in the simplest case ψ splits into two terms representing the two possible results of a measurement:

$$\psi = \psi_1 + \psi_2. \tag{1}$$

Assuming $\psi_1 \perp \psi_2$, the corresponding probabilities p_i are $|\psi_i|^2$ (with $i = 1, 2$), provided that ψ has been normalized. We must not say that already before the measurement the system possesses *one* of the two properties 1 or 2 and that we only do not know which property this is; for ψ_1 and ψ_2 may interfere. This means that there exists at least one observable a, whose mean value contains terms of interference between ψ_1 and ψ_2, i.e. $\bar{a} = \bar{a}_1 + \bar{a}_2 + 2\bar{a}_{12}$, or

$$\langle\psi|a|\psi\rangle = \langle\psi_1|a|\psi_1\rangle + \langle\psi_2|a|\psi_2\rangle + 2\mathrm{Re}\,\langle\psi_1|a|\psi_2\rangle.$$

The cross term shows that ψ implies certain effects caused only by ψ_1 and ψ_2 in common. According to von Weizsäcker I therefore speak of a statistical *coexistence* of the two properties 1 and 2 in the state ψ. Without these interference terms we would have to deal with classical probability calculus, and the uncertainties could be interpreted as a consequence of our ignorance only.

2. *Division.* The point in the measuring process is now to split ψ into its components in such a way that interference between them cannot occur. The two components have to be isolated by a physical process; so there must be an interaction with some measuring device.

(a) Extension. In order to describe this interaction the Hilbert space of the object has to be extended by that of the measuring apparatus. $\Psi(Q)$ being the Schrödinger function of the apparatus, we have the following transition:

$$\psi_1 + \psi_2 \rightarrow (\psi_1 + \psi_2)\Psi. \tag{2a}$$

A simple product, however, may be assumed only before the interaction takes place. According to Schrödinger's equation, the total state is later changed in such a way that a simple separation is no longer possible, not even after the interaction has ceased. There exist correlations between the object and the apparatus. This is a consequence of the remarkable fact that in combining two systems in mind, within quantum theory the direct product of the state spaces has to be formed and not the direct sum as in classical theory. The correlations are of great importance for the theory of quantum mechanical measuring disturbances, since they are the main reason for the loss of coherence.

(b) Recording. In most cases the interaction changes the state of the total system in a complicated way; of course the orthogonality of the two components $\psi_i\Psi$ is conserved. If, however, the coupled instrument is suited to measure $i = 1, 2$ it must have the following properties. The component $\psi_i\Psi$ turns into a state $\psi_i'\Psi_i'$ which may be separated again after the interaction has taken place, but with different states of the instrument. Because of this i-dependence, the final state $\psi_1'\Psi_1'+\psi_2'\Psi_2'$ of the total system cannot be separated. The components Ψ_i' as well as Ψ are normalized. However, it is not generally possible to derive their orthogonality; but considering a *completely* dividing apparatus, the probability of the two 'pointer positions' Ψ_1' and Ψ_2' happening together must vanish. Otherwise the components would not be completely isolated. We assume this condition to be fulfilled, indicating it by the notation Ψ_i instead of Ψ'_i. Then

$$|\psi| = 1, \ \langle\psi_i|\psi_{i'}\rangle = p_i\delta_{ii'}; \ |\Psi| = 1, \ \langle\Psi_i|\Psi_{i'}\rangle = \delta_{ii'}, \ (i, i' = 1, 2).$$

If the apparatus is *non-disturbing*, that is, if we may neglect all interactions which in principle can be avoided, ψ_i' equals ψ_i. Hence the recording may be described by the formula

$$(\psi_1+\psi_2)\Psi \rightarrow \psi_1\Psi_1+\psi_2\Psi_2. \tag{2b}$$

It follows from the orthogonality of the pointer positions Ψ_i that it may now be difficult to find observables with non-vanishing interference terms. In most cases the Q-integration yields zero in connexion with simple operators, especially if we have to deal with many degrees of freedom. The coherence of the two components is then considerably reduced.

(c) Abstraction. From now on the state of the apparatus is only important for reading the state of the object. The latter is obtained by revoking our extension of the Hilbert space. Two different things are achieved by this reduction: the state of the instrument is eliminated, and as a consequence of this abstraction, the state of the object splits into two non-coherent parts:

$$\psi_1\Psi_1+\psi_2\Psi_2 \rightarrow \{\psi_1, \psi_2\}. \tag{2c}$$

The result is a thermodynamical quantum state; for $\{\psi_1, \psi_2\}$ is the statistical ensemble of the microstates ψ_1 and ψ_2 with the relative frequencies $|\psi_1|^2$ and $|\psi_2|^2$.

The effect of the division therefore may be summarized by the formula

$$\psi_1+\psi_2 \rightarrow \{\psi_1, \psi_2\}. \tag{2}$$

After the division has been made the two components are not able to interfere any longer, because they are not superposed but are just elements of a set. Hence, in the mean values (including the probabilities) the interference-terms do not any longer occur.

3. *Reading.* As soon as we know the result $i = 1$ or $i = 2$ the object is again in a mechanical quantum state:

$$\{\psi_1, \psi_2\} \rightarrow \psi_i, \qquad (i = 1 \text{ or } 2).$$

The probability for the reading i is $p_i = |\psi_i|^2$.

In order to get the new probability amplitude ψ', the Hilbert vector ψ_i has finally to be normalized. Collecting (1), (2) and (3) we obtain the formulae

$$\psi \to \psi', \qquad \psi' = \psi_i/|\psi_i|, \qquad (i = 1 \text{ or } 2)$$

for the state reduction. From this derivation it follows that the discontinuity can by no means be avoided, because the transition from $\psi_1\Psi_1+\psi_2\Psi_2$ to $\psi_i\Psi_i$ does not satisfy the Schrödinger equation of the total system.

A replies: But you must not assume a mechanical state for the measuring device because it is impossible to know 10^{20} co-ordinates or even more. We are rather concerned with a thermodynamical state and the discontinuity may therefore be understood as in classical theory: it follows from the mere *selection* from a statistical ensemble, the Schrödinger motion remaining untouched. The thermodynamical character of the measurement becomes evident from the irreversible character of the recording. The considerable increase in entropy shows that even before the reading the true measuring-value has already been established.

B replies: The thermodynamical situation must certainly be kept in mind, but this has nothing to do with the question whether the Schrödinger-waves are continuous or not. It does not affect my above argumentation, if Ψ, Ψ_i etc. is replaced by statistical ensembles $\{\ldots \Psi^\alpha \ldots\}$, $\{\ldots \Psi_i^\beta \ldots\}$ respectively, the final state having perhaps a much higher entropy than the initial one.[4] Because of the unitarity of the motion, each element of the ensemble contains the total state of the object; that is, in each element the state ψ is present with its total probability amplitude ψ_i.

A replies: But you must not forget that it is not the statistical ensemble of ψ-functions which gives the proper description of a thermodynamical state in quantum mechanics, but the *mixture*. For as opposed to classical theory, completely different ensembles may be statistically equivalent within quantum theory. This is a characteristic consequence of the quantum-mechanical superposition principle. A class of equivalent ensembles is by definition a mixture and is described easily by von Neumann's probability operator $\sigma(q, q')$, which is hermitean, non-negative and of trace 1. In formulae:

$$\sigma = \sigma^* \geqslant 0, \ \langle \sigma \rangle = 1.$$

The connexion with the corresponding ensemble $\{\ldots \psi^\alpha \ldots\}$ is given by the equation

$$\sigma = \sum_\alpha |\psi^\alpha\rangle\langle\psi^\alpha|.$$

We now can easily formulate the fundamental conceptions of thermodynamics: according to Boltzmann the value of the *entropy* is

$$S = -k \ \langle \sigma \log \sigma \rangle.$$

Here the negative trace $-\langle \sigma \log \sigma \rangle$ may also be called the logarithm of a generalized 'statistical weight' G of the state, so that $S = k \log G$. Accordingly, the entropy is a negative measure of the information contained in σ, or a positive measure of our *ignorance*. Hence, by the reading the entropy is decreased a little. In quantum theory[5]

[4] For each element Ψ^α may produce ensembles $\{\ldots \Psi_{\alpha\gamma i} \ldots\}$ so that $\beta = (\alpha, \gamma)$.

[5] In classica ltheory S always contains an additive constant which remains undetermined, and in the micro-state we get $S = -\infty$. So Nernst's heat theorem already indicates a quantum effect, and the entropy constants contain both the 'quantum of entropy' k and the 'quantum of action' h.

$S \geqslant 0$, where $S = 0$ means a minimum of ignorance, or the existence of a microstate ψ which is equivalent to σ. A well-known example of a mixture with different ensembles is an unpolarized photon (or electron).

This equivalence of different ensembles must be taken into consideration also when we discuss the measuring process. The original ensemble contains both ψ-components; but after the irreversible process has occurred, we have to replace it by a new ensemble adapted to the two pointer positions. This transition from one ensemble to another is a purely subjective or logical act which does not affect the Shrödinger equation. Each microstate might be followed up continuously, because the elements of the mixture are only 'rearranged'. In the new 'assortment' (consisting of other elements than the original one) the reading is only a selection. Hence, the state reduction is essentially of 'Liouville's' type.

B objects: This is an interesting idea; but if we wish to have an exact theory, there is no possible mathematical formulation of it. This can be seen clearly if each of the ensembles $\{\ldots \Psi^{\alpha} \ldots\}$, $\{\ldots \psi^{\beta}{}_{i} \ldots\}$ etc. is replaced by its corresponding mixtures σ, σ_i and if one realizes that the temporal development of the mixture does not depend on the ensemble which has been used for interpreting it. The coexistence of the values $i = 1, 2$ cannot be made to disappear by means of a unitary motion. This becomes evident if we consider the reversed process, which also satisfies the Schrödinger equation. For in this case the interference terms cannot arise from nothing. The irreversibility of the recording does not mean that all interference terms vanish; it means that they lose their physical significance. In practice, operators with non-vanishing interferences are no longer 'observables'. Therefore, in the process of abstraction we are to some extent justified in omitting the interference terms, though their full mathematical *existence* cannot be doubted. The objectivity of the measuring values i can only be obtained by the logical act of abstraction. Strictly speaking, however, their coexistence before the reading cannot be denied.

A now says: I agree. But you have supposed that macrophysical bodies strictly obey the quantum mechanical laws. This extrapolation goes very far and is not plausible.

B remarks: Whether or not the quantum theory is valid on the macroscopic level, we don't know. But if we take the theory as it is, and if no hidden parameters are assumed, then a normalized ψ cannot be considered a continuous quantity.

Thus the dialogue. Finally I want to make the following remark. The interpretation according to which ψ is not a real field, does of course not imply that the *atoms themselves* are not real. It says, that the *physical concepts* of the atoms have direct reference only to our knowledge of these entities.

Discussion

Bastin. I wish to describe a view of the nature of the process of observing an elementary particle which arises out of a theory[1] of the process of extrapolation of our local, macroscopic physical theory to the unfamiliar conditions of the very large and the very small.

According to this theory the limits to observation that are associated with elementary particles can be completely understood only if we pay attention to the theoretical and mathematical language on which our investigation of the microscopic realm is based. Also, on this theory, it is intrinsically impossible to separate the physical properties of elementary particles from the properties of the experimental observing systems and therefore of the theoretical description of the whole situation upon which the choice of observing system is based. This point of view is in a very direct way an extension of those well-known interpretations of quantum mechanics according to which the limits to the observation of quantum systems arise from an irreducible interaction between observer and what is observed. Both points of view stress that the characteristic properties of quantum systems require an explanation different in kind from the explanations of macroscopic physics. In both it is recognized—for example—that the discontinuities in structure that we encounter in connexion with elementary particles are different in kind from the discontinuities in structure we finally arrive at if we examine successively smaller samples taken from a heap of sand.

I have argued that the properties of any physical object need to be seen as essentially dependent on the whole set of concepts in terms of which we describe it. I propose therefore to incorporate this view into the beginnings of a physical theory by considering the measurement or observation of any physical object to be effected by a sequence of physical operations or decisions (each involving our whole theoretical descriptive technique) and which develops in time towards a definite degree of precision. Information about the object, or any given characteristic of the object, is thus built up at each stage of the sequence. If at some stage in the sequence there were a specially large increase in our knowledge about the object (as might happen for example if a photon were to produce a recoil electron which was then observed in a cloud-chamber) then it might be convenient to speak of that stage as our 'observation' of that object. In general however the decision that the available information given by the sequence constitutes an observation, will be largely arbitrary.

Let us now consider the objects that have the special property that a definitely known small number of sequences of the type we have introduced leads to the

[1] This theory is due to E. W. Bastin and C. W. Kilmister and some account of it can be found in a series of papers called 'The Concept of Order': I, The Space-Time Structure, *Proc. Camb. Phil. Soc.* **50** (1954) 278. II, Measurements, *Proc. Camb. Phil. Soc.* **51** (1955) 454. III, Relativity as an Extrapolation Theory, *Proc. Camb. Phil. Soc.* **53** (1957) 462. IV, Quantum Theory as an Extrapolation Theory (To be published).

measurement of the set of attributes of each such object. These objects will be elementary particles. According to my view then, the difference between observation of an elementary particle and observation of a macroscopic object consists in this: in the case of the elementary particle our observation cannot be amended, checked or in any way refined because further distinct sequences do not exist. In the case of a macroscopic object, on the other hand, further sequences giving further information about further attributes of that object can in principle be produced indefinitely. This property of macroscopic particles—that they seem to possess an indefinitely extendable set of attributes which become known as we successively refine and alter our measurements—clearly lies deep in our experience. For this reason it is valuable to be able to formulate the characteristic property of elementary particles by ascribing to them *an exhaustible set of attributes* (a phrase due to H. Bondi)

It remains, to end this note, to suggest one important step in the process by which the sequences I have introduced enable us to derive particles with an exhaustible set of attributes and to incorporate these into a physical theory from which a quantum mechanics can be derived. It is necessary first to connect these sequences explicitly with the study of the structural forms underlying the language and formalism of physical theory. The essential step then consists in assuming—on the basis of an adequate empirical enquiry—that these structural language forms underlying physical theory should be closed and finite. It is clear in a general way that the connexion of sequences with the structural forms might be expected to carry the finitary property of the structural forms over to the set of attributes of the particles. The details of this connexion cannot, however, be discussed here.

Bohm. I would like to call attention to an important problem concerning the theory of measurements, first raised by Schrödinger. He supposed a hypothetical experiment, in which a single photon passed through a half-silvered mirror. This photon is either reflected or transmitted. If it is reflected, nothing happens. If it is transmitted then it activates a photo-electric cell, which fires a gun that kills a cat which was placed inside a small box.

After the experiment is over, but before any person has looked, the wave-function for the combined system is a linear combination of functions which represent a dead cat and functions which represent a live cat. But at this time it is not only impossible to say whether the cat is dead or alive; it is impossible even to say that the cat is either dead or alive. Of course, when somebody looks he then either sees that the cat is alive or that it is dead—and adjusts the wave-function accordingly. Now if we wish to have an objective treatment of the whole process, that is to say, a treatment where the observer plays no essential role, then there must be something more in the theory than the wave-function. For the wave-function does not give the most complete possible description of reality, as is usually assumed. This suggests that quantum mechanics is incomplete, that there should be in addition to the wave-function some further parameters which tell you what the actual state of the system is after the interaction. After the apparatus has functioned but before anybody has looked, the system is already in some state—and then the observer looks and he finds what it is. The reduction of the wave-packet takes place objectively, that is without the aid of the observer, but with the aid of those additional parameters.

Feyerabend. I don't think that this radical procedure is justified, and I think that the paradox can be solved within quantum mechanics in its present form and interpretation. One has only to consider that, when the interaction is over the combined wave-function is of such a kind that a macroscopic observer cannot discover any difference between the statistical results which it implies and the statistical results implied by a mixture in which the measuring apparatus (or the cat) can be said to be in one of various different states. Hence, if one takes into account the fact that the observer who looks at the cat (or the device which is used for ascertaining the state of the cat) can only distinguish macroscopic events, states, etc., one is allowed to identify the wave-function and the mixture. And if one is allowed to make this identification, then the assumption that the cat is in a definite state even before anybody has looked at it, will not lead to any contradiction.

Bohm. That is very similar to the idea that I was proposing—in the large scale there are some classical variables not satisfying quantum theory.

Feyerabend. That is a misunderstanding. On the large scale there are all sorts of variables. Some of them can be measured by the macroscopic observer, some can't be measured by the macroscopic observer or by a macroscopic measuring device. But if the macroscopic observer takes into account only those variables which he can measure then he will find no difference between the combined wave-function which forbids him to say that the cat is in a well defined, though perhaps unknown state (dead or alive) and the mixture which does not forbid him to say this.

Bohm. But then the observer is being given a fundamental role and the fact that it is in a definite state seems to depend on the observer once again.

Vigier. The Schrödinger paradox points to the fact that there is something which has happened at the macroscopic level and which we have not been able to describe. There is the fact that the cat is either dead or alive and this fact does not come into the description of the process as this description is purely statistical. But this brings us back to the argument that the only knowledge we have at the macroscopic level is a statistical knowledge.

Groenewold. In the description which Dr. Süssmann has given of the measuring process he has taken into account the various steps of the interaction between the object-system and the measuring instrument. The point which to my mind is the most important and the most interesting one is the transformation of the pure state into a mixture; this point can be expressed by saying that in some way the coherence between the states on the right-hand side is destroyed. Let me discuss this destruction of coherence a bit more in detail using as an example the experiment which Professor Vigier discussed yesterday, viz. the two-slit experiment. If we are going to measure whether the particle is going through one slit or the other of the screen, we know that then the interference picture is destroyed, which can be expressed by the destruction of the coherence between the part of the wave which goes through the upper slit and the part of the wave which goes through the lower slit. Now there is a possibility of regaining the coherence. Assume, for example, that we try to determine whether the particle has gone through the upper slit or the lower slit by taking a movable screen and measuring the recoil. Then the place of the screen becomes undetermined and the interference pattern is faded out. But now we may, after the particle has passed, decide to measure not the recoil, but the position of the screen and then select only those for which the screen is found near to a certain position. In this case we have retained the interference pattern, but we have lost the possibility of saying through which of the slits the particle has come. We can therefore let the two waves interfere again by making a suitable selection. But this becomes different if we now go one step further, and say, in the way von Neumann does, that in the measuring process we are concerned with a series of links where each system is coupled to the former system, because we must observe the screen with some apparatus and then we must observe that apparatus and so on. Now if we have more than one apparatus after the screen, then it is no longer possible to restore the coherence. In order to make the interference once more we have not only to select something from the first apparatus but also from the second one, and that is completely impossible if you analyse it. The phase relations between the systems are distributed over the various apparatus and we can't use them any more. So if there were only one link between the object system and the recording system it would already be impossible to make interference. But this is not the only possibility to obtain destruction of coherence, as there are various different places where one can find this destruction. In this connexion the most important point is this: it is one of the paradoxes of the discussion of von Neumann that this chain of links has to be followed into the brain of the observer; i.e. we either get an infinite chain or we have to follow the chain into a region where it is difficult to apply physics. But we must not forget that at some earlier place there comes the recording of the measuring instrument, and the recording has to be made in such a way that the state of the recording system is not affected in a relevant way by the next observation. This is only possible if the recording is made in an irreversible way and in a macroscopic system and I think that this is the main reason why in the discussion of the measuring process the macroscopic character of the measuring process comes in. This is also a point where the destruction of coherence comes in. Coherence cannot be restored as the system is too complicated. We may be able to describe it by some linear combination of wave-functions, but in this place this becomes completely meaningless.

Süssmann. If one changes quantum mechanics then it may well be that one can describe the situation in a different way, but I want to restrict myself to quantum mechanics as it is. Here—and this concerns Dr. Feyerabend—I think I have proved that the assumption of a classical observer as he introduces it is inconsistent with quantum mechanics. I also have the feeling that Professor Groenewold wanted to discuss away the interferences which I think are preserved, although one may of course be able to abstract from them by a kind of logical act. Within a strict theory the proof which I have given is still in force, which means that on the basis of quantum mechanics one cannot doubt this co-existence of properties, although they may lose their physical meaning in the case of macroscopic bodies such as cats and the like. But their mathematical existence within a strict formulation of quantum mechanics is beyond doubt. In order to understand the situation in the cat-paradox we must realize that the Ψ-function of a cat is not identical with the cat, but that it expresses our information about the cat. If you consider this, then the whole situation loses its paradoxical character. It is no longer paradoxical to say that there are interference terms between the dead cat and the cat alive, for operators with non-vanishing interference terms are very complicated and cannot be realized by any physical means. Thermodynamics seems to provide us with a good analogy: according to the theory a brick may rise to the roof of a house, and it is not possible to deny this possibility. The same applies to dead and alive. What is going to happen should not be taken as a matter of course; we cannot simply say—and this is another argument against Dr. Feyerabend—that macroscopic bodies don't behave like that, for as the phenomena of super-conductivity or super-fluidity show, quantum mechanics is better than our definitions of classical bodies. These phenomena are macroscopic phenomena which are simply absurd when seen from a classical point of view; not much less absurd than the extremely 'weak' co-existence of dead and alive or the extremely improbable rising of a stone. In their discussion of the possible quantum measurements Heisenberg and others have shown that the uncertainty of position and momentum of macrophysical bodies is essential: these uncertainties are the reason of the destruction of coherence mentioned by Professor Groenewold. Thus it is impossible to consider macroscopic bodies along classical lines.

Pryce. In formulating the cat paradox one has started by assuming that besides the cat one deals with a microsystem, the photon. One says 'Take the photon' and then from this one draws certain apparently paradoxical conclusions. Now this is a gross over-simplification of the way in which one has to apply quantum mechanics to the real world. For one starts with a macroscopic world, one is doing experiments in a macroscopic world; I cannot take a single photon at will. In general I have to accept photons from a source which I cannot completely control. I could, of course, refine the approach and try to set up an imaginary apparatus in which I could take a photon. But I think if one oversimplifies at the beginning of the formulation of a problem like this one shouldn't be surprised if one's oversimplified conclusions look paradoxical.

Hutten. The whole theory of measurement in quantum mechanics was created by a philosophical problem, namely the problem, What can we know? The study which has been called the theory of knowledge and which we have inherited from the Greeks proceeds from the idea that the objective reality is something which we can know completely and which is specifiable by a finite number of parameters. Within classical mechanics this idea does not lead to any serious difficulty. But it is, of course, quite unfair to apply the classical standard to the case of quantum mechanics and to declare that quantum-mechanical description is incomplete. Of course, one could say that classical description is also incomplete; for one can always make it incomplete but we do not worry about that. If, for example, I look out here and see a tree and then turn away, then, while I am turning my back to the tree, anything may happen; the tree may disappear completely into thin air, or it may explode, or all sorts of other things may happen—we cannot say which. That shows that our knowledge is incomplete already in the classical case.

In one sense it is trivial to say that scientific theories are incomplete, for all theories will be superseded by new ones that are better approximations to the facts. Newtonian mechanics is incomplete in this sense, for it cannot, and was not designed to, treat of quantum phenomena.

It is important to see that, in order to judge whether a theory is complete or not, we have also to know its domain of application. We believed originally that Newtonian theory applied to all mechanical phenomena; later, we learned that relativity mechanics is needed when we want to describe phenomena involving high energies and speeds. This does not mean that Newtonian mechanics is incomplete in a serious sense; it can still deal with all the phenomena on a given plane, or level, which represents its proper domain of application.

But a theory may also be incomplete in the sense that it cannot cope with the phenomena on the level for which the theory was intended. Quantum mechanics is sometimes accused of being incomplete in this second, serious, sense. In order to arrive at a verdict, we must say what the level of description is to be; and most people would say, I think, that quantum theory was designed to deal with atoms and molecules, i.e. the atomic level.

It is of course true that it can deal also with some sub-atomic phenomena of a relatively simple kind, especially when these are closely connected with atomic phenomena, e.g. certain processes in nuclear disintegration. But it is noteworthy that, in so far as quantum mechanics can deal with elementary particles at all, it is only the stable particles, e.g. the electron and the proton, that can be treated.

Thus the fact that we need a new theory to describe sub-atomic phenomena does not imply that quantum mechanics is incomplete in the serious sense that it fails in its proper domain of application. It may well be that, if and when a new theory of fundamental particles is developed, we shall have to restrict the domain of application of quantum mechanics and assign certain phenomena to the new theory which, before, we treated with the help of quantum theory.

To say that quantum mechanics must be able to treat of *all* 'non-classical' phenomena is a mistake, the same mistake which the mechanists committed in the last century when they thought that Newtonian theory applied everywhere, e.g. the elastic theory of light.

Körner. Dr. Süssmann says that the theory, as illustrated by the example of the cat, results in a statement giving information about the cat. Professor Bohm says that this information is not sufficient. The cat is either alive or dead, but the existing quantum theory does not enable us to find out which. Therefore, I think, there is no disagreement between them about what Dr. Süssmann calls the strict logical consequences of quantum theory. It appears that Dr. Süssmann is concerned with showing what follows from quantum theory as it stands, whereas Professor Bohm points out certain gaps in a broader context including quantum theory—gaps which by his new theories he is trying to fill.

Bohm. I think that is more or less correct. I would like to add just one thing. One can perhaps see the problem more sharply in the following way: let us admit that the quantum mechanics at present tells us *something* about the cat under the condition that one photon was going in. On the other hand, with respect to this condition surely the cat knows more, the cat—or some human observer that we use in its place—knows something which it is apparently not possible to put into the wave equation of the first observer. Of course, the cat could in principle make another wave function, which describes itself as either dead or alive. But we are getting into very difficult paradoxical problems if we try to say that quantum mechanics is a complete description of everything that can be known, that is of all knowledge that can exist with respect to a given situation.

Süssmann. In most points I think we would agree. But consider, for example, the Stern-Gerlach experiment where a beam is split into two by a magnetic field. In this case one cannot say that the electron is in beam 1 or in beam 2 and that we only do not know it, for there is a difficulty, namely the possibility of interference. The point of disagreement was whether in the case of the cat these interference terms must still be assumed to exist. Bohm does not seem to like those interference terms because the cat is a macroscopic system which, he believes, is either in one stage or another. I say that strictly speaking one has to assume that they exist but one can show at the same time, as Professor Groenewold has explained, that they are practically without any effect.

Bohm. I would even admit that the interference terms may well be there, and I agree with you that they are normally of extremely small importance. But the other problem is what parameter in the theory describes the fact that there is a cat which is either alive or dead. There is this additional information, which apparently can't be described by our physical theory. Hence there is something missing, which shows that present quantum mechanics cannot be the complete theory it is always supposed to be.

Vigier. Professor Pryce brought up the important question whether one can trigger macroscopic phenomena by phenomena occurring at a quantum-mechanical level. I think the answer is Yes. You could start with an electron, and with an apparatus which allows you to detect and multiply the current created by one electron. If you do this then a serious physical problem arises because now one can induce macroscopic phenomena by microscopic phenomena at the quantum-mechanical level. You can, for example, trigger an H-bomb which you have put into this room. If you admit this fact, then you must also admit that at the macroscopic level there is some information which does not enter the wave-function. This is the deep meaning of the Schrödinger paradox.

And now to Dr. Süssmann's point that the wave-function is only an information function and that the cat is not reducible to that wave function. If you grant us that, then I think you come into conflict with Professor Rosenfeld, because the basis of the orthodox interpretation is precisely the fact that the wave-function covers everything physical in the system. This is true at the quantum-mechanical level, but it is also true at the macroscopic level which is just a collection of quantum-mechanical particles, after all.

Pryce. I agree in part with what you say but this is a very difficult problem. One difficulty I have in mind you have not quite covered. You put in a radium atom to trigger it, and the radium atom will or will not disintegrate after a certain time, and it is not under your control when that triggering takes place. When I said you cannot take a photon, I was rather at the next level; I thought you cannot trigger a photon-emitting atom to deliver you a photon when you want it, nor can you make a radium atom disintegrate when you want it, but this is I think not strictly relevant to the problem.

Mackay. I have always taken it that $|\Psi|^2$ was a measure of the probability, not of a state of affairs, but of an event. If one follows the quantum process to the brain of the observer, $|\Psi|^2$ measures the probability of the event 'observing the cat', in one state or another. If one follows the process only to the event of the impact of the photon on the counter or the electron on the counter, $|\Psi|^2$ measures the probability of photon-impact. To clarify the point, let us replace the cat by a rapidly moving film on which the photon or the electron makes a black spot. Then you could determine by later observation not only that this event has happened but even when it has happened. At no time is the film—or the cat—in two states. What has two states is the range of possible outcomes of your observing-the-cat, until you observe the cat. After you observe, without any magical interactions, this range of possibilities collapses to one, the observed one. The same situation is a commonplace of information theory. Does the Ψ-function ever predict more than the probability of events; does it ever in fact predict the probability of states of affairs?

Pryce. I would say that the Ψ-function is concerned with the outcome of measurements and not events.

Öpik. Is it fair to say that anybody has ever claimed that quantum mechanics is complete in the sense that it gives us all the information that there is? I think we don't even have to consider the paradox of the cat—I think even the Einstein-Podolsky-Rosen example shows that there is something in Nature that we cannot know by quantum mechanics. So is it not proper to say that quantum mechanics gives us or might give us all the knowledge that is ever obtainable although there is something more in Nature? Now going back to the cat, I think the paradox can be resolved in this manner. In this experiment, we—unless we make an observation—can only know the wave-function which consists of two terms, one representing the cat as dead and the other one as alive. It doesn't give us the information whether the cat is definitely dead or alive, but it gives us all the information which we can obtain. The cat knows more, sure enough, but in this experiment the cat must be regarded as part of Nature, and even in the Einstein-Podolsky-Rosen example we don't know what will be there in Nature when we have made only the first measurement.

Groenewold. It has been asked why a cat is used. Discussing the recording process one can introduce the concept of the reliability of the recording which means that the recording is more or less insensitive to other influences, like Brownian motion and so on. This has been discussed, especially in other connexions, by Brillouin who, I think, introduced this notion of reliability which is directly connected with the entropy-change in the recording process: one has to pay for it by negentropy. By raising the price in negentropy out of proportion, e.g., in a recording device in which animals become killed, one just produces quite spectacular effects.

Landsberg. Normally when one specifies a thermodynamic state, all one can say is that the system is in a fairly large phase cell of phase space. Hence one would expect in any account that makes reference to thermodynamics to have some kind of coarse-grained probability or a specification of the size of the cell in which the system is. This I have not seen here. The second point I wish to make is connected with the paradox of the cat. I don't know what the initial state is, but if it is an electron in a box with perfectly reflecting walls of infinitely high potential energy, then, of course, the electron will never be absorbed by any apparatus whatsoever. If you want to allow for the electron to be somewhere absorbed and to trigger off a reaction, one of the potential energy walls will not be infinitely high. There will then be a definite probability for the electron to pass into your triggering system. This will have to be taken into account in your wave-function and, presumably, if you approximate the potential in a suitable way, you will be able to find a probability for the electron to come through, and for the cat to be killed. It is true that the numerical answer is a probability, but we would have used the best available theory. At least it has the merit that the same theory with similar assumptions does not also lead to another probability. This would be a paradox in the strict sense. So I don't quite see at the moment what precisely the paradox is, granting, as previous speakers have emphasized, that the interference terms are unimportant. Is not the basic difficulty that probability statements cannot be tested by single occurrences?

Süssmann. With regard to Professor Vigier's question, I would like to say that the Ψ is not the atom and not the cat either. I would agree that apart from the Ψ-function there is also something more. The Schrödinger equation for Ψ contains all the laws of nature—but apart from those laws there is also something else, namely the initial conditions, the historical features, the accidental properties of things, the events. These are of course not fully contained in the wave-function, but predicted by it only with probability. Physical theories do not contain all the parameters which would be necessary to deduce all we know; for besides physics there is history.

One can of course say that Ψ gives only information about measurements. This is correct as long as one does not want to know the properties of the things (atoms, cats, etc.). But if one wants to know whether the electron is here or there then one is bound to say that the statements about future experiments, if they are correct, forbid us to say that the electron is either here or there, one only does not know where; on the contrary one is forced to admit the statistical co-existence of both—the electron is so to speak partly here and partly there. In strict quantum mechanics it is not allowed to speak of events (which would provide a decision) before a measurement has taken place. This is my answer to Dr. Mackay.

As regards the second question of Dr. Landsberg; if the probability that the cat is dead is 99·99%, then of course, there is no paradox; but if one arranges the experiment in such a way that the probability is only 50% then the paradox arises because of the existence of interference terms.

Feyerabend. We have a measuring device and the outcome of the measurement is indicated by a pointer which has only two possible positions, either pointing up or down. Now when the interaction with the system to be measured is over two different questions may be asked. The first question is whether from the combined state of the system and the measuring device one can derive a statement to the effect that the pointer will be in a well defined, though perhaps unknown, position. This is the question which Bohm and Vigier have been asking and this question must be answered in the negative. The second question which is of importance for the theory of measurement is: is the statement that the combined system is in a certain combined state, compatible with the statement that the position of the pointer is already well defined? According to the strict account those two statements are not compatible (which shows, by the way, that the negative answer to the first question does not imply, as Bohm and Vigier seem to believe, that quantum mechanics is incomplete. For the combined wave-function is not too 'poor' to say anything about the position of the pointer, it strictly *forbids* us to make a definite statement about the position of the pointer). Therefore the strict account forces us to introduce such things as 'quantum-jumps' which lead us from the combined state to the classical level where the cat is definitely either dead or alive and where the pointer has a definite, though unknown, position. My point is that this is due to the incompleteness of the strict account which does not consider (a) that the measuring apparatus is a macroscopic system, and (b) that the observer who looks at it or the device (photographic camera) which is used for ascertaining its state cannot determine all its finer properties. (a) and (b) allow us to replace the combined wave-function by a mixture, not because a quantum-jump has happened in nature but because the error involved is negligible. Hence, a complete theory of measurement which takes into account the special (viz. macroscopic) properties of the systems concerned is no longer faced by the cat-paradox and it does not contain quantum-jumps either. It contains nothing but the equations of motion and some special assumptions about the character of the systems involved in the measurement. My objection to Dr. Süssmann is therefore simply that his account, although correct, is incomplete. Of course, he is not content with the combined wave-function; he wants to have this mixture in order to be able to describe the measuring apparatus in a more or less classical way. But instead of taking into consideration the approximations which this transition involves and justifying them on the basis of the special properties of the measuring-device, he introduces, as many physicists before him (e.g. Heisenberg), the jumps as unanalysed wholes. Therefore his strict account is not at all as strict as it looks, as it leaves out the interferences anyway—but without in any way justifying the procedure. This is the reason why I cannot consider his account, or any similar account, to be a satisfactory one. This is also the answer to Dr. Landsberg's first question. For when introducing macroscopic observers we must at the same time introduce coarse-grained densities. In fact a macroscopic observer is defined by certain (coarse-grained) possibilities of subdividing phase-space.

SIXTH SESSION

Chairman: Professor R. B. BRAITHWAITE

W. C. KNEALE: What can we see?

W. B. GALLIE: The limits of prediction.

G. RYLE: Predicting and inferring.

What can we see?

by

W. KNEALE

(1)

A SCIENTIFIC correspondent writing in *The Times* of 17 July, 1956, about New Ways of Examining Atoms said 'There are several ways of "looking" at atoms, although for most of them the word "look" must remain to some extent in inverted commas.' After this curiously worded opening he explained a new technique of projecting ions from a very finely pointed electrode, and stated cautiously that the method had produced 'impressively clear pictures which leave little doubt that it is the positions of atoms which are being seen'. Then, turning to the more familiar electron microscope, he asserted without hesitation that it had made possible 'direct pictures' of crystal lattice planes, and even went so far as to say that by its use crystal lattices and their imperfections had been 'directly seen'. But when he came to talk about sub-atomic particles, he felt once more the need for caution and said 'The nucleus can be "seen" only from its interaction with particles which have made inelastic collisions with it'.

My purpose in this paper is not to discuss modern instruments of observation, about which I know no more than I have read in popular accounts like that just mentioned, but rather to consider what sorts of things we can properly claim to see, and I have quoted from the article of *The Times* correspondent only because it shows in a striking way how an intelligent man accustomed to expressing himself in print may be puzzled about the propriety of using the simple English word 'see' in unfamiliar circumstances. My enquiry is in large part linguistic, but not, I hope, trivial. The intellectual discomfort which we feel when we have to make up our minds about the application of old words in new contexts may direct our attention to features of ordinary usage that we have not hitherto noticed explicitly and so help us to solve some ancient problems of philosophy. And apart from that, since language is not merely a vehicle for the communication of thought but also an instrument of thinking itself, it is a mistake to be impatient about linguistic questions unless they are manifestly of the sort that can be solved by tossing a coin.

Sometimes philosophers and philosophizing scientists tell us that seeing in a minimum sense is mere reception of sense-data of a certain sort, but that in most contexts it involves also interpretation of the data within a theory. The theory, they say, may be just the set of common beliefs which Lord Russell has called the metaphysics of the stone age, or it may be a system of scientific hypotheses, but in either case what we see depends in part at least on what we are looking for. This doctrine is so widely received and so respectable that I have no wish to attack it, but I cannot agree that it offers a sufficient answer to my question. For the technical phrase 'sense-data' requires elucidation, and the word 'interpretation' is metaphorical in this context.

If we want a proper understanding of the situation, we must not remain content with such a formula, which is at best a very general summary of the features common to all kinds of perception, but examine the peculiar facts of vision and the peculiar ways in which we talk about it. In what follows I shall sometimes mention the other senses, but only for purposes of comparison.

(2)

Let us begin, then, with that usage of the word 'see' in which we say that we see bodies such as sticks and stones. This is certainly the most primitive usage, i.e. that which was established first in the history of our race and also first in the history of each individual. Sometimes when there is need for special precision, we say that we can see only part of the surface of a body, e.g. one side of a piece of paper; but this way of talking should not be regarded as a *correction* of the other. For a man who admits that he has seen one side of a piece of paper cannot properly deny that he has seen the paper, and no one (except perhaps Bishop Berkeley when writing of God in his *Principles*) has ever supposed that it might be possible to see an opaque solid in the sense of seeing all parts of its surface and all parts of its inside at once.

Having accustomed ourselves to saying that we see the surfaces of bodies, we may go on to say that we see colours and stripes and spots and patterns of various sorts on those surfaces. Nor need we stop there; for we may say also that we see changes of bodies and their markings, e.g. that we see the movement of the second hand of a watch round its dial.

The last point is important for various reasons, but in particular because it shows that there must be something wrong with a recent suggestion that what we call seeing is never an experience with duration but always an achievement of detection. There is indeed a common use of 'see' in which it is equivalent to 'detect by sight'; and it may perhaps be the prevalence of this use which makes it seem unnatural to say 'I am seeing' or 'I have been seeing' except in specialized phrases like 'I have been seeing pupils all morning', where 'seeing' is equivalent to 'interviewing'. But it is interesting to notice that a person who has succeeded in detecting something by sight may express his achievement by saying 'I can see it now'. Here the phrase 'can see' implies that the speaker has come into a state of discernment which may continue for some time. And later on such a person may describe his experience by saying 'When once I had spotted the thing, I could see it clearly for several seconds' or more simply 'I saw it clearly for several seconds'.

We have discovered already a good deal of complexity in our common talk about seeing. But there is more to come. When I say that I see my spectacle case, the fact that I use the phrase 'spectacle case' to describe what I see shows that I recognize it to be a spectacle case. But when I say of another man that he sees his spectacle case, only the context can show whether or not the word 'see' is supposed to imply recognition, and the same is true of statements about myself in the past tense. When, for example, I describe a search which I have made for my spectacle case, I may say either 'It was staring me in the face, but I did not see it' or 'I must have seen it without recognizing it'. Neither of these linguistic usages can be said for certain to be derivative from the other, but it is obvious that seeing with recognition is more complicated than seeing without recognition in that it involves subsumption of the object seen under a concept.

In so far as seeing with recognition can be ascribed to animals that do not talk, the concepts which it requires must be independent of language, and it is arguable at least that some are innate. But we can safely say that most of the concepts used in recognition of visible objects are acquired by learning and that some could not be acquired without language. Cats have to learn to recognize dogs, and they do so without much difficulty; but they show no signs of being able to recognize books as such. If, therefore, I hear it said that a cat saw a book, I take this to mean that he saw it in some sense which did not involve recognizing it as a book. It is difficult, however, to say just where the boundary comes between recognition which requires the use of language and recognition which is possible for animals. We say that some animals are frightened by moving shadows, but can an animal recognize a dark patch as a shadow? Or is the notion of a shadow accessible only to those who have some rudimentary theory of the propagation of light? In any case it is clear that much of the recognition done by human beings depends on their possession of rather complicated beliefs about causal connexions. When Robinson Crusoe saw the footprint in the sand of his desert island, he was amazed precisely because he saw it as a footprint, i.e. as a hollow which had been caused by the pressure of a human foot on the sand.

(3)

After the usage, or rather group of usages, which seems to be most primitive, we must notice next the earliest extension, namely, that by which we speak of seeing things in pictures. Since pictures of various sorts are among the oldest evidence we have for the existence of human beings, we may safely assume that short ways of talking about them have been current for many thousands of years, and it is even possible that in the past these locutions had something to do with the importance of pictures in magic. When a modern man talking to another about a picture by Landseer says 'The beast you see in the foreground is a stag', his hearer feels no inclination to stick knives in the representation. But such a remark uttered before a lively picture by a prehistoric artist might have a profound effect on a literally minded caveman.

The phraseology which we use in talking of pictures painted by men has been found equally appropriate for talking of photographs, cinema shows, X-ray shadows, television scenes, radar images, and all the representations produced by modern scientific apparatus of the kind mentioned at the beginning of this paper. Indeed we often use the word 'picture' itself in all these various contexts, and the reason is fairly obvious. In all these cases we can, if we choose, say that what we see is a pattern of light and colour on a surface. If instead we say that it is a picture of Charlie Chaplin, or of the bones in a man's body, or of an iceberg hidden from ordinary sight by fog, or of the lattice planes of a crystal, we do so because we think that it has been produced in such a way as to resemble the original of which we say it is a picture. In some of these cases a savage who knew nothing of the apparatus by which the pattern of light and colour had been produced might be prepared to say that he saw a picture, merely because it resembled something he had seen in the ordinary way;

but in other cases, and particularly in those which interest *The Times* correspondent, the savage would probably see no reason at all to use such a word as 'picture'. In short, our willingness to treat something as a picture may depend entirely on our knowledge of physical theory, and so *a fortiori* may our willingness to use the word 'see' in that derivative sense in which we speak of seeing a thing when we look at a picture of it.

In this connexion it is important to distinguish between cases in which the resemblance of picture to original might in principle at least be confirmed by ordinary visual inspection and those in which there could be no such confirmation. Even people who know very little about optics assume that photographs taken in the ordinary way resemble their originals, because they have often compared photographs with their originals in the past; and they are prepared to make the same assumption about pictures on radar screens as soon as they have independent evidence of the general reliability of the pictures obtained in that way. The fact that radar involves use of radiation which does not affect the human eye is of no more importance to the ordinary man than the fact that some photographs of very far distant objects are taken by infra-red light. It is true, of course, that while an iceberg is still shrouded in fog the ship's navigating officer cannot see it in the ordinary way to compare it with its picture on his radar screen; indeed it is just for this reason that radar is valuable. But the confidence of the navigating officer in his equipment is based on comparisons which he has made at other times between what he saw in the primitive sense and what he saw in the derivative sense by radar. The situation is very different, however, when apparatus is designed to produce pictures of molecules or even smaller particles. For analogy is then our only justification for the use of the word 'picture' and for that derivative use of the word 'see' which goes with it. It may be a very good analogy, but it is one which can be appreciated only by those who know something of physical theory.

I have assumed throughout this section that we can speak of seeing an X in a derivative sense whenever we can speak of seeing a picture of an X in a primitive sense. But it is interesting to notice that the inclination to use the word 'see' in its derivative sense is strengthened when the picture which we see in the primitive sense is a moving picture, and still further strengthened when we have reason to believe that the picture is contemporaneous or nearly contemporaneous with its original. When we see the moving picture of the performer on a television screen it seems quite natural to say that we see the performer, and similarly when we see the shadows cast by the bones of our feet as we wiggle them in one of the X-ray instruments used by sellers of shoes, it seems quite natural to say that we see our bones. But in neither case is there any serious danger of misunderstanding. If need arises, we are always prepared to distinguish the derivative usages with appropriate qualifying phrases such as 'by television' or 'by X-rays'. It seems that there is here an element of make-believe which comes most easily in the conditions mentioned above.

(4)

So far we have considered only cases in which it is possible for us to say that we see bodies. We have noticed various extensions of usage for the word 'see', but they have all presupposed our seeing of bodies. Are there in fact any other usages, whether primitive or derivative? In recent years many philosophers have become so hostile to the talk of sense-data which was introduced by Professor G. E. Moore and Lord Russell that they speak as though it were improper and philosophically dangerous to say we see any thing but bodies. I think this is a queer kind of obscurantism. In ordinary life we claim to see many objects, such as the sky and sparks and flashes and glows of light, which are neither bodies nor things obviously dependent on bodies, and also some other objects, namely reflections, which though certainly dependent in a way on bodies, can nevertheless be seen without the seeing of bodies in the primitive sense of 'see'. It is true that these claims are not so frequent as our claims to see bodies, and perhaps they are not so important for practical life, but they are sufficient to establish the point that seeing is not necessarily the seeing of bodies.

The modern philosophers to whom I have referred sometimes try to support their thesis by saying that sight, unlike the other distance senses, hearing and smell, has no special object apart from bodies, or in more obviously linguistic terms, that there is no word related to 'see' as 'sound' is related to 'hear' and the noun 'smell' to the verb 'smell'. Here again I think they are mistaken. Although we most commonly talk of seeing bodies of various sorts, we have words such as 'sight', 'spectacle', 'scene', and 'view' with which to indicate the special object of vision when we wish to concentrate attention on that. In what follows I shall use the word 'view' for this purpose but I should make clear that I am not thinking of that use of 'view' in which we speak of getting a good view of something; for it may be said that the whole phrase 'get a good view of' is then to be understood as an equivalent for 'see clearly'. What I have in mind is rather the use of the word 'view' in aesthetic contexts, as when, for example, it is said that we should see the view from a certain height or that a certain group of buildings present an impressive view to anyone standing in a certain position. And in order to make quite clear that a view in this sense is not just the set of those parts of the surfaces of certain bodies which can be geometrically projected through a certain point onto a plane it is sufficient to remark that a view we are recommended to see may be something that can be seen only in certain conditions of illumination. Those who wish to ensure us aesthetic pleasure may conceivably tell us that we should see the view which presents itself to anyone looking east from the top of Snowdon at sunrise on a misty morning. I think it unlikely that I shall ever learn whether that particular view is indeed beautiful; but it seems evident to me that what the enthusiasts wish to commend is a special object of sight, and that special objects of the same status, though not perhaps of the same interest, present themselves to our inspection whenever we open our eyes. We do not commonly talk about these, because we are interested chiefly in the bodies that surround us; but when a teacher of painting tells his pupils to paint what they see, it is a view rather than a set of bodies to which he directs their attention.

In my example of one man's recommending another to see the view from the top of Snowdon at sunrise I have used the word 'view' much as the word 'sound' is used when it is said that jet aircraft make an unpleasant sound; for a view in the sense of my example is something that may recur from time to time. But we often use the word 'view', just as we often use the word 'sound', to stand for something with a date, and it is this sense which seems to be basic, though the other may be equally common.

Because painters are interested in views for their own sake, they sometimes use the word 'view' in the titles of their pictures, and so by an easy transition the word 'view' has come to be used in certain contexts as a synonym for 'picture'. But the best that even a naturalistic painter can hope to produce is a patterned surface which makes it easy for us to practise make-believe, whereas the views of which I have spoken have depth. They are indeed public objects, like pictures, but not of the same status. For the seeing of a picture presupposes the seeing of some body on whose surface the picture is to be found; but the seeing of a view does not in this way presuppose the seeing of a body. On the contrary, the seeing of a body presupposes the seeing of a view, much as the hearing of a body presupposes the hearing of a sound.

It is important, however, to notice at this point a difference between the way in which we speak of the special objects of sight and the way in which we speak of the special objects of the other distance senses. We say that bodies make or cause sounds and smells, but never that they make or cause views. If we talk at all about the relation, we say rather that bodies present views, where the word 'present' is obviously intended to suggest that the connexion of a body with a view of it is more intimate than the connexion of a body with any sound or smell which it causes. This impression is confirmed by another usage. We say sometimes that the presence of a body in the neighbourhood may be *inferred* from the occurrence of some sound or smell, but very rarely, if ever, that the presence of a body may be inferred from the occurrence of a view. Most commonly we speak without more ado of seeing bodies; and in those special circumstances in which we talk about views our purpose is not to set out evidence for a belief in the presence of bodies, but rather to abstract from such beliefs, or, to speak more strictly, from the practical interests which commonly go with expression of such beliefs.

Why should there be this difference? I think the explanation may be simply that for human beings sight is correlated with touch in a much closer and more detailed fashion than any of the other senses can be. Our language is a product of the social life of the animals we are, and it naturally reflects our peculiar circumstances. Now we commonly guide the movements of our bodies by sight with great precision and without any feeling of hesitation or perplexity; but there are only a few sounds and smells which directly affect our conduct, and they do not make possible any detailed adjustments. If, like bats, we could avoid small obstacles by using our ears for echo-location, or, like some species of ants, we could find our way about by smelling the shapes of things, we might perhaps talk of hearing and smelling bodies exactly as now we talk of seeing them. Bodies are primarily objects of touch in the large popular sense of that word which includes not only the capacity to feel contacts and pressures but also an ability to recognize the positions of our limbs and a derivative ability to discover the shapes of things by movements of exploration. Since, however, the perception of bodies by touch is involved in any action we may undertake to alter our environment, it is not surprising that it should provide the framework within which we try as plain men to co-ordinate the deliverances of our other senses, nor yet that we should speak most confidently of perceiving bodies by that other sense which is most closely connected with control of our action on bodies. At a later stage in the development of physical theory this obsession of ours with bodies may perhaps be a hindrance to understanding, but it is a natural result of the circumstances in which our theorizing starts.

When we say that we see bodies *directly* and refuse to admit that we infer their presence from views as we sometimes infer their presence from sounds or smells, we show by this way of talking that at the time of speaking we have no doubt about the reliability of views as signs. If occasionally we have some doubt, as when, for example, we are trying to discern an object at a great distance, we fall back on the language appropriate to the description of views and say that we see coloured shapes. It is interesting to notice that such talk is sometimes found necessary by scientists reporting what they see through ordinary telescopes or microscopes. In these cases the need for non-committal language may be due not merely to the difficulty of describing something seen at the margin of visibility and without benefit of stereoscopy, but also to the fact that any material objects which can be discerned in such circumstances are very different from all those with which we are familiar in ordinary life. On the other hand, if a view brings with it immediate confidence about some object or event even more remote from vision than a body, we may conceivably go on to say that we see that also. Thus, for example, we may say that we see embarrassment in a man's face, not because we are in any way disposed to accept behaviourism as a philosophical doctrine, but simply because the view which we see as we look at his face evokes a certain response in us without need for any inference on our part. In similar circumstances we sometimes say that we hear anger or disappointment in a man's voice, though we certainly do not think that either of these emotions exists in a sound.

(5)

If I am right, no public object of any kind can be seen except in the seeing of a view. But at this point someone may object to the way in which I have spoken of views, not because he thinks that the objects of vision must always be bodies, but rather because he thinks I have made a mistake in talking of views as public. In the theory of perception it has been assumed almost universally that private sense-data are the only objects whose seeing, hearing, smelling, etc. is presupposed in the perception of bodies, and in accordance with this assumption words such as 'view', 'sound', and 'smell' have often been cited by philosophers as specialized substitutes for their generalized technical term 'sense-datum'. To anyone who takes this philosophical practice for granted it may seem that I am trying to put forward a new kind of extreme realism, perhaps what Lord Russell called the metaphysics of the stone age. But this is not my intention: I am merely trying to preserve the usages of ordinary language. When one man says to another 'Look at this view' and the other replies 'Yes, it is fine' or alternatively 'I do not think it is very remarkable', there is surely no room for controversy about the fact that they are talking of a public object which could be photographed with a camera. I would go further and maintain that it is obviously good sense to say there may be views when there is no one about to see them. But I am willing to assert this only because I think it is obvious that to say that there is a view to be seen from a certain place is the same as to say that any one with normal sight would have a certain experience if he were there.

The analysis that I offer is not phenomenalistic, because I am quite prepared to admit that a subjunctive conditional statement of the kind I have just cited requires for its truth that there should be something actually going on at the time and place under consideration. Plain men who talk of views may know nothing of the physical theory of light, but what they say reveals a place in our intellectual scheme for such a theory. On the other hand, my analysis of the notion of a view does involve the assumption that there are visual sense-data. For if I were asked to say what sort of experience a person with normal sight would have in the place where there was a view to be seen, I should have to reply that the experience in question would be that of seeing something in that sense of 'seeing' in which we say that we see after-images; and I take it that visual sense-data are just such objects as we may claim to see in that sense of the word 'see'.

No doubt philosophers have made many mistakes in the past when discussing sense-data, and I prefer for my own part to speak of *sensa* in order to avoid some misleading suggestions of the word 'data'; but I think that there are worse confusions in the criticisms that have been urged recently against all talk of private sense objects.

It has been argued, for example, that there must be something wrong in saying that we see visual sense-data because the word 'see' is properly a word for recording the detection of objects in the common world. But it is a sufficient reply to point out that no unphilosophical person of any education feels the slightest difficulty in saying that he sees after-images from time to time or that he sees an essentially private three-dimensional scene whenever he looks into a stereoscope. We have noticed already that the word 'see' is used in a multitude of different contexts: if now we say that the use of the word in one of these contexts requires explanation by reference to its use in another of these contexts, it should be clear that we are not prepared to allow that it has just the same sense in all the various contexts.

Again, it has been argued that there is not, and never can be, any language for talking of sense-data because language is always social in origin and therefore adapted only for use in communication about public objects. This objection is fatal to any reductionist theory which requires that talk of public objects should be *replaceable* by talk of sense-data, but it has no force against a suggestion of the kind put forward above. When we say that the seeing of public objects involves the seeing of sense-data, we do not commit ourselves to the obviously incorrect statement that talk of sense-data could be either introduced or maintained without talk of public objects. What we assert is indeed something that could not have been formulated at all at the beginning of language. But we have now learnt how to tell each other about our private experiences by constructing phrases of the form 'It is as though I were looking at an X', and with this development of language we have acquired a power of analysis which enables us to reveal the assumptions underlying our more primitive usages.

Some philosophers who do not wish to go so far as to say that talk of sense-data is absurd have argued nevertheless that it is useless because it is no more than an alternative to the device of constructing sentences with the phrase 'it is as though'.

But this attack rests on a misconception of the purpose for which talk of sense-data has been introduced. The aim of sense-datum theorists is not to provide a new terminology for describing experiences in detail, whether they be normal or abnormal, but rather to indicate what ordinary experiences have in common with extraordinary. If I am asked to describe what I see when I use a stereoscope, I say 'It is just as though I were looking at Westminster Abbey'. But this remark does not provide a direct answer to the question 'What do you see?'; and although it shows clearly enough that there is something happening very like what happens when I look at Westminster Abbey, it provides no general description of that event. If, however, I say 'I see a complex visual sense-datum such as I should see if I were looking at Westminster Abbey', these objections cannot be raised. In practice introduction of the much-debated terminology of sense-data amounts to no more than a licence to use the phrase 'sense-datum' in such ways as this, and it seems to me not only harmless but very useful in directing attention where attention must be directed if we are ever to get a satisfactory theory of perception.

(6)

What morals can we draw from this survey of English usage? We have discovered that the objects we may properly claim to see fall into many different categories, and that the sense of the word 'see' differs from context to context according to the nature of the objects we claim to see. It is therefore foolish to dogmatize about the meaning of the word from consideration of a few examples, and in particular it is foolish to speak as though bodies were the only things we could properly claim to see. For although talk of seeing bodies may belong to the most primitive stratum of our language, it involves assumptions that are far from simple. On the other hand, we should not fall into the opposite error of supposing that we have as it were a continuum of usages without any fixed boundaries anywhere. For among the usages we have distinguished some at least are related to others in a definite order of presupposition, and it is of great importance for the philosophy of perception that we should understand this clearly. No one can see an atom except in the sense in which we say we see something when we see a shadow picture of it. But in order to see a picture a man must see a pattern of light and dark on a surface. And in order to see a surface he must see a body. And in order to see a body he must see a view. And in order to see a view he must see a visual sensum.

The limits of prediction

by

W. B. GALLIE

WHEN we say that an event is unpredictable we risk being misunderstood. Hence philosophers have distinguished unpredictability in principle from unpredictability in practice, and physicists have insisted upon the peculiar, because probably ultimate, grounds of the unpredictabilities that arise in quantum physics. But these are not the only distinctions we need: there is a surprising diversity in the kinds of ground upon which unpredictability can be attributed to events, and even more surprisingly there are marked logical disparities in the consequences of establishing (or urging) unpredictability in different kinds of case. I shall defend these claims by comparing and contrasting two cases or areas of unpredictability which have been detected by contemporary philosophers: my underlying thought being that, since the limits of prediction are so strangely various, they may well indicate hidden complexities in this and kindred notions, which figure so familiarly in our applied logic that as usual we have mistaken the familiar for the simple and clear.

It has been maintained[1] that discoveries, inventions, artistic creations, etc. cannot be predicted, because to predict them would be to have made them before they actually were made, which is self-contradictory. I believe that this claim contains a point of substance, although as it stands it is far too sweeping; one can easily think of discoveries and inventions that either actually have been, or that conceivably might be, predicted.[2] But now, to come to the point which this objection misses, consider the following example. A firm engages a team of scientists—physicists, economists, etc.—to prepare an estimate of their productive progress over the next ten years. But it is quite possible that one of the experts will report that in his field such *revolutionary* changes are under way that any prediction made now, on the basis of his science's current methods, about production in ten years' time must be utterly valueless. He will thus report the predictably unpredictable character of certain developments.

Paradoxical though this sounds, the situation described is believable and indeed familiar enough. Why does it arise? Certain new (guessed at or vaguely predicted) discoveries are, it is alleged, going to alter drastically the well-established methods of predicting—and hence of controlling and producing—certain physical and industrial processes. But relatively accurate predictions about the results of such processes can be made only when the established methods of predicting (and of

[1] E.g. by Professor H. B. Acton and Mr. Maurice Cranston.

[2] Thus a government 'lays on' a powerful team of scientists, acting on the prediction that, given time, peace, apparatus, etc., the team will produce a required discovery or invention within a specified time. Or a spy is set to report on a great scientist's work: if he is intelligent and well-informed the spy may at some point be able to predict the all-important outcome of the work before the scientist himself can see or state it clearly. Or we can conceive an apparatus that could be fitted, say, to an artist's solar plexus and would enable us to predict his artistic products before they actually come into his head, or to his lips or his fingers.

controlling and producing) *within* the industry can be taken as fixed, or at least as subject to change only within definite limits and upon generally accepted grounds; and, conceived as thus limited, changes in these predictive methods or habits can be included in any normal prediction of a firm's or industry's development. More simply, the predictive or other intelligent habits and methods of those running the industry must be regarded as given, if its developments are to be predictable with any accuracy. What our disconcerting expert has done is to suppose—or to predict on relatively vague grounds quite external to the system studied—certain revolutionary changes in these predictive habits, and, by implication, the adoption of *new* predictive habits not logically derivable from those regarded as given or as parts of the system as it is functioning now.

Mutatis mutandis, I think the same could be said about developments in any branch of knowledge or human endeavour. Whenever entirely new principles, not derivable from those commonly accepted as 'governing' the activity in question, are introduced —as, e.g. entirely new conjectures sometimes are in the case of knowledge—then the revolutionary change-over which results is not *pre*-dictable just because predictions made *before* its introduction are based on principles and premises which *ex hypothesi* lack the special explanatory force or virtue which it is the distinction of the new revolutionary principles to supply. This seems to me the point of substance in the claim from which our discussion began. So far all I have done is to describe it in terms of the contrast between the characteristic predictions of science, capable of being reformulated with ever increasing precision, and such inevitably relatively vague quasi-predictions or warnings of revolutionary changes to come as were made by the disconcerting expert in our example; but I shall try, before I conclude, to move on to at least a partial explanation of this kind of unpredictability.

Meanwhile I will simply add that the more one indulges in such quasi-predictions the more one must regard the future as 'open', i.e. the less can one *think* about it in the sense of describing situations of such and such (predictable) character. Thus our belief in the progressive character of the predictive capacities of men could lead us to a limit at which their future thoughts and actions could not be conceived by us, descriptively/predictively, at all. And yet, paradoxically, it seems possible for us to *believe* this.

I want now to contrast, in respect of its logical status and consequences, this type of unpredictability with that discussed by Professor Popper in his article 'Indeterminism in Quantum Physics and in Classical Physics'.[3] Here Popper tries to show that, just as in quantum physics there are events which cannot be predicted because of inescapable interaction between the means of observation and the system observed, so within classical physics, contrary to general belief, there are certain predictive tasks that cannot conceivably be carried through so as to conform completely with what would seem to be logically permissible and desirable requirements.[4] More specifically, Popper claims to show that a predictor, set to work upon ideally

[3] Published in the *British Journal for the Philosophy of Science*, Vol. 1, pp. 117–133 and 173–195.

[4] Unpredictability in these cases is due, Popper maintains, to certain quite inescapable features of the processes of observation and reporting and calculation which are necessary to all prediction: they arise, primarily, because any predictor must be an *amplifier*, but are most obvious when the system to be predicted is (or contains) a further predictor (or predictors) required to 'advise' the original predictor of its own present or future states without taking notice of which its own predictive calculations would always remain incomplete.

complete information, is being asked to perform before a specified time operations which in the nature of the case, must be pursued after that time. I cannot here discuss his detailed arguments: I will, however, mention three principles which appear to guide, and are necessary to, his whole undertaking.

(1) Popper writes throughout in terms of a physical predictor; but this is simply a methodological device to ensure recognition of the physical embodiment of any predictor within, and as an interacting part of, the system he studies, and, in particular, as strongly interfered with by that system. Recognition of this is of peculiar importance to Popper's thesis, quite apart from the partial parallelism it here shows to that of quantum physics, since it helps to emphasize that every genuine prediction (in contrast, e.g., to 'clairvoyance') is a process—including a *physical* process subject to definite *physical* conditions—of deducing consequences from information and theory.[5]

(2) Any predictor's results depend logically upon a particular theory which we may regard as 'built in to it'. Besides being necessary for the specification of any predictive task, the use of a particular theory in all predictions serves to underline the point just made—viz. that all prediction is a process that takes time.

(3) For Popper, determinism in science means simply predictability; and the general thesis of determinism, which he claims to have refuted, is accordingly that any specified prediction task can in principle be performed. We must note, however, how very limited is the kind of *in*determinism which Popper claims to establish; for he repeatedly asserts that none of his arguments precludes the possibility of any given predictive task being completed, i.e. of a logically complete explanation, based on the latest relevant information, being given *after* the event in question has taken place.[6] It might indeed be more usual to say that if every phase of a system can be completely explained, even after its occurrence, in terms of relevant laws and initial conditions, then every phase of it is completely determined. The fact that some of its phases cannot possibly be *pre*dicted (and therefore that advance assertion of their *predetermination* would lack its sole possible source of empirical meaning or value) seems to tell us something not so much about the status of the system, as about the limits—including the physically imposed limits—of our foreknowledge of it.[7]

Let us now try to see and state the logical disparities between the two kinds of case we have considered. Unpredictability, in the case or on the grounds which Popper discusses, is a logical consequence of what is seen on careful inspection to be a contradictory demand or task. Given adequate appreciation of certain factors, including the necesssity for every predictor to be physically embodied and to work by deduction from a theory, we can see that the ideal of a prediction based upon the completest (i.e. including the latest) relevant information is an impossible one: it violates temporal possibilities somewhat as the demand for a certain geometrical construction may violate spatial ones. In brief, the impossibility is seen to be inherent in the activity prescribed once it—and its situation and means and methods—are fully described.

At first sight the same might seem true of the kind of case which we first considered.

[5] This is essential to Popper's basic 'Tristram Shandy' argument.

[6] Here, of course, the logical parallel with the situation in quantum physics breaks down.

[7] That Popper himself is aware of this is clear from the extremely interesting closing sentence of his paper.

If there are going to be revolutionary changes in certain predictive methods, it certainly *seems* contradictory to expect our present predictive methods to predict these and their consequences. There would, however, be nothing *contradictory* in the assumption that there are always available at every stage of investigation certain higher-order principles of prediction by which the next revolutionary stage in predictive methods *could* in principle be predicted before it actually arrives. (What should, of course, be said against this assumption is that there is no evidence, and no prospect of evidence, for it, and that there is nothing in scientific procedure or achievement to suggest it).[8]

But how then shall we explain our earlier thesis that a revolutionary change in e.g. predictive methods *cannot* be predicted? This possibility is precluded—or rather we are forced to *discount* it—in so far as we look forward to or entertain hope regarding the future of science in a rather special way. We have come to expect that science will show the kind of progress that includes the springing of revolutionary surprises upon its practitioners: or, in a little more precise language, that science will continue to show developments that are at once (a) *characteristic* and *satisfying* and yet (b) unpredictable and in no sense necessary. Let me emphasize, however proper and desirable and pleasant such revolutionary developments may be they are at best *propria*, in the Aristotelian sense; they are *not* essential features of scientific practice, for all that, for reasons I cannot now discuss, some of the greatest of all philosophers of science, e.g. Kant and Peirce, thought they were. There is no inherent reason why scientific progress should not continue in any subject and yet be dull, or why, for that matter it should not—for a variety of possible reasons—come to a stop. For our purpose, however, what matters is this: to *deny* the impossibility of predicting scientific advances is not contradictory—bad scientific judgement or taste or ethic though it may display. And here, therefore, we have a clear logical difference in the grounds of unpredictability as between the present case and Popper's.

A second disparity between our two cases is this. We have seen that Popper's thesis in no way precludes the possibility of our giving a (to certain specifications) ideally complete explanation of an event *after* it has occurred, even when that event was in principle un*pre*dictable (to the same specifications). But in the case of an unpredictable discovery or invention, it is at least highly doubtful whether a logically complete explanation of it after its occurrence could ever be provided, viz. an explanation in terms of initial conditions and universal laws considered jointly sufficient for the deduction of the discovery in question (Does anyone seriously believe that any discovery could be shown to have been, predictably, due-to-be-made, due-to-be-seen, no longer escapable, before it actually *was* made?).

[8] It is one thing to claim on the basis, say, of numerous successful short-term predictions in a given field, that we should look forward to being able in future to predict more complicated and longer-term changes in the same field. It is quite another thing to claim that we *could*, theoretically or in principle, predict *now* all the changes in intellectual attitudes and methods which will be required to make those future (more complicated, but as yet quite unspecified) predictions. The former hope reflects the actual scientific experience of piecemeal advance: the latter expresses an intellectual attitude which would appear to be well on the way to omniscience—though alas it gives no indication of how we are to get there. The former hope—in the steadily increasing success of scientific predictions—contains no presumption that the successive phases in the improvement of predictive methods must themselves make up a (theoretically or in principle) predictable whole. Evidence that they do so, viz. a completely deterministic *historical* account of how any great scientific discovery or revolution took place, is to date simply not to hand; and, for what this consideration is worth, one cannot imagine anything that we would recognize as history even beginning to provide it.

Had time allowed, I would have liked to suggest how other disparities, partially parallel to those discussed, arise in other cases of unpredictability: viz. (1) those due to interventions of the human will, and (2) those due to the assumption, on different conditions and with different intentions, of randomness in nature.[9] But perhaps what I have shown suffices to give force to the question: How can we know what we mean by a determinist system until we have examined all the radically different grounds on which 'determinism' can significantly be questioned or denied?

[9] Imagine a man who, living in a society of predicting psychologists, revolts against it and decides to live, in certain respects, as unpredictably as possible, i.e. so as always to prove the predictors wrong. On what conditions can we conceive of him succeeding? I suggest the four following, as illustrations of the further disparities I have in mind.

1(a) He is himself a predictor, at least the equal in power of any of his fellows, so that he can always predict their next prediction of his behaviour and can accordingly act to contravene it. But presumably in this case his own predictions are made by methods current in his society; consequently, for all that he enjoys a privileged position for the anti-predictionist or anti-conformist exercise of his own will, the possibility of a full (causal) explanation of any of his choices, after it is made, is in no way precluded. 1(b) Alternatively our anti-conformist might be an unusually fertile inventor or discoverer in respect of ways of living: i.e. he might find himself continually impelled to initiate new principles or precedents of action, with the result that many parts of his conduct cannot be predicted and, further, cannot be fully (causally) explained, after their occurrence. (The parallelism between these two cases and those discussed above seems clear). 2(a) Our anti-conformist's conduct, although unpredictable for either of the above reasons, may yet admit of the following familiar analysis and treatment. Various recurrent items in it are abstracted: then, on the assumption that they are shuffled or randomized, probabilities can be assigned to their recurrence under specified circumstances. But this procedure, even if adopted in the face of apparently inescapable unpredictabilities, in no way *logically* precludes the possibility that our anti-conformist's conduct might turn out to be explainable after the event, or might even be predictable, although in a more indirect manner. 2(b) As against this let us suppose that our anti-conformist is equipped with an apparatus which, on the occurrence of certain stimuli (news of a new prediction about his behaviour) has the effect of randomizing certain parts of his behaviour. Usually, of course, it would be possible for the principle of construction of this apparatus to be discovered, so that reliable probabilities could be assigned to the occurrence of different features in our hero's behaviour as at assumption 2(a) above. Alternatively, however, we might suppose that the apparatus is so constructed that once opened up it begins to operate on different principles; so that the possibility of predicting our anti-conformist's behaviour is logically excluded. This situation, or any strict analogue of it, would seem to be of metaphysical rather than of scientific interest. It suggests the extreme point of opposition to predictability or scientific determinism; but it is altogether freakish—there is absolutely no reason to think that any part of nature works as if to the one aim of completely frustrating our curiosity. Yet one gathers that this sense of randomness has seemed to many scientists to be the only real alternative to logically complete determinism.

Predicting and inferring

by

G. RYLE

To predict is to assert that something will happen or will be the case at a time later than the making of the prediction. It is to assert something in the future tense. A person who makes a prediction may be just guessing, or asserting something that he believes on mere hearsay, or prophesying from what he believes to be inspiration. He may even predict what he believes or knows will not be the case, like a share-pusher in order to deceive or like a doctor in order to encourage. But sometimes a prediction is a reasoned prediction. The author expects something to happen because he has evidence that it will do so. Some predictions, but not all, are the conclusions of good or bad inferences. The fact that these are nowadays the most highly respected predictions must not lead us to suppose that a prediction is, *ex vi termini*, the conclusion of an inference. To predict is not itself to infer; it is not necessarily even to declare a conclusion of an inference. Old Moore's Almanac is full of predictions which are not conclusions of inferences, even bad ones. Conversely, it is not necessarily the case that the conclusion of an inference is a prediction. The inferences of a detective, an historian, a geologist, a palaeontologist and a cosmologist are very often inferences to past events or states of affairs. The inferences of a doctor, a general and a bridge-player are very often inferences to contemporary states of affairs. Not all inferred conclusions are in the future tense. This point is worth making since there is at present something of a vogue for tying up problems about induction with the special notion of inference to the future. But inferences to the unobserved has-been and inferences to the unobserved is-now are just as respectable as inferences to the unobserved is-to-be. The only difference of importance is that the future is inevitably unobserved now, whereas the what has been and what is now *might* have been observed or be being observed, instead of having to be inferred.

The vogue of concentrating on scientists' predictions has had another damaging effect on popular views about science. Many people speak as if the forecasting work of astronomers and meteorologists was typical of all scientific investigation—as if, that is to say, the chemist, the nuclear physicist and the endocrinologist all had their advance information to give us about things to come about next Wednesday week in something like the way in which the Nautical Almanac gives us advance news about the positions of the stars and the times of high and low tide days or years ahead, or like the way in which meteorologists give 24 or 48 hour forecasts of the weather. But it is clear that the provision of forecasts of these kinds is no part of the business of most sciences, not even of astronomy or meteorology save when these are *applied*. Ask the biochemist for information about anything that will be happening tomorrow week, and he will laugh and tell you that prophecy is not his business. No, the way in which reasoned predictions do belong essentially to the business of any scientist is quite different. He predicts not what will be going on in the world at large, but, for example, what will be the result of the experiment he has himself set up inside his own laboratory. What occurs there, if all goes well, is something which he himself had deliberately and carefully tried to get to occur; and usually, save when he is giving a demonstration or exhibition, he tries to get it to occur in order to test his still tentative theory, that in such and such specified and controlled conditions just such a happening or state of affairs does ensue. His predictions are conditional experimental predictions—experimental both in the sense of being tentative and in the sense of being made for the sake of testing a theory.

They are not forecasts of a future state of the public world, but tentative inferences to a future state of the object under experiment in his own laboratory, under conditions designed and created by himself. Since the actual outcome of the experiment is meant to verify or falsify the theory which generated the inference to it, that inference was in some degree tentative. If the theory was already known to be true, or else to be false, there would be no point in setting up an experiment to show whether it was true or false—save, again, for demonstration to pupils, i.e. for didactic ends. Whereas the forecasts in the Nautical Almanac or weather forecasts are meant to inform the public and not to test theories or to teach them.

Certainly, when the researcher's theory has been definitely or adequately established, it can then, very often, be turned to practical account, i.e. applied to the world outside the laboratory to generate inferences to past, present or future happenings *not* under control conditions, as well as to generate techniques for bringing about or preventing the happening of such things. Part, though not the whole of the *application* of a theory consists in inferences to happenings or states of affairs in the world, i.e. to happenings or states of affairs the occurrence of which is not due to the intentions of the theorist and the labours of his technical assistants. Notice that the theory which generates, *inter alia*, inferences to the future, present and past states of affairs, is not itself an inference or a budget of inferences to future, present, or past states of affairs. The theory itself is stated in tenseless terms, or rather in terms which are tense-neutral, as the terms of an algebraical formula are number-neutral. It does not itself assert that anything in particular has happened, is happening or is going to happen. I mention this obvious point because we sometimes hear theories described as predictive theories or as explanatory theories, phrases which might be misconstrued to mean that the theories themselves are or contain predictions or explanations of particular matters of fact. (I am not here talking about the theories of detectives or historians. These are, normally, hypotheses about particular happenings. Even if definitively or adequately established, they will not rank as laws. This is not their business.)

From now on I want to concentrate on what I have called 'experimental inferences,' including experimental inferences whose conclusions are predictions, that is those inferences which a person testing a theory or hypothesis makes more or less tentatively, in order to confirm or else upset the theory that generates the inference. If the theory *works* then, *inter alia*, the particular inferences made on the basis of it, if validly drawn from true observational premisses, will be successful, i.e. their conclusions will turn out to be true. This is part of what we mean by saying that the theory works. But we must notice that there can be theories or hypotheses which are experimentally empty, since they do not empower us to make any particular inferences, or, therefore, to test the theory by the successes or failures of any experimental inferences. For example, a person may have the theory that whatever happens anywhere is due to Fate. But from this theory he can derive no specific inferences to anything that is going to happen or has happened. It is an inferentially hollow theory. Some theories, like some doughnuts, are partly hollow and partly not. I want to concentrate on the testing of non-hollow theories by the successes and failures of the particular inferences generated by them. Notice first, a point I have already made, that the fact that someone *asserts* something in, say, the future or the past tense, does not by itself involve that he has inferred. He might just be guessing, or making things up or repeating something that he had been told. Notice, second, that even when his assertion is both the conclusion of an inference and turns out to be true, this is not enough for us to grade his inference as a good one. He might have inferred a true conclusion from premisses some or all of which were false, or he might have inferred invalidly. In either case his arriving at a true conclusion would be a matter of lucky coincidence. For example, a seismologist might come to the true conclusion that there had been an earthquake at a certain time and in a certain place, though he was arguing from false newspaper reports of tidal waves reaching the shores of the ocean at certain times. Or he might argue from good seismographic data, but make a howler or two in his calculations, and yet, by luck, arrive at a true conclusion about the locus and the time of the earthquake. In neither case would we allow or he continue to claim that his inference showed that his seismological theory had worked. For it was not his theory but mere luck which had got him to the right answer. No marks are bestowed upon his inference by the mere truth of its conclusion. Consequently no credit or discredit is reflected back on to his theory. Though he intended to test his theory, what he actually performed did not test it.

While a mere prediction, i.e. an assertion in the future tense, may be called successful, simply if it turns out true, an *inference* to a conclusion in the future tense can be said to have succeeded or come off only if (1) the conclusion turns out true, (2) the observational premisses were true, and (3) the drawing of this conclusion from those premisses is valid, i.e. does not embody a sheer miscalculation or logical howler.

As the epithet 'successful' is equivocal, let us call a prediction which comes out right merely a 'happy' prediction, however arrived at or even if merely guessed. And let us call an inference a 'scoring' inference if its conclusion is both true and correctly drawn from true premisses. I will say that a theory scores, or makes a score, if a factual inference based on it is a scoring inference. Now if I have conceived a non-hollow theory or hypothesis, and if I want to establish it to the satisfaction of myself and my colleagues, I shall certainly try to make inference-scores with it. But—and here we are getting a look at the old problem of induction from what is, I hope, a slightly new angle—I shall not be required by you or by my own conscience to assemble masses and masses of parallel inference-scores. It is not a matter of drowning surviving doubts under a Niagara of repetitions.

In an important way, I have shown you that my theory works, up to a point, if I have shown it generating just one inference-score; I have shown that it works rather well if I have shown you a fair variety of non-parallel inferences scoring.

But there is, I think, no likelihood of your being discontented with these inference scores merely on the ground that there have not yet been quite enough of them—as if it were a case of statistical inference being objected to on the ground that the sample extrapolated from was too small a fraction of the population extrapolated to.

Indeed, I might say, subject to a *dementi* to be made in a moment, that the problem of induction is not a problem about the legality of arguments from samples to populations, whether closed or 'open' populations; it is rather a problem about the legality of arguments from inference-scores to the truth and adequacy of the theories or hypotheses that generate those inferences. But now I want to withdraw this phrase 'the *legality of arguments* from inference-scores to the truth of theories'. For the maker of the theory or hypothesis does not *argue* from the scoring of the grounded inferences to the conclusion that the theory that generated them works. He *shows* that it works by showing it working, and he shows it working by showing inference-scores being made. Or, in other cases, the critic shows that the theory does *not* work by showing it not working, i.e. by showing inference-scores being attempted but not made. For example, someone had the theory that bats avoid bumping into obstacles when flying about a dark room not by seeing but by hearing where the obstacles are, and that they hear where they are by picking up echoes of noises emitted by themselves. This theory generated, *inter alia*, the concrete factual inferences (a) that this bat Sally (let's call her) will avoid the wires stretched across the room even when her eyes are sealed over; (b) that this bat William will hit wires if his ears are sealed down, and will continue to blunder into some wires when one ear is sealed down and the other not; (c) that this bat Charlie will hit wires if his squeaking apparatus is put out of action though his ears are not interfered with. These three concrete inferences all scored; and so showed that, anyhow up to a point, the theory worked. But the experimenter did not, I suppose, formulate a premiss-conclusion argument of the queer pattern '*Because* the factual inference about Sally scored and the factual inference about William scored and the factual inference about Charlie scored, *therefore*, the theory works.' He had *shown* it working, not *inferred to* its working.

So if by 'inductive inference' or 'inductive argument' we mean to be referring to a special kind of inference or argument from scoring-inferences to the truth of the theory generating them, then I think that there is no such special kind of inference or argument—not merely that it is not an inference of the, in itself, quite reputable pattern of inference from sample to population, but that it is not a kind of inference at all.

We do indeed discover laws; we do indeed establish or upset hypotheses by making experimental inferences and seeing whether they score or not; and we do indeed teach pupils and satisfy critics by showing them these inferences scoring. But not all discovering is inferring; not all establishing is proving; not all instructing is arguing.

So far I have been speaking vaguely of a theory 'generating' the particular factual inferences, which are, so to speak, the encashments of it. I want to say a bit more about this. When I say that my bat-expert's theory *generated*, among others, the particular factual inference that because William's ears were sealed down therefore he would blunder into the wires, I do not mean that this factual inference was *deduced* from the theory. For an inference or argument is not a proposition, and so cannot be something that follows or does not follow from a proposition.

For the same reason, the driver who argues 'I have seven gallons of petrol left in my tank, and two in the can, so I have nine gallons of petrol altogether' does not *deduce* this argument from the equation $2+7=9$ or from the conjunction of this equation with factual propositions about the amounts of petrol in the containers. He deduces the factual conclusion that he has nine gallons left from the factual premiss that he has seven gallons in the tank and two in the can. But the deduction of this quantitative conclusion from this quantitative premiss is not itself a conclusion deduced from anything else. For *it* is not true or false but only valid or fallacious, and so is not the sort of thing that could be deduced. But still knowledge that $7+2=9$ *is* necessary for the deduction—only necessary not as knowledge of the truth of a premiss may be necessary if a conclusion is to be known to be true, but in quite another way. A child who has learned that $7+2=9$ has already learned that 7 somethings plus 2 somethings make 9 somethings, and so has, in a way, learned that 7 gallons of petrol plus 2 gallons of petrol make 9 gallons of petrol. And having learned this, then on finding that there are 7 gallons in the tank and 2 in the can, he knows what conclusion to draw—or rather he just draws it, in full knowledge of what his title is to draw it, namely the arithmetical truth that $7+2=9$.

However, though there is an important analogy, there is also an important difference between this sort of case, and the cases that we are considering. The child knows, and everyone knows, that $7+2=9$. Its truth is not in question and is not up for testing. It is not an empirical law or hypothesis. But we are dealing with inference-generating theories which are not truisms and are up for testing. Even if the formulation of the theory incorporates some general equations, still these are not algebraical truisms but candidates for the status of laws of nature, or bye-laws of nature. They are an essential part of what is up for testing. Still, the way in which they generate tentative, experimental inferences is, for what concerns us, the same as the way in which the arithmetical truism $7+2=9$ generates the untentative factual inference 'there are 7 gallons in the tank and 2 in the can, so there are 9 gallons all told'. In either case a piece of sheer miscalculation will result in the generated inferences not necessarily being false conclusions, but being invalid arguments.

In our cases, unlike the case of the gallons of petrol, the scoring or the non-scoring of the generated experimental inferences is what goes to show that the theory generating them does or does not work well, or fairly well or very well. (There is, I suppose, no question of a theory ever being claimed to work perfectly well for all conceivable applications. There is always room for further amendments.)

I want to stress the point made before that it is not just the fact that the *conclusions* of these experimental inferences turn out right that renders them scoring inferences. Rather it is the fact that these true conclusions are legitimately derived from true observational premisses. The specific mode or route of derivation is of crucial importance. For this is the place where the structure of the theory exhibits itself. It exposes its nervous system in the nerves of the concrete inferences that it generates.

The only important thing that I have tried to do is this. (1) I italicized the too commonly ignored distinction between predicting and inferring, or between statements in the future tense and arguments the conclusions of which may be, but may not be, in the future tense. (2) I then tried to switch the centre of gravity of disputes about induction, verification, confirmation, infirmation, etc., from the happiness or unhappiness of predictions on to the scoring or non-scoring of concrete inferences and in particular of concrete experimental inferences. I argued (or perhaps I only declared) that the relation between a theory and the experimental inferences that it generates is such that these do indeed *show* that the theory works or does not work, since they show it working or failing; but there is no question of there having to exist a special sort of argument, to be called 'an inductive argument', *from* the successes and failures of the inferences *to* the truth of the theory. *A fortiori* there is no question of there having to exist a sort of inductive argument the cogency of which increases with the sheer multiplication of favourable instances, in the way in which the evidential value of a sample really does, in certain conditions, increase, up to a point, with increases in the ratio between its size and the size, if it has one, of the population of which it is a sample.

Discussion[1]

Ayer. I want to begin by touching on this question of direct and indirect perception. It is extremely important particularly for the philosophy of science, and I don't know whether Mr. Kneale realizes how extremely vague this distinction is in ordinary speech. For example, take the case of hearing—have I heard Caruso? Well, one would be inclined to say 'no', only on gramophone records, and hearing him on a record isn't hearing him. It is not quite clear why it is not hearing him, perhaps because of the time lag, because he is dead. But then suppose that one hears someone broadcasting, does one hear him? Yes, but supposing his talk is not live but recorded, must it be said that then one doesn't hear him? This is clearly absurd. Now it is not the instrument that is in point here, for then I would not get to hear somebody over the telephone; neither is it the time dislocation—there is always some time dislocation and it seems arbitrary to suppose that the perception is indirect when there is a large one and direct when there is only a small one. But then again with seeing. Kneale talked of seeing bodies and seeing pictures of bodies but how sharp is this distinction? Does one see someone when one sees a photograph of him? No, one would say. Does one see him when one sees him in the cinema? No, one would say.

Kneale. Yes, I produce a photograph of this conference, and say 'Look that's Braithwaite, can't you see him?'

Ayer. Suppose someone says 'Have you ever seen Braithwaite?' One would be inclined to say, 'No I have not seen Braithwaite, I have only seen a photograph of him.' With television it is already a little more doubtful; how often do you say 'I have met you, and I remember where—on television.' Now all this does suggest that the distinction between direct and indirect perception is a pretty arbitrary one. We tend to say indirect when there is spatial dislocation, so that the reason for saying you see him indirectly is that you don't see him in the place where he is, and also because of the intervention, or partial intervention, of some instrument. Well, of course we don't in the least mind people wearing glasses, we don't mind a microscope because it's still direct, but very often there is some spatial dislocation, for example when you are a bit drunk then you may see things in the wrong place. This seems to suggest that naïve realism is not so naïve as one would think it was, although I don't in the least believe in the splendid accuracy of ordinary language—this seems to me absolute rot, and any analysis of this kind shows what rot it is. I think what Kneale is proposing is that we should try to make our ways of talking about seeing more uniform; for example he wants us to say that in all cases we see views and then ascribe the differences to the different ways in which the views are related to bodies,

[1] In order to guarantee a thorough discussion of the first two papers of this session Professor Ryle has kindly suggested that his paper should not be discussed.

and this seems to me to be a great advance. And there are two questions I would like to put to him, first what is this truth that seeing a body always entails seeing a view? Is this simply a piece of legislation on his part; and secondly, does he not think that any arguments which would lead him to say that seeing a body must entail seeing a view must also lead him to say that seeing a view entails seeing a visual sensum in the sense in which visual sensa are private?

Kneale. On the distinction between direct and indirect—I think that what Professor Ayer has shown is that these words 'direct' and 'indirect' themselves are subject to a sort of systematic shift according to context. One can very well use the word 'direct' in one context in order to make a contrast with 'indirect' in that context, although in some other context one would want to say that what was formerly called 'direct' was now to be called 'indirect'. In answer to the last question I want to say that we can't see a body without seeing a view, and for this reason, that when anyone claims he has seen a body it is always reasonable to tell him to paint a picture of the view he saw when he saw the body. If he says there wasn't any view, it is reasonable to reply 'You can't really have seen the body'. He might of course say, 'I did see the body; but if you ask me to draw a picture, I don't know what colours to put for the shadows.' But this is explained by the fact that we don't always attend to the views we see. To the further point about sensa I would say, Yes, I think there must be private sensa if there are views. I do not want to people the universe with a lot of new entities, saying that I have discovered views as a chemist might say he had discovered a new element. When I say there are views, I am merely drawing attention to a way in which we talk, and after doing so I want to go on immediately to say that, in asserting the existence of views, I am only claiming that in certain conditions all normal persons would have certain experiences. That is why I am committed to talking about experiences.

Feyerabend. Mr. Kneale has given us an analysis of the various uses of the word 'to see' which is much less dogmatic than the analyses one usually finds. He admits that there are various uses of the word 'to see'. Now very often the result of such an analysis is turned into prescriptions for future usage which might have some kind of conservative effect, it might tend to preserve the usages which we have had so far. As to this conservatism I would first of all say that it exists. It is often maintained that one cannot 'see' an electron—as using the word 'see' in this context would mean violating the rules which one has discovered by analysing past usage. And this in spite of the fact that the new rules can easily be explained to everybody. My question is now simply whether Mr. Kneale would also like to make such prescriptions.

Kneale. I certainly don't want to set myself up as an authority on the English language such as the French Academy claims to be for the French Language. I don't want to say that, having written my little dictionary on the word 'see', I require everyone to conform. We can only make restrictive rules of that sort for technical terms. The point of philosophical analysis is not to keep people on the right track in ordinary life or science, but rather to save ourselves from getting into philosophical muddles, to give ourselves, as it were, a map of our intellectual world.

Bastin. If I understand Mr. Kneale he is saying this: it may be sensible to say we have seen an electron, but if we do we must be clear that 'seeing' in this case can only be what it is if we have in our minds as well a whole physical theory of the electron and a familiarity with, and understanding of the experimental set-up within which we see it. Now I am sure this badly needs saying about elementary particles but I think we shall have missed what we can learn from the extreme case that they provide if we fail to realize that it is often also true of macroscopic objects. Think how we say we see an aircraft when a brilliantly lit contrail is being drawn across the sky at 40.000 feet.

Kneale. One might say 'I have seen an electron track' much as one might say 'I have seen an aeroplane trail in the sky' and yet hesitate or refuse to say 'I have seen an electron'. I think that at the present stage of the development of the English language that is the position. At present, if asked 'Have you seen the aeroplane which is making a noise', I should reply 'I can't say I have seen the aeroplane, but I have seen its trail.' In another 50 years we may possibly come to say 'I have seen the aeroplane.' But while we all know what it is like to see an aeroplane in the ordinary way, there is nothing analogous in the case of the electron, and so talk of seeing an electron trail must always depend on having a certain physical theory. If you bring a savage, or indeed any person who hasn't had scientific training, to look at a cloud chamber and ask him 'What's this?' what can he say? But in the case of an aeroplane you can get the man into a position where he sees both the aeroplane and the trail it makes.

Hesse. In talking about whether we see atomic particles we must distinguish two kinds of experiments. First there are pictures and quasi-pictures where we say that we see for instance a tree in the picture because we know what it is to see it not in a picture. In this sense we see atoms in a picture only because we are using a particle model for atoms, and we imply that they have the same relation to the picture as the tree has to its picture, in the behaviour of light beams, lenses, and so on. But there are also experiments giving photographs of tracks and so on. The analogy here is with aircraft making vapour trails, and we don't normally say we see the aircraft, but tracks made by the aircraft, because we know what it is like to see it on the airfield. What about meson tracks? I cannot see that this observation is different in status from that of atom-pictures just because we cannot say according to the analogy that we see the meson. The point is important because it is sometimes said that particles detected 'indirectly' have a different theoretical status from those which are photographed. But if a particle, for instance a photon, cannot in principle be photographed by any radiative process, is it sensible to say it is detected any more indirectly than atoms? Such particles are merely detected in the only ways possible for them. There is a different distinction from this which is referred to when it is said that a new particle is 'discovered'. There, for example in the case of the neutrino, what counts as 'discovery' is not the ability to photograph it, but detection by any means which are independent of the original experimental results, that is, lack of energy balance in certain reactions, which suggested its existence.

Polanyi. Mr. Kneale has said in the discussion that we may see the particulars of a face without attending to them. I suggest that in that case we attend to the face *in terms of its particulars*. We would see something different if we looked at the features of a face in themselves, not as parts of a face. It is not clear to me how Mr. Kneale distinguishes between 'views' which are seen *as clues* to the presence of a body or *as seen in themselves*. The distinction is indispensible.

Kneale. I think the situation is enormously complex, but that it may be possible by care to distinguish cases in which the constitution of sensa depend in part upon our intellectual set, i.e. upon our beliefs and so forth. There are other cases in which the constitution of our sensa does not depend in that way on our intellectual set. Consider the following case:

A circle which is not completely closed is presented tachistoscopically. The observer reports quite sincerely that he sees a circle, and this is sometimes called psychological completion. Now the name of psychological completion is not a happy one, because it suggests that a certain part of what is seen is physiological and that the rest is supplied by his mind as an hypothesis; but it isn't like that, since the man is not aware of the difference which I have represented by the distinction between a continuous line and a dotted line. He does not recognize the left hand part as the genuine datum, and the right hand part as the supplement. Hence the completion takes place at a sub-conscious level, and if you ask whether it is dependent on the intellectual set, the answer can only be settled by experiment. In some cases, it may turn out that the completion is dependent on the intellectual set, i.e. on the observer's being familiar with the objects he is looking at and having certain habits of expectation.

Englman. My remark concerns the current usage of the words 'to see' rather than the reality or otherwise of what we see. It seems to follow from what has been said before that the word 'see' should be used in a sense which refers to the optimal way of seeing, and I think this throws some light on the controversy between Professor Ayer and Mr. Kneale where the problem was apparently whether one does or does not hear Caruso. I think the distinction is that if one has the chance to hear Caruso in life, then one does not 'hear' him from the record. Similarly, there is a clear relevance to what Dr. Bastin said about whether we are seeing an electron or an aeroplane. One *can't* see an electron better than by a track but one *can* see an aeroplane in a more concrete way than by looking at the track it creates.

Kneale. If new possibilities of observation are developed which were not thought of by our ancestors and which are therefore not provided for in present language, we shall have new puzzles. Suppose we flew past Caruso very fast while he was singing a high note, so that the pitch of his voice apparently rose while we approached and fell while we went away. If you were then asked 'Have you heard Caruso?' you might say, 'Yes, in a sense, but not properly'.

Hutten. I was very glad to hear that people have accepted the view that what we see depends on the experience we have; therefore, if people have certain experiences which others lack, they have a use of the word 'to see' which is different from the use of others. Now if we admit that the use of the word 'to see' can be extended to cover new experiences compared with those of ordinary discourse, then we must also admit that our use of the word may be based often on experiences which are either not very good ones or which have been interpreted by false theories. Thus established use is often very misleading: historically speaking, it goes back to the old Greek epistemology which is taught even today, and this epistemology is in fact nothing else but a special case of the, in some sense, incorrect psychological theory of the Greeks. This theory is a static theory and it amounts to saying that there is an object and a mind and that an act of seeing connects the object with the mind. This is a static view which overlooks that seeing is actually a process. Then it is, of course, an idealization to say that sense-data are reliable and mistakes come in as result of interpretation. Naturally, one is not always conscious of the theories used for interpretation if one says that one sees something, but these theories also do not change too rapidly. In any case we need a better theory of seeing, a theory of the interaction between human beings and objects. This has very great bearing on the mind-body problem. We say, of course, that we see elementary particles. We do object violently to saying that we see sense-data or patterns of sense-data. In fact the question of *eidola* is very difficult whether the *eidola* are psychological things or physical things. If they are psychological things then I suggest saying that I have *eidola* but I never see them. I can see an electron because I am quite sure that it is a thing which has nothing to do with my mind. But if we shift from the physical context to the psychological context then we have to describe something different, and then the use of the word is changed.

Landsberg. I want to ask a question about the motivation of this sort of work. The procedure appears to be as follows: you start from everyday language, you notice that the word 'see' is used in various contexts; then you omit the contexts and, so to speak, consider the world of all possible contexts; and then you try to analyse and discuss whether you should say 'see directly', 'see indirectly' and the like. You leave us in the end with instructions on how to use the word 'see' in everyday life. But in everyday life we don't use this sort of approach. What we do is always to describe the situation more completely—at least by context or implication. We talk about seeing specified objects on specified occasions. I have been very much impressed by the fertility of people's examples, such as flying past Caruso and 'hearing' him as one does so. I do not know what you possibly *could* say apart from just that 'I heard him when flying past'. There is no obvious merit which I can see at the moment in suppressing the circumstances of my aural sensation and proceeding to the question: 'Did I really *hear* him?' We have also to remember that language develops, so that if you have today analysed the whole domain of conceivable contexts of the word 'to see', I am afraid you may have to do this again next year when new experiments have been made, and new contexts been found for words such as 'seeing' or 'hearing'.

Kneale. To explain the motivation of all this sort of work would involve going over the history of philosophy during the present century. If you ask me about the motivation of my own work, I think the answer is that I have been worried by what other philosophers say. They claim to be reporting ordinary usage, and yet what they report doesn't seem to me to be ordinary usage. But once this sort of query has been started the only way for a philosopher to deal with it is to enter into the game himself, at least so far as to get clear what can be done in this way. I am inclined to agree with Professor Ayer that it isn't the end of all philosophy, but I do think that it may be a necessary present stage.

Mackay. About 'seeing an electron', I think that we ought to say that we see a *body* only when we know what to answer if someone asks—are you sure it is a body and not something else? For example, a spot appears on a cathode-ray tube screen. Are we seeing a body? We apply a voltage to the plates and we say 'the spot' moves across the screen tracing out a line; but if you apply the voltage quickly enough, there isn't in fact a spot any more, what happens is that a fan of electrons strikes the screen, and if anyone took the resulting line as evidence that there was a spot, he would be in trouble. This is, I think, one of the reasons why one can be intellectually unconvinced by cloud-chamber photographs, while one is not unconvinced by aeroplane cloud-trails.

Secondly, I should like to point out an interesting distinction (I am not sure whether it has significance in atomic physics), between two degrees of immediacy in seeing, namely between seeing in the sense of *being in visual contact with* a situation, (e.g. through binoculars) and seeing in the sense of *having a visual representation of* it (e.g. in a cinema). By being in visual contact or in visual communication I mean that in principle one could imagine *information currently originating from oneself* appearing (implicitly or explicitly) in what one is seeing. It is a little like being potentially in control of what one is seeing. I think there is a very fundamental difference in our sense of reality in the two cases.

Braithwaite. To turn now to Professor Gallie's paper. He has made some most interesting distinctions between different sorts of situations in talking about unpredictability, and I hope that he will develop some of them in a little more detail, since he has been very self-denying in restricting his paper to 15 minutes only. I just want to comment on the last situation he described which he suggested might be unpredictable in an almost absolute sense if Nature was all the time changing its causal laws. Of course, if the way in which Nature was changing its causal laws was by a kind of randomizing mechanism, then it would be possible over the long run to make predictions, since we could learn from experience what randomizing mechanism Nature was using. So we should have to suppose that Nature is not using a randomizing mechanism. But even if Nature were to change its laws in such a way that we could never make predictions, there would still be a sense in which we could adapt our behaviour to Nature, namely, by using Wald's minimax method for making the best of the worst of all possible worlds.

Gallie. One could still do one's best, but it would seem to me to be a very poor best, which would nearly be the same as if we could not adapt ourselves at all.

Bohm. The discussion this morning brings us back to two old questions—one is the question whether the 'principle of science' is prediction or something else perhaps. The second point is the question of induction as raised by Hume. As to the first question—certainly we are interested in the practical uses of prediction, and we also use prediction as a criterion for the correctness of our theories. But it seems to me that the principal purpose of science is to find out what actually exists in nature and what the laws are. The question of induction, I think, needs to be treated like this. Given any set of data we can very often abstract a law from this set of data. Now when we test such a law under new conditions, we may find that it doesn't work, and we then propose a new law which subsumes the old law as a special case. Now this raises the question, is there a law at all, is not prediction a tautology because you say that prediction works when it works. That is also not true because we know from long experience that when we operate with the scientific method, generally speaking we do obtain a law that works in a much broader domain than that of the facts with which we started. This is a basic characteristic of nature. The fact that such a law works has nothing to do with our taste or pleasure, but it means rather that nature permits itself to be treated in this way.

Gallie. The difference perhaps is that I seem to be approaching science from what one might call a more humanistic or a more humble standpoint. Thus I attach more weight to the particular situations from or within which we frame the experiments that give us our knowledge.

Bohm. I think you are right that science must look at experimental systems. But it also must do another thing; it must try to make a general theory of nature, the best that it can do at any one moment, in order to try to explain the general course of the development of our theories.

Cohen. Mr. Gallie suggested that the problem of determinism is more complicated than we supposed because there are various senses of predictability to be taken into account. I would suggest that even his identification of the problem of determinism with the problem of predictability must be called in question. Suppose we think of the general theory which Professor Bohm has been suggesting—that there are infinitely many levels where one may find statistical laws or causal laws or both together. Now if this is so then one might say that in this sense everything is determined because at any level we may either find a causal law or we may find another level at which those things which are not determined at the first level become determined. This would be at least one sense in which we could say that everything is determined. Yet it seems to me that there is also an important sense in which it would be false then to say that everything is predictable. This arises because prediction is after all an activity and it is reasonable to suppose that prediction is something that can take place after a finite period of study—after carrying out a finite series of experiments in a finite series of domains. If this is so, then there is at least one lack of parallelism between predictability and determinism. You could also argue the other way (and in rather more practical terms) that it is possible for everything to be predictable though not determined. Even if some people would say there are really undetermined events and you can't predict any one of these—well, then someone might have a hunch and predict what is going to happen. All this seems to show that there is a difference between a formulation of the problem in terms of everything is determined and a formulation of the problem in terms of everything is predictable. Of course, we can modify the version of the criterion in terms of predictability by saying that everything must be predictable on good reasons. But we are then saying 'there must be laws'. In other words, to assimilate the notion of complete predictability to determinism we have got somehow, as a logician would put it, always to quantify over propositions or properties. The notion that everything is determined seems to be capable of a formulation in terms of something like this: there are propositions of certain kinds from which can be deduced other propositions describing an event. Or alternatively, any properties which an event has are correlated with other properties. Now I think on the other hand, the temptation to use the predictability language may be called an 'extensionalist' one, since the relation of predictability holds between a person and an event. This is a possible interpretation but there may be other ways of doing this. But at least it does seem to me necessary—at least on Professor Bohm's view—to separate these two problems of predictability and determinism.

Gallie. If you divorce determinism from prediction and think of determinism as being—I think that I caught this properly—something which just holds timelessly, then I think you are saying something that is meaningless. Just as it takes time to predict, because you have to make the observations and to apply the laws and so on, so I think the determinateness of the system is something which takes time to show itself. It is senseless to say that the universe is determined at an instant.

Cohen. This bears out what I have been suggesting, and in any case I am myself very sympathetic with this extensionalist attitude. I agree that you cannot say that something is determined unless you say what actually happens when people are actually making predictions—*if* you don't want to talk intensionally in terms of relations between properties.

Gallie. This is extensionalist only in the sense that I want facts.

Rosenfeld. On this last point I would say that it is our language which implies the reference to certain conditions in which the difference can be tested and therefore it is not a question of deciding whether one is an extensionalist or not, it is a situation in which we find ourselves and we cannot escape it. And my point is, it is not because we are human and happen to be on the earth.

Gallie. We have certain things at our disposal and we have to start from that. It is no good saying that an event's being determined just means that it is predictable by the methods now available. An event is determined only when its determinateness could be shown by using any proper method of prediction. It would be a great mistake to say that we are confined to a particular kind of prediction.

Rosenfeld. I am not suggesting that predictions must be limited to tests which we can actually make but the criterion should be that the tests which we imagine, even if they are not realizable materially, should be describable in terms which do not violate any one of the laws involved in the statement to be tested.

Gallie. Of course we might then change the question slightly. You say you must not violate any laws which are involved in the statement of quantum theory but you might slightly change quantum theory.

Rosenfeld. But that is another problem.

Alexander. I don't see what is wrong with the view that there can be predictions of discoveries—that *x* will be discovered. And in connexion with this Professor Gallie took his example of a case where, owing to technological advances that were somehow unforeseen, no prediction was possible of future developments of something, and he described this as the predictable unpredictability of the future. But he says that there might be a change of our predictive habits. Well, can this ever be predicted? Is it logically possible to predict that future prediction will be based on different principles and premisses? I can see the point about premisses, but could we ever predict that we will need a new *method* of prediction? Surely, we don't know we need a new method of prediction until our present method breaks down and then can no longer predict.

Gallie. If someone says there are going to be absolutely revolutionary changes in our predictive habits, this is not strictly a prediction, rather it expresses an attitude which we have to the future progress of science. Of course I agree that there are many minor changes in our premisses and so on which could be predicted. I mentioned the case of a clever spy, spying on a man engaged in physics; he gets the answer even before the physicist arrives at it. You could invent plenty of cases where such a prediction would be easy but when you get changes in predictive principles then it seems to be impossible.

Alexander. But can we ever have justification for expecting these in the near future sufficient to make any difference to our behaviour now?

Gallie. Well, I don't know about the present conference; it is possible. We just don't know.

Ayer. A few words about Gallie's man who is living in a society of predictors and wants to make fools of them. There is the premise that they are all equally good predictors, and I suppose that given the same evidence they reach the same conclusions and are always or in most cases right. What is suggested is that he therefore would be able to predict what the others would predict about him and they of course would also be able to predict what he would be able to predict about their predictions of him. The important thing is that if they have access to the same evidence they will come to the same result about actual behaviour. Now Gallie says the man can always make this go wrong by perversity, but the answer is of course that if there are laws governing this behaviour, and if the information about the initial conditions is available to these persons then he won't behave differently. What Gallie is raising is therefore not a logical point but simply the old free will problem. What lies behind all this is the idea that human beings are not subject to deterministic laws, and therefore they can always make fools of anybody who tries to predict what their behaviour will be. Now this may be just false, but I don't think that Gallie's sort of method is a legitimate way of setting bounds to the knowledge we can obtain in the field of physiology. And in the same spirit I suggest with regard to the invention that if you want to predict this, it would not be by considering just the state of science now and wondering how it is going to develop.

Gallie. The first point that you have made I might answer like this. The predictions that might be available about the perverse behaviour of that person would be predictions about the behaviour of this kind of chap in this kind of situation. These predictions will apply to a class of persons behaving in a certain situation, but he is outside this situation or is a new term in the new situation and until he has actually carried out his action you can't have your class completed so as to make a general law.

Hutten. I want just to illustrate this point by a reference to the history of science. In 1900 there were certain problems in physics, namely, concerned with the theory of specific heat and the theory of black body radiation. Planck who introduced the quantum of action to solve them was actually dismayed and tried always to explain the apparent discontinuity in a continuous way. It was not possible before Planck's discovery was made to predict in any sense of the word how the development of these theories would proceed. In fact, it was quite possible that the situation was wholly unpredictable. On the other hand, I take as an example the acceptance of the relativity theory and the prediction of the properties of the gravitational field. This was predicted long before it was discovered, it was a deduction as it were, from the theory and then, when it was discovered it was no surprise at all. Therefore, I would suggest that there is a whole spectrum, so to speak, from complete unpredictability, on the one side, to complete predictability on the other, and it would be false if one were to take one or the other as the standard model.

Körner. How far does Professor Gallie's argument depend on contingent facts and how far is it *a priori*?

Gallie. Let me go back to my perverse individual, my anticonformist. Before he makes his last anti-conformist move there will be generally available evidence to show that certain laws hold of the behaviour of a person of his kind. But he is always one move ahead of his fellow predictors; knowing the natural expectations he can always contravene them; his expertise is in improvising perversely. This is not to say that his moves cannot be causally explained after the event. This brings us to the question—can they be causally explained on the same general principles, in accordance with the same general theories, as have explained his moves to date? Perhaps altogether new explanatory principles and procedures will be needed. How we should expound this possibility, and how we should justify our claim in any particular situation that altogether new principles of explanation are needed, are of course difficult questions. But surely to talk about the general character of the Universe won't help us here. Our business, to quote Goethe, is 'not to solve the riddle of the universe but to enlarge the boundaries of the accessible'.

Rosenfeld. It seems to me that this attitude of Professor Gallie, with which I am in complete sympathy, should be denied by anyone believing in Laplace's idea.

Mackay. I think it is important to realize that this is not a paradox involving a community of beings of unknown physiology, as Professor Ayer seems to suggest. We could take it for granted, for the sake of the argument, that the physiology is fully understood. It is rather a paradox of coupled information systems, which one can analyse in such a way that the solution is quite clear—it is a solution of oscillation—there is no stable solution. One can put it a little more constructively and realistically in this way: if one wants to assert that there exists now a 'true' proposition describing the future action of one of the members of this community, this is 'truth' of such a kind that it cannot be *entertained as certain* by that member, even if we take a deterministic physiology for granted. If this member were to attempt to entertain such a proposition the action of attempting would be self-nullifying, because it would deny the conditions under which the proposition could meaningfully be said to be certain. In short, he would have to put the same apparatus both to deliberating and to entertaining as already fixed. This, I think, is part of what we mean by our consciousness that we are free—it is, to be brief, that a would-be 'certain' description of our voluntary actions is not only impossible to offer to us but inconceivable to be entertained by us as certain. It is therefore quite compatible to say that within a certain community all the members are unpredictable to to one another, and yet nothing within the community is unpredictable to one outside. The activity can be wholly determinate and yet at the same time unpredictable to each member.

Ryle. Isn't this like the proposition that Mr. Snooks is going to be surprised? The point about this is that you don't tell this to Mr. Snooks, probably because if you do he won't be surprised.

Mackay. Yes—but there is a further point: This logical indeterminacy applies equally to any actions which depend on the proposition for their direction. For example, it may be that Mrs. Snooks is tired of finding Mr. Snooks complaining about the breakfast, so she calls in a psychologist to predict what Mr. Snooks' preference will be tomorrow. Now if it happens that Mr. Snooks is so perverse that whatever he sees her cooking, he will prefer something else, no advances in psychology will help her, even if she doesn't tell him her prediction explicitly.

Feyerabend. I would like to make a contribution to the discussion between what has been called the extensionalists and the Spinozists or the Laplacians. The Extensionalist, as I understood him, analyses determinism in terms of predictability whereas the Spinozist would try to analyse determinism as a property of the universe. Now I suggest the following formulation of determinism which is independent of observers: I start with a syntactical definition: *a theory is deterministic with respect to a class K of variables*, if, and only if, a conjunction C of statements to the effect that some of the variables of K have a certain value at the time t can be derived from the theory together with another conjunction of statements which again contains only variables of K—not necessarily the same as in C—and which asserts that those variables had some other value at some other time $t' < t$. On the basis of this definition I propose to formulate *determinism* thus: The world is deterministic if and only if the class of all variables can be sub-divided into sub-classes in such a way that for every sub-class there exists a theory which is deterministic with respect to that sub-class and which is true. Two remarks about this formulation of determinism: first it is a statement about the world because it involves the concept of truth. It does not involve anything about observers. Secondly, it can be tested and can also be refuted. For assume that quantum theory in its present form is true and that the Neumann-proof is correct. This would imply that no true and deterministic theory exists with respect to the class of variables of elementary quantum mechanics, hence, determinism in the form which I have just suggested would be refuted.

Gallie. I admit that in this form determinism could be refuted, but I do not think it could be confirmed.

Feyerabend. But this does not matter, perhaps it can be confirmed.

Gallie. But if it is all one-sided then it does matter.

Feyerabend. It can even be confirmed: within classical mechanics we could confirm it because classical mechanics was deterministic and we had also confirmation to the effect that this theory was universal in the sense that all variables could be defined in its terms; so it could be confirmed; but I am not keen on confirming it—it can be refuted.

Rosenfeld. May I ask how you can speak of truth without observer. I thought that the truth of a statement relates on its being possible to have a meaning for an observer.

Feyerabend. I do not define this statement of determinism in such a way that the defining sequence contains anything about observers, about possibilities of prediction, and so on. It only contains the notion of a theory being deterministic which is a syntactical notion, together with the concept of truth—how we *test* a true theory is an altogether different matter.

Gallie. If you only take one test referring to one of these sub-classes of variables—just one little exception would refute your determinism. Hence you could never improve or strengthen the case for determinism.

Feyerabend. This only shows that the statement of universal determinism is a hypothesis, that it is an empirical statement.

Rosenfeld. Laplace who is the supreme authority, I suppose, for that idea proposes it in connexion with an observer; of course, his observer was an exalted being but with human qualities.

Feyerabend. But here I would be even more radical than Laplace. I would say that the statement of determinism is a statement about the world and not about observers. Although this statement can be tested by observers—this does not mean that it asserts something about them.

Rosenfeld. The last is the only sensible way of understanding determinism but I would also contend that it was also Laplace's idea.

Vigier. With the last statement of Professor Rosenfeld we are back to our old quarrel again: does the scientific statement have a meaning outside observers? We say Yes; he says No. Now this is a question which can only be settled by practice, it is not a question in which logic can decide. There exists the science of geology which informs us about times when no observer existed. And I think that even in the time of the big Saurians the laws of quantum mechanics did apply to molecules inside this Saurian although I cannot go and see because unfortunately they have vanished. Also the whole idea of the developement of the universe on the basis of laws and of facts which we observe now, is a valid scientific edifice. This is my first point. The second point is about Laplace. Nobody wishes to return to Laplace's determinism. Bohm and I myself are very strongly against Laplace's determinism in the form which Laplace has given it. The whole point here is the question of infinity. If you find a finite ensemble of laws and an ultimate set of laws, then you are back at Laplacian determinism. But there is no such finite ensemble and closed set of laws. There is always a larger context out of which this finite ensemble of laws can be approached. This is also related to Professor Gallie's paradox—this man, this joker, is outside the context of prediction of the society of predictors.

Rosenfeld. The first point about the observers is a completely trivial point. I do not see the slightest difference between prediction about the future and retrodiction about the past: both are based on present evidence. All that we can say about those Saurians is based on what we can see of them. And all that we can say about the state of the universe when it was first being formed is also based on the known laws of physics—with some degree of idealization, of course; the reliability of those retrodictions, as well as the reliability of predictions, depending on whether the amount of idealization is excessive or not. I cannot see the least philosophical difference between descriptions of the state of the world in the secondary epoch and the description of the world as it is today. It is the same scientific procedure which is applied in both cases. But with respect to the last point about the finiteness and the infinity of levels, I would not regard this as a new point at all: it is a familiar point, and no person in the world more than Bohr would insist upon this dialectical conception of science and of our knowledge. I think I am not betraying his philosophy when I describe it like that. But it is only a framework, and the question whether to fill it with subquantal monsters or with things that you know from experience is a completely different one.

Bohm. I don't quite see the equivalence between prediction into the future and retrodiction into the past. When I predict about something that will happen tomorrow then I can wait until tomorrow and see whether it happens or not. But if I retrodict that there was a monster on the earth a thousand million years ago then I have no way of going back and seeing whether it was really there. All I can do is to see that various consequences of this hypothesis continue to be verified. The second point is this: we find ourselves here in existence at a certain time and we find that we came from something that existed earlier and therefore we suppose that there was a time when there were no human beings on the earth. Now if we suppose that the only meaning of a hypothesis is what an observer might see, then we cannot understand what we mean when we say that there was a time when there was no intelligent life, after which intelligent life came into being and became capable of perceiving. This is why I want to say that we frame our hypothesis not basically on what an observer might observe, but rather, about what is in being. We then say secondarily that if a certain thing is in being, then an observer who happens to be around could observe certain consequences. If he isn't there he can't observe them, but this doesn't change the fact that they are there. Of course, we must take the whole universe in our definition of the meaning of being. We must not say that what is in being is just the universe without us. Rather, it is the universe with us in it. We are part of being and therefore when we observe something we may well change it. If this happens to a significant extent then we must remember that being includes us, our minds, our thinking, our actions and so on. Now in this sense Bohr made a very important contribution when he stressed that the observer plays both an active and a passive role—that we are both actors and observers on the stage of life. But this is not in contradiction with the notion that there is a life and there is a stage upon which we can act and observe. To say that there is no life and no stage and that there is nothing but potential or actual observation, and that this is the only thing that has meaning, I don't understand.

Rosenfeld. I protest against this complete distortion of what I have been saying.

Ayer. I think that Professor Rosenfeld gave the wrong answer to Professor Vigier and that Professor Bohm gave the wrong answer to Professor Rosenfeld. Professor Rosenfeld was quite right in saying, of course, that in making conjectures about either the past or the future we do depend upon present evidence, but of course this is not at all the same thing as to say that in talking about the past or the future we are talking about present evidence. Here Professor Vigier is quite right against Professor Rosenfeld. On the other hand I don't think that the distinction which Professor Bohm made is very important. It is quite true that we shall be around to verify a few of our predictions, but we don't live very long and the great majority of the statements about the future remain unverified by us, by him or me or Professor Rosenfeld, just as do the majority of statements about the past. I suggest that if

Professor Rosenfeld does maintain this position he must do it in a form that would escape Professor Vigier's trouble about the Saurians. He must say that in talking about the Saurians he is talking not about anything he did observe but about something somebody might have observed, had he been there, even if he wasn't there. To make this theory work, you have got to do it in terms of the possibility of making the relevant observations and not in terms of actual observations. This, I think, might be a difficult thing to do.

Rosenfeld. I am glad that you have mentioned that—this is exactly what I meant. But I didn't mention it explicitly because I thought it was quite obvious.

Feyerabend. I want to underline what Professor Ayer has just said. In their discussion with Professor Rosenfeld, Professor Bohm and Professor Vigier have confused a special problem of quantum mechanics with a general problem of epistemology. It is true that quantum mechanics in its present form and interpretation has some subjectivistic leanings. But in the earlier discussion about determinism Professor Rosenfeld went much further than this. He seemed to assume that the fact that we *need observers in order to test* a statement—whether of classical physics or of quantum theory—implies that the statement, every statement, *is also partly about observers.* I have tried to point out that such an inference is completely unjustified. More especially I have suggested how to formulate the problem of determinism in a way which does not make it a problem about observers although I have at the same time tried to formulate it in such a way that observers can test it and can decide whether or not it is true.

Rosenfeld. If a statement does not contain any reference to an observer—how can such a statement be tested? How can it even be understood?

Gallie. Perhaps I can do something here. It seems to me that we want to relate determinism not to the observer but to the observable. In this sense I mean there were processes going on and there were laws before observing beings were on the earth and if there was a law before there were any sensitive beings, this law would be manifested, in Popper's language, as the propensity of certain systems to produce certain effects. But those effects we can only describe as if we could somehow, directly or indirectly, have observed them. There is another point for Dr. Feyerabend. Einstein for example propounded deterministic theories. On the other hand there are grounds, e.g. von Neumann's proof, for denying that in certain fields a deterministic theory is possible. I suppose Einstein could have retorted that the difference is that in his theories the variables are well chosen, whereas in other theories they are not. Would not this rebut your disproof of determinism?

Feyerabend. But then quantum mechanics would be false, whereas I have made the assumption that quantum mechanics is true.

Vigier. I was very happy about what Professor Ayer said and I also agree with Professor Rosenfeld, for this is the first time I have heard Professor Rosenfeld disagree with a plain, positivistic sentence. I would put the thing in a stronger form: I do not think that things which exist are things which might have been observed. This is where the split comes in a very clear form.

Rosenfeld. I don't say that. Don't continue on that line because I do not say that things only exist in so far as they could have been observed. All the statements we make about the world are necessarily descriptions of a state of affairs, of mind, of material, that an observer might perceive if he were placed in those particular circumstances.

Vigier. Let us say then we agree that the world exists outside any observer. Did the laws of quantum mechanics apply to the world at a time when there were no observers present?

Rosenfeld. Of course.

Vigier. O.K. If you say then, that the laws of quantum mechanics did apply at that time, then the laws of quantum mechanics are real, objective, statistical laws of nature, which have nothing to do with the observer, and are verified whether there are observers or not.

Rosenfeld. No.

Vigier. You can't change your position and say something two minutes ago and another thing now. Let's go into the time when there were no observers at all, then you would say that the world did exist at that time in an objective way, that the laws of quantum mechanics did apply at that time in an objective, real way, and that means that the laws of quantum mechanics are real, objective, statistical laws which have nothing to do with observers or things which might have been observed, since nobody was there and couldn't possibly have been there.

Braithwaite. But they could only be known by observers.

Vigier. That is quite a different question. It is true that you get to nature through scientific practice and scientific elaboration, this is one side of the question. But what we say is that the laws that you get are real objective approximations of the real objective properties of matter. That is what is contested basically. There might have been no observers whatsoever and the laws of quantum mechanics did still work. And once this is admitted you have the right to suppose that there might be a deeper level and to admit the possibility of explaining statistical laws in terms of this level.

SEVENTH SESSION

Chairman: Professor M. FIERZ

F. Bopp: The principles of the statistical equations of motion in quantum theory.

H. J. Groenewold: Objective and subjective aspects of statistics in quantum description.

The principles of the statistical equations of motion in quantum-theory

by

FRITZ BOPP

1. *Introduction*

I am going to talk about the problem of interpretation of elementary quantum mechanics. This problem has various aspects:

1. Indeterminism,
2. Indeterminability,
3. The impossibility of an objective account.

There are certainly still other aspects, which we shall not touch upon in this context. I propose to treat here mainly the problem of objectivity.

For that purpose I must define what I understand by saying that it is possible to objectivize a certain process.[1] About a month ago we celebrated the 100th birthday of Heinrich Hertz, according to whom the 'possibility to objectivize' is the same as the 'possibility to form pictures of things' in such a way that the logically necessary consequences of the pictures are pictures of events which happen according to the necessities of nature. There is no doubt that those pictures are not identical with their objects. But if they exist they can, in our plans, represent the objects. It is in this sense that I shall talk about the 'possibility of objectivization'.

According to common opinion quantum mechanics does not allow for objectivization in this sense because we need two conceptions, the conception of a particle and the conception of a wave, and it is impossible that at the same time both can represent the same object.

I have no doubt that this philosophical attitude is compatible with quantum mechanics of today. I also do not propose in this context to change the present theory. I only want to discuss the question whether or not the philosophical decision to drop the possibility of objectivization is a necessary consequence of quantum mechanics, and I think that one can demonstrate mathematically that there is no such necessity.

According to our definition of objectivization we can only prove this statement by providing well defined pictures for quantum processes. It was recognized long ago that Born's statistical interpretation of Schrödinger's wave function suggests a way to this goal. We only need to consider the particles as the objects proper in the sense of Hertz and to interpret the waves as relating to statistical ensembles of particles.

[1] During the symposium there emerged another definition of this notion of objectivity which is obviously the rule in quantum mechanics as well as in any sensible physical theory. In the present paper we are not concerned with this conception.

Particles and waves of this kind are compatible in nearly the same way to that in which particles and sound waves in an ideal gas are compatible.[2]

There is still a strong inclination to pass over this suggestion. The difficulties which seem to be connected with this interpretation become evident as soon as we realize that the quantum-statistical equations of motion cannot be subsumed under any type of statistical equations of motion which is known so far. Hence one cannot think that it will be possible to derive the quantum-statistical equations of motion from the equations of motion for a deterministic model in a way which is immediately comparable with that leading from Newton's equations to the equations of classical statistical mechanics, and I think that this is also asserted by Bohm and Vigier.

But there are two ways of proving the view that quantum mechanics deals with particles, whose motion is described only statistically. I shall only briefly refer to the first one, for it has been treated in detail in a publication in *l'Annales de l'Institut Henri Poincaré*. It is based upon the following theorem[3]:

> Any quantum-mechanical system, pure and mixed states included, can be mapped into a statistical ensemble of particles in a certain phase-space; hence also every quantum-mechanical process can be correlated to a movement of this ensemble.

Once again I would like to emphasize that this is not a thesis which may be subject to discussion, it is a mathematical theorem.

This theorem asserts that the picture of particles whose motion can only be described statistically is a consistent picture which, in the sense of Hertz, may represent the objects such that we do not need to give up the possibility of objectivization. This is also not contradicted by the fact that the quantum statistical equations of motion are of a rather uncommon kind, a fact which also follows from the principles I am going to enounce presently.

2. *Formulation of the principles.*

I repeat: I want to point out that quantum mechanics, as it stands, is a new kind of statistical mechanics describing the motion of virtual ensembles of particles or of systems of particles, and that it is possible to derive the quantum equations from principles which are connected with the notion of moving ensembles.

In order to simplify the discussion we consider a single particle moving in one dimension. I think that this will not lessen the generality of our consideration.

Two of the principles mentioned above define the notion of ensembles of particles moving in phase-space.

1*st principle*:

> There exists a phase-space, in which a particle has a definite position at any time.

[2] Of course there is an essential physical difference beween quantum-waves and sound-waves. In the first case we have virtual ensembles, i.e. ensembles of possibilities, and in the second case real ones. But from a purely logical point of view both ensembles are comparable at least if we consider only the linear terms in Boltzmann's integrodifferential-equation, neglecting interaction between the sound-waves.

[3] F. Bopp, La méchanique quantique est-elle une méchanique statistique classique particulière?, *Ann. l'Inst. H. Poincaré*, tome XV, fascicule II, 1956, pages 81 à 112, Paris.

We state here that the particle will follow a certain orbit in phase-space and that the motion is completely determined. Therefore, in referring to the 1st principle, we are speaking of the principle of determinism. But we do not assume that we are able to know the positions in phase-space exactly. From an extremely positivistic point of view it seems to be contradictory or at least meaningless to state at once the principle of determinism and the impossibility of knowing exactly the well determined states. But we shall see that it is possible and useful to distinguish between 'determinedness' and 'determinability'.

Even in classical mechanics it is not possible to observe exactly a particle's position in phase-space, as Born has pointed out recently.[4] Therefore it is not sufficient to consider the particle in a single situation only. We must consider all situations compatible with our observations and the arrangements of our devices. Hence the subject of research is an ensemble of particles representing all possible situations of the single particle we are speaking of. For this ensemble we assume the

2nd principle:

> The virtual ensemble of particles representing the possible situations of the single particle in consideration is a statistical ensemble.

This principle states the possibility of statistical descriptions, and it is logically independent of the first principle.

Hence we have probabilities for finding the particle in different regions of phase-space. To avoid unessential complications we stipulate that the phase coordinates p, q can only assume a finite number of values according to

$$p = ma,\ q = nb,\ (m, n, \text{integers})\ -N \leqslant m, n \leqslant +N. \tag{1}$$

Obviously $(2N+1)^2$ is the number of points in this phase-space.

Let W_{mn} be the probability for finding the particle in (m, n), then we have obviously

$$W_{mn} \geqslant 0,\ \sum_{m,n} W_{mn} = 1, \tag{2}$$

and the ensemble is defined by the whole set of probabilities

$$\mathbf{W} = (\,..\, W_{mn}\, ..\,). \tag{3}$$

Taking each probability as a coordinate in a barycentrical system we can represent the ensemble by a point within a tetraeder of $(2N+1)^2$ corners in a $((2N+1)^2-1)$-dimensional space.

According to the first principle these probabilities are at any time completely determined by the probabilities at some other time. Therefore the first time derivatives $\dot{W}_{mn}$ of the probabilities W_{mn} are certain functions of these probabilities themselves, and these functions must be linear ones, for it is evident that there is no interaction at all between the particles of a virtual ensemble. Hence we get the

3rd principle:

> The equations of the motion of ensembles are linear differential equations of first order in time.

[4] M. Born, *Phys. Bl.* **11**, 49, 304 (1955); M. Born, D. F. Horton, *J. Phys.*, **192**, 201, (1955).

This principle states the superposition law and leads to the equation:

$$\dot{W}_{mn} = \sum_{r,s} S_{mnrs} W_{rs}. \tag{4}$$

According to the second equation (2) we add:

$$\sum_{m,n} S_{mnrs} = 1. \tag{5}$$

If we would further accept the inequalities

$$S_{mnrs} \geq 0, \text{ if } (m, n) \neq (r, s) \tag{6}$$

we would obtain a stochastical system of equations. But the essential point of quantum mechanics is that we cannot accept these inequalities.

Equation (6) are a consequence of the proposition that each ensemble can be realized, i.e. that we are able by observation to reduce in a completely unlimited way the region in which we are certain to find the particle. Bearing in mind that we cannot immediately perceive positions in phase-space and that we need at least two observations in ordinary space in order to identify positions in phase-space, we see that it is by no means evident that probability distributions in phase-space can be reduced to a point. Whether or not this is possible obviously depends on the properties of our instruments only, and it does not depend on the question, whether the motion of the particle is determined or not. Hence we arrive at the following definition of the notion of 'determinability': *a physical system is determinable, if the conditions of the measurements of momenta and space-positions allow us to reduce the distribution function of the representative ensemble to a single point.* A system which does not fulfil this condition will be called indeterminable. In quantum mechanics we postulate the principle of indeterminability:

4th principle:

There are realizable and nonrealizable ensembles.—The boundary line between both sets of ensembles is a constant of motion.

This principle is essentially the same as condition VI in a paper, published 1955.[5]

The statistical equations (4) define linear transformations of the tetraeder mentioned above. In our case the only surfaces which can be invariant with respect to linear transformations are the ellipsoids. Hence, the fourth principle provides us with a certain group of linear transformations, defined by the invariant surfaces which separate the realizable and the nonrealizable ensembles.

Obviously this group of transformations is a subgroup of the halfgroup defined by equations (4) and (5). But the group of quantum statistical motions is still more restricted. It can easily be shown, that we get equations which are equivalent to those of von Neumann, if we add the more restrictive Bohr frequency-condition:

5th principle:

The characteristic frequencies of the equations of motion of ensembles can be written as differences of two frequencies, each of which belongs to the same set.

It will be shown that this principle contains the fourth principle.

[5] F. Bopp, *Bay. Ak. Wiss., Math.-Naturw. Kl.*, 1955, p. 9.

3. *Derivation of von Neumann's equation.*

This is the form in which I read my paper at the Colston Symposium. During the session I dropped the very simple proofs. But it seems to be desirable to add them now in a supplementary section.

We start from equation (4) summarizing the principles 1, 2 and 3. It is convenient to use the matrix notation:

$$\dot{W} = SW. \tag{7}$$

Here the matrix S has $(2N+1)^2$ rows and columns. According to the fifth principle, the eigenvalues of iS should be equal to $\omega_m - \omega_n$.

Now we want to prove the following theorem: If Bohr's frequency condition holds for the matrix iS, then an affine transformation will turn eq. (7) into von Neumann's equation:

$$i\hbar\dot{Z} = HZ - ZH. \tag{8}$$

Here Z is the state matrix, otherwise called density-matrix or statistical matrix, and H is the Hamiltonian. Both matrices have $2N+1$ rows and columns.

In order to prove this theorem we rewrite eq. (8) using its different components:

$$i\hbar\, \dot{Z}_{mn} = \sum_r (H_{mr}Z_{rn} - Z_{mr}H_{rn}). \tag{9}$$

Taking into account that the Hamiltonian is a Hermitean matrix, we get from equation (9), writing it in a form comparable to eq. (4):

$$i\hbar\, \dot{Z}_{mn} = \sum_{r,s} \{H_{mr}\delta_{ns} - H^*_{ns}\delta_{mr}\}Z_{rs}, \tag{10}$$

i.e. if we return to matrix-notation, now considering Z as a vector of $(2N+1)^2$ components:

$$i\hbar\dot{Z} = (H \otimes 1 - 1 \otimes H^*)Z. \tag{11}$$

Here $\otimes$ means the Kronecker product.

Obviously equation (11) provides us with the same spectrum as equation (8). Therefore Bohr's frequency-condition holds for the Matrix

$$1/\hbar\,(H \otimes 1 - 1 \otimes H^*) \tag{12}$$

According to the fifth principle it should also hold for iS. If the spectra of both matrices are identical, then there exist an affine transformation

$$H \otimes 1 - 1 \otimes H^* = i\hbar A\, S\, A^{-1}, \tag{13}$$

and the theorem is proved, if we take into account that, given iS and its spectrum $(\omega_m - \omega_n)$, there exist Hamiltonians with the spectrum (ω_m), e.g. the diagonal matrix with the frequencies ω_m as diagonal elements.

It is very remarkable that in these derivations we have not used the fourth principle. This principle holds automatically, if the fifth is given. But, I think, it is reasonable to formulate both principles separately, because the fourth principle is of a more intuitive character, whereas the fifth principle is more technical.

4. *Mean values in phase-space.*

What about the mean values in phase-space? asks Rosenfeld. Wigner and other authors have shown that it is impossible to define non-negative distribution functions giving the same mean values as quantum mechanics.

These well known statements are based on certain assumptions, which can be made but which are not necessary. Both representations of quantum mechanics, the usual representation and the representation of the present paper, are completely equivalent. Therefore we must change Rosenfeld's question, if we are to see the point he wants to make.

Let $Z(t)$ be the state matrix of a quantum-mechanical system, and $f(p, q, t)$ the corresponding distribution function. Let G be the operator of a certain quantity, and $g(p, q)$ the corresponding phase-function representing the *same* quantity. Then the following equation holds (for the mean values of G and $g(p, q)$, assumed to be equal):

$$\overline{G} = Tr(GZ) \equiv \overline{g(p, q)} = \int g(p, q)\, f(p, q, t)\, dpdq, \tag{14}$$

which holds identically for all $Z(t)$ and $f(p, q, t)$.

By virtue of equation (14) a unique correspondence is established between Z and f and consequently between G and g, and we must ask: what about the correspondence between the representing expressions for the physical quantities?

The answer is given in detail in the paper, referred to in footnote 3. Referring to this paper and writing correspondences of operators according to

$$G = \underline{g(p, q)}, \tag{15}$$

we state:

$$\begin{aligned} \underline{q}_{\text{here}} &= \underline{q}_{\text{Schrödinger}}, \\ \underline{p}_{\text{here}} &= \underline{p}_{\text{Schrödinger}}, \end{aligned} \tag{16}$$

and

$$\begin{aligned} \underline{(q^2)}_{\text{here}} &= \underline{(q^2)}_{\text{Schrödinger}} + l^2/4, \\ \underline{(p^2)}_{\text{here}} &= \underline{(p^2)}_{\text{Schrödinger}} + \hbar^2/l^2. \end{aligned} \tag{17}$$

In this equation l is a certain length, describing the accuracy of measuring space positions. According to quantum mechanics we can assume that l may be as small as we want. Therefore the difference between $\underline{(q^2)}_{\text{here}}$ and $\underline{(q^2)}_{\text{Schrödinger}}$ may be neglected.

The crucial point of Rosenfeld's question is to be found in the second equation (17). It states: The smaller l, the worse for the difference between $(p^2)_{\text{here}}$ and $(p^2)_{\text{Schrödinger}}$. If we do not want the additive terms in equation (17), then it is not possible to construct non-negative distribution functions as Wigner has proved.

But why should we not want them? There is no reason for such an assumption. It is completely sufficient that there is no difference between the statements of both representations of the theory. We want to show this explicitly for a measurement of the mean square of p.

Whatever operation we perform in measuring p^2, we must use some device, which transforms differences of momenta into differences of positions. We only *observe* distances in space and then we *interpret* them as momenta. This is possible according to the second equation (16). But for the mean square the difference between the quantum value and the new value will be equal with the constant in the *first* equation (17), which can be made as small as we like and which is completely different from the constant in the second equation (17).

It is a remarkable feature of the statistical transcription of quantum mechanics that we cannot speak of the second equation (17), if $l = 0$, i.e. if we postulate the possibility of ideal measurements of positions. Perhaps this is a point of deeper interest. But at the present moment I do not want to press this point.

These considerations are certainly more detailed than those belonging to the usual interpretation of quantum mechanics. They are richer because we are using rather intuitive pictures which leave open future possibilities. But I cannot see that they are more involved, as they are mathematically equivalent to the usual interpretation.

5. *Relation to stochastic processes.*

Bohm asked a question about papers I published some time ago[6] on the relation between quantum statistical equations and stochastic equations. There is certainly no equivalence between both kinds of equations, as we have seen in section 2 and as becomes clear when one considers principle 4. If we want to introduce stochastic equations or even deterministic equations we must change quantum mechanics more or less. But the introduction of determinism does not necessitate such modifications. For we have seen that it is an essential feature of quantum mechanics to adopt principle 1, which postulates determinism even if we are not able to determine the state of a physical system exactly.

It is this point which I want to stress here. Considering the objection that simplicity is lacking, it seems to me preferable to separate the question whether or not there is determinism from the question whether or not there exist relations to stochastic or even to deterministic equations. As we have seen in section 4 it is possible to answer the first question without any modification of the theory and hence without other complications than those familiar from the usual interpretation of quantum mechanics.

But I agree that it is possible and even necessary to consider the second question as well. I shall indicate briefly, what I have to say on it:

1. There are statistical equations of motion satisfying the 4th principle, whose solutions are nearly the same as the solutions of the related stochastic equations. The manifold of these solutions is of the same power as that of the motions which agree with Newton's equations.

2. There are also statistical equations satisfying the 5th principle and consequently the 4th one too, the solutions of which are again nearly the same as certain random walks. But it is not yet proved that they are as numerous as is necessary.

6. *The problem of symmetry.*

If Heisenberg were present, he would point to the lack of symmetry between

[6] F. Bopp, *Z. Naturforschg.* **10a,** 783 (1955); **10a,** 789 (1955); *Z. Phys.* **143,** 233 (1953).

waves and particles, and he would maintain that the statistical picture is a kind of revival of the materialistic ontology.[7]

The second statement is purely philosophical. Since the days of Newton physics has implicitly adopted the principle that it does not provide us with reasons for ontological decisions. Hence, we have the strong feeling that the fact that the statistical interpretation is compatible with different philosophical opinions, and also with the materialistic ontology constitutes a kind of indirect proof for it. But it is impossible to speak of a revival of that ontology. We do not believe in such a revival. Reasons for this fundamental decision are only to be found beyond physics.

With regard to the lack of symmetry, we want to point out that it is a very familiar fact that the mathematical form of a theory is much more symmetrical than its interpretation.

We know, for instance, that the Hamiltonian equations of classical mechanics are invariant with respect to canonical transformations, and we also know the importance of this property. But nobody will agree that the canonical momenta, calculated by some more or less involved canonical transformations, are as evident as the momenta introduced by Newton. Obviously there must be something to justify this situation, and the reason for it must be found outside the mathematical framework of the theory. I think that this reason is to be found in the fact, that we can observe space positions, whereas we are not able to see positions in momentum space. Hence the lack of conceptional symmetry is an immediate consequence of the non-existence of phase-space-spectacles.

It is for the same reason that the conceptional symmetry breaks down in quantum mechanics. It is of course true that we observe interferences. But nobody has ever seen the waves. We are only counting particles or measuring the intensities of beams of particles.

These statements will hold even from a strictly positivistic point of view. For it is generally admitted that we cannot observe Schrödinger's functions or von Neumann's state-matrices. We only observe mean values, if not single events only. Hence a strictly positivistic theory should provide us with equations connecting such mean values, as it is done by Peierls in some papers on the quantum theory of fields. Now the probabilities, given in section 1, just define a complete set of mean values. which is sufficient to represent the quantum-mechanical system.

[7] W. Heisenberg in *Niels Bohr and the Development of Physics*, London, Pergamon Press, 1955, p. 19, section 3.

Objective and subjective aspects of statistics in quantum description

by

H. J. GROENEWOLD

If not already for the sake of brevity my discussion would be clumsy, it still would be so for the sake of principle. The principle being that theories of quantum observation are usually either vague or formalistic and unphysical. Now just for the sake of brevity I principally shall be vague and formalistic.

The two main notions of simple non-relativistic quantum mechanics are those of motion and measurement. Further we are apt to use the notion of the quantum state of a quantum system. A pure quantum state may be represented by a state vector in the appropriate Hilbert space $\mathcal{H}$, but it is more suitable to use a statistical operator **k**, which may represent a mixture of incoherent pure states as well. The dynamical motion of the system during a time interval (t_a, t_b) is represented by a unitary operator $\mathbf{U}(t_b, t_a) = \mathbf{U}^{-1}(t_a, t_b)$, which induces the transformation

$$\mathbf{k}(t_a) \rightarrow \mathbf{k}(t_b) = \mathbf{U}(t_b, t_a) \,.\, \mathbf{k}(t_a) \,.\, \mathbf{U}(t_a, t_b). \tag{1}$$

The simplest kinds of measurements are those, which are designed to distinguish between various linear subspaces $\mathcal{H}_m$ of $\mathcal{H}$. In fact such an 'idealized' design is too schematical in various aspects and could at best approximately be realized (Wigner 1952). Let us consider the case that the subspaces are orthogonal and complete. Expressed in their projection operators $\mathbf{K}_m$ that means

$$\mathbf{K}_m \,.\, \mathbf{K}_n = \delta_{mn}\, \mathbf{K}_m \,;\, \underset{m}{\boldsymbol{S}}\, \mathbf{K}_m = 1, \tag{2}$$

where $\boldsymbol{S}$ symbolically stands for summation or integration over the discrete or continuous domain of values of m. If all subspaces are 1-dimensional the measurement is said to be maximal, though not everybody does believe it is. The influence of the measuring process on the object system may formally be described by the destruction of coherence between the various subspaces $\mathcal{H}_m$. As according to (2)

$$\mathbf{k} = \underset{mn}{\boldsymbol{S}}\, \mathbf{K}_m \,.\, \mathbf{k} \,.\, \mathbf{K}_n\,, \tag{3}$$

this means that the intervention of the measuring process induces the transformation (Lüders 1951)

$$\mathbf{k} \rightarrow \mathbf{k}' = \underset{m}{\boldsymbol{S}}\, \mathbf{K}_m \,.\, \mathbf{k} \,.\, \mathbf{K}_m = \underset{m}{\boldsymbol{S}}\, \mathrm{tr}(\mathbf{K}_m \,.\, \mathbf{k})\, \frac{\mathbf{K}_m \,.\, \mathbf{k} \,.\, \mathbf{K}_m}{\mathrm{tr}(\mathbf{K}_m \,.\, \mathbf{k})}. \tag{4}$$

For a state with normalized $\mathbf{k}$ we may define the 'degree of mixing' e.g. by

$$M(\mathbf{k}) = -\mathrm{tr}(\mathbf{k} \ln \mathbf{k}) \,, \tag{5}$$

which is positive except for pure states, where it is zero though some people think that even a pure state is a kind of mixture. $M(\mathbf{k})$ remains constant under the transformation of motion (1), but under the transformation of intervention (4) it increases, unless $\mathbf{k} = \mathbf{k}'$, in which case the state and the measurement are said to be perfectly matched. Therefore the intervention of the measuring process in the object system cannot be simply described by the approximation of a motion of the system in an external classical field. This does not mean that quantum mechanics could not account for the destruction of coherence between the distinguished subspaces anyhow. But I cannot account for this most fundamental feature of the measuring process just in this brief talk. It has been touched upon still more briefly in yesterday's discussions. For today it is only in order to divert the suspicion from the observer of personally committing this destructive act, that I shall assume that the result of the measuring process is automatically recorded in a more or less permanent way. For this it is very essential to have a macrophysical recording system (e.g. punched tape or photo emulsion). Further in a way of speaking imagine that every sample $S^{(K,A)}$ is enclosed in a box B, with a window W, which has to be opened in order that the recorded measuring result may be read. After the measuring process is finished and so the result has been recorded, the observer comes into play, opens the window, and reads the record. It is fundamental that the record is not essentially affected by the reading. If the observer reads the result 'm', then he changes the statistical operator assigned to the object system according to the transformation

$$\mathbf{k}' \rightarrow \mathbf{k}''_m \frac{\mathbf{K}_m \,.\, \mathbf{k} \,.\, \mathbf{K}_m}{\mathrm{tr}\,(\mathbf{K}_m \,.\, \mathbf{k})}. \tag{6}$$

The probability that just the result 'm' is found is equal to the weight

$$w_m = \mathrm{tr}(\mathbf{K}_m \,.\, \mathbf{k}) \tag{7}$$

of $\mathbf{k}''_m$ (7) in $\mathbf{k}'_m$ (4). w_m is normalized if $\mathbf{k}$ is normalized, i.e. if $\mathrm{tr}(\mathbf{k}) = 1$.

The transformation (6) of the reading occurs immediately, even if it would be effective over large distances in ordinary 3-dimensional space. But that would not matter even in a relativistic theory because it cannot be connected with transmission of signals. This might suggest that the statistical operator (and the state vector as well) is not an entirely 'objective physical reality'. This by no means implies that it would be an entirely 'subjective mental construction' of the observer. The character of the statistical operator (and the meaning of the quoted terms) have to be analysed more carefully.

There is no common agreement whether quantum description in general may have a meaning already for a single observation of a single event. Almost common agreement might be attained that at least it has a physical meaning for a large number of observations, all on the same object system or a large number of identical ones and all with the same apparatus or a large number of identical ones, the records being read by one or more observers. Identical systems are understood to have the same relevant physical properties. For all these observations the object system and the apparatus should be prepared in a definite way. In practical applications, where observations are actually performed, the probability (7) is in fact used as an approximation (I do not say limit) for the relative frequency in a large number of observations. Thus the operational interpretation of the probability of a measuring result is statistical anyhow. This minimum statistical interpretation, which to a certain extent might be acceptable for almost everyone, is sufficient for the moment. Those who believe that it is non-maximal will no doubt try to go beyond. As far as I see nobody ever succeeded, not even at this symposium.

Formally the statistical interpretation may be more appropriately described in terms of a statistical ensemble (or probability collective) $\mathcal{E}^{(N;\,K,\,A)}$, in which each of the N samples $S^{(K,A)}$ represents a single observation on either the same or an identical object system K with either the same or an identical apparatus A. This only provides a more convenient and precise way of speaking. The ensemble is entirely fictitious and the samples have no mutual physical interaction whatever. I also consider partial ensembles like $\mathcal{E}(N; \mathbf{k})$ in which only the object system K in the state represented by the statistical operator $\mathbf{k}$, but not the apparatus A, is reckoned to belong to the sample $S^{(K)}$. In the statistical interpretation the relative frequency of an event in the ensemble is for a sufficiently large number N of samples approximately given by its probability.

By the transformation of the intervention of the measuring process (4) the partial ensemble $\mathcal{E}(N; \mathbf{k})$ is transformed into $\mathcal{E}(N; \mathbf{k}')$. If thereafter the recorded measuring results 'm' are read on all samples $S^{(K\,A)}$, the partial samples $S^{(K)}$ may according to this labelling be divided into subensembles $\mathcal{E}\,(N_m; \mathbf{k}''_m)$. They are represented by the statistical operators $\mathbf{k}''_m$ resulting from the transformation of reading (6). The number N_m of samples $S^{(K)}$ of the subensemble $\mathcal{E}\,(N_m; \mathbf{k}''_m)$ is for sufficiently large N approximately related with the probability w_m of 'm' (7) by

$$N_m = N w_m\,. \tag{8}$$

So far I have considered a single measurement repeated on all N samples $S^{(K)}$ of the ensemble $\mathcal{E}\,(N; \mathbf{k})$. Merely for sake of brevity I shall speak for the moment as if each intervention of the measuring process in the object system occurs within an infinitely short moment of time. In order to connect observation of physical change and the formal description of dynamical motion in terms of $\mathbf{U}\,(t_b, t_a)$ together, we need two or more measurements on each sample $S^{(K)}$ after certain intervals of time. As for all samples the relative circumstances must be the same, we may by a suitable choice of the zero point of the time scale for each of them say that a corresponding measurement is made at the same time for all of them. If the measurements are preceded by a preparation, that may for the present purpose be considered as a special kind of initial measurement from which a particular measuring result is selected.

So let there at consecutive times $t_1, t_2, \ldots t_s$ with a corresponding series of various apparatus $A_1, A_2, \ldots A_s$ be made a series of measurements, which each distinguish between in general different sets of subspaces $\mathcal{H}_{1,m_1}, \mathcal{H}_{2m_2}, \ldots \mathcal{H}_{s,m_s}$ respectively. Now let us again put every sample $S^{(K,A_1,\,A_2,\,\ldots\,A_s)}$ into a box B with windows W_1, $W_2, \ldots W_s$ which have to be opened in order that the recorded measuring results

'm_1', 'm_2', ... 'm_s' may be read. Say that after all recordings have been made the observer (or a team of them) first opens the set of all windows W_{a_1} and reads the recorded results 'm_{a_1}', then opens the set of all W_{a_2} and reads the recorded 'm_{a_2}' and so on in an order of the measuring times $t_{a_1}, t_{a_2}, \ldots t_{a_s}$, which is an arbitrary permutation of $t_1, t_2, \ldots t_s$. After each jth set of readings he may on the ground of the acquired information about the labelling 'm_{a_j}' make a further selection of the samples $S^{(K)}$ into (sub)^j-ensembles. Except for the trivial case that all measurements are perfectly matched to each other, only the final division into (sub)^s-ensembles will be independent of the permutation.

After the jth set of readings has been performed, someone might be curious about the probabilities of those recordings, which still are stored behind closed windows. All these probabilities may be derived from the 'conditional' probabilities (probabilities are always conditional)

$$w_{m_{a_{j+1}} m_{a_{j+2}} \ldots m_{a_s} / m_{a_1} m_{a_2} \ldots m_{a_j}} = w_{m_1 m_2 \ldots m_s} \Big/ \underset{m_{a_{j+1}}}{\mathbf{S}} \; \underset{m_{a_{j+2}}}{\mathbf{S}} \ldots \underset{m_{a_s}}{\mathbf{S}} \; w_{m_1 m_2 \ldots m_s} \tag{9}$$

that a sample $S^{(K, A_1, A_2, \ldots A_s)}$ which behind the opened windows shows the recordings 'm_{a_1}', 'm_{a_2}', ... 'm_{a_j}' has just '$m_{a_{j+1}}$', '$m_{a_{j+2}}$', ... 'm_{a_s}' recorded behind the remaining windows. $w_{m_1 m_2 \ldots m_s}$ is the (not necessarily normalized) basic probability that for the chosen types of measurements under the fixed conditions of preparation the complete set of recordings is just 'm_1', 'm_2', ... 'm_s'. Since two days ago some of you might perhaps be inclined to speak here of propensity. The theoretician may try to calculate the conditional probabilities (9) in some way or another and the observer may test them by opening the remaining windows and comparing the numbers of samples in the corresponding subensembles.

If in spite of this unpractical and moreover unexciting situation the poor theoretician is expected to act as a practical man, he will no doubt begin by begging the observer to open the windows in the conventional order of $t_1, t_2, \ldots t_s$. Then after having received the information of the first j sets of readings, he would like to be able to assign to the samples labelled 'm_1', 'm_2', ... 'm_j' on the ground of the transformations (1), (4) and (6) a statistical operator

$$\mathbf{k}''_{m_1 m_2 \ldots m_j}(t) = \mathbf{U}(t, t_j) \,.\, \mathbf{K}_{j,m_j} \,.\, \mathbf{U}(t_j, t_{j-1}) \ldots . \mathbf{K}_{1,m_1} \,.\, \mathbf{U}(t_1, t_i) \,.\, \mathbf{k}(t_i) \,.\, \mathbf{U}(t_i, t_1) \,.\, \mathbf{K}_{1,m_1} \ldots . \mathbf{U}(t_{j-1}, t_j) \,.\, \mathbf{K}_{j,m_j} \,.\, \mathbf{U}(t_j, t) \tag{10}$$

valid for the time interval $t_j < t < t_{j+1}$; if he only knew the initial statistical operator $\mathbf{k}(t_i)$ at a time t_i before the first measuring intervention. As the sequence shows regression for non-maximal measurements, (10) essentially depends on $\mathbf{k}(t_i)$. In such cases the most practical auxiliary rule (Elsasser 1937), which actually is a very fundamental statistical 'random' principle, is to take of all statistical operators $\mathbf{k}$, that are consistent with the available information that one for which the degree of mixing $M(\mathbf{k})$ (5) is maximal. For the initial state this gives $\mathbf{k}(t_i) = \mathbf{1}$. Usually this is sufficient. If it might occur that the calculated probabilities would not almost agree with the observed relative frequencies, $\mathbf{k}(t_i)$ could in principle (as long as the processes are within the domain of validity of quantum mechanics) be readjusted so as to bring about agreement. Such a readjustment could formally be represented by a fictitious preparation measurement before the first measuring intervention considered hitherto, but I shall not dwell upon this complication. So for the time interval $t_j < t < t_{j+1}$ the theoretician assigns

$$\mathbf{k}''_{m_1 m_2 \cdots m_j}(t) = \mathbf{U}(t, t_j) \,.\, \mathbf{K}_{j,\, m_j} \,.\, \mathbf{U}(t_j, t_{j-1}) \ldots .\, \mathbf{K}_{2,\, m_2} \,.\, \mathbf{U}(t_2, t_1) \,.\, \mathbf{K}_{1,\, m_1} \,. \\ .\, \mathbf{U}(t_1, t_2) \,.\, \mathbf{K}_{2,\, m_2} \ldots .\, \mathbf{U}(t_{j-1}, t_j) \,.\, \mathbf{K}_{j,\, m_j} \,.\, \mathbf{U}(t_j, t). \tag{11}$$

Then for lack of information about the remaining recordings he derives, merely with the help of the transformations (1) and (4), for a time t_f after the last measuring intervention the statistical operator

$$\mathbf{k}'_{m_1 m_2 \cdots m_j}(t_f) = \underset{m_{j+1}}{\mathbf{S}} \; \underset{m_{j+2}}{\mathbf{S}} \ldots \underset{m_s}{\mathbf{S}} \; \mathbf{U}(t_f, t_s) \,.\, \mathbf{K}_{s, m_s} \,.\, \mathbf{U}(t_s, t_{s-1}) \ldots . \\ .\, \mathbf{K}_{j+1,\, m_{j+1}} \,.\, \mathbf{U}(t_{j+1}, t_j) \,.\, \mathbf{k}''_{m_1 m_2 \cdots m_j}(t_j) \,.\, \mathbf{U}(t_j, t_{j+1}) \,.\, \mathbf{K}_{j+1,\, m_{j+1}} \ldots . \\ .\, \mathbf{U}(t_{s-1}, t_s) \,.\, \mathbf{K}_{s,\, m_s} \,.\, \mathbf{U}(t_s, t_f). \tag{12}$$

From this he finds according to (6) and (7) the conditional probability

$$w m_{j+1} m_{j+2} \cdots m_s / m_1 m_2 \cdots m_j = \mathrm{tr}(\mathbf{K}_{s, m_s} \,.\, \mathbf{U}(t_s, t_{s-1}) \ldots .\, \mathbf{K}_{j+1,\, m_{j+1}} \,. \\ .\, \mathbf{U}(t_{j+1}, t_j) \,.\, \mathbf{k}''_{m_1 m_2 \cdots m_j}(t_j) \,.\, \mathbf{U}(t_j, t_{j+1}) \,.\, \mathbf{K}_{j+1,\, m_{j+1}} \ldots .\, \mathbf{U}(t_{s-1}, t_s) \,)/ \\ \mathrm{tr}(\mathbf{k}''_{m_1 m_2 \cdots m_j}(t) \,) \tag{13}$$

for the set of recordings 'm_{j+1}', 'm_{j+2}', ... 'm_s'.

Granted the validity of simple non-relativistic quantum mechanics within a certain restricted domain of applicability and the schematization of this description of quantum observation, all quantities which may be derived from the theory and tested by observation may be calculated from either the particular or general conditional probabilities (13) or (9) or the unnormalized basic probabilities $w m_1 m_2 \ldots m_s$. Even those, who believe that still other quantities do have some 'objective' physical meaning, might agree that at least the conditional probabilities have an 'objective' statistical physical meaning as an approximation for the relative frequencies of macrophysically recorded measuring results. If so, that will do for the moment.

Now from our lofty position of critical spectators we may either by inserting (11) into (13) or starting from $\mathbf{k}(t_i) = 1$ and using (1), (4), (6) and (7) write the unnormalized basic probabilities as

$$w_{m_1 m_2 \cdots m_s} = \mathrm{tr}(\mathbf{K}_{s, m_s} \,.\, \mathbf{U}(t_s, t_{s-1}) \ldots .\, \mathbf{K}_{2, m_2} \,.\, \mathbf{U}(t_2, t_1) \,.\, \mathbf{K}_{1, m_1} \,. \\ .\, \mathbf{U}(t_1, t_2) \,.\, \mathbf{K}_{2, m_2} \ldots .\, \mathbf{U}(t_{s-1}, t_s) \,). \tag{14}$$

This form is built up merely from unitary operators $\mathbf{U}(t_b, t_a)$ which represent the dynamical motion of the object system and projection operators $\mathbf{K}_m$ which characterize the types of quantum measurements. It does not contain any statistical operator representing some state of the object system. From (14) all observable quantities may be calculated. Formally it represents the quantum mechanical formalism in its most concentrated form. If all the measurements are maximal, the (1-dimensional) projection operators $\mathbf{K}_{j,\ m_j}$ in (14) may be factorized into the corresponding state vectors and their adjoints and only in this case (14) forms a Markoff chain.

No doubt several amongst you do consider this concentrate as extremely poor. So it is. So poor indeed that it not even provides the possibility of introducing a cat-or-whatever paradox. Blessed are the poor in spirit.

The other way round we may, using (9), split up (14) into (11) and (13). In this way a sharp distinction is made between the recordings 'm_1', 'm_2', ... 'm_j' about which information has already been obtained and 'm_{j+1}', 'm_{j+2}', ... 'm_s' about which information has not yet been obtained, but still may be obtained. If we start from the direct relation (14) and then define the statistical operator $\mathbf{k}''_{m_1 m_2 \cdots m_j}(t)$ by (11), it appears as a very efficient auxiliary quantity, which represents the acquired information in its most concentrated form. It may be considered as representing the $(\text{sub})^j$-ensemble of samples $S^{(K)}$, which are selected according to the labelling 'm_1', 'm_2', ... 'm_j'. Under the dynamical motion of the object system it transforms according to (1) and under a measuring intervention according to (4). The probabilities of the recorded measuring results may be derived from (7) and every time new information is obtained from a further reading of recorded results, the statistical operator is reassigned according to (6). There we are back at the starting point, though perhaps a little bit more conscious of the auxiliary character of the statistical operator (and the state vector as well) and its conditional meaning with respect to the assimilated information. Let me just give an unpractical illustration.

(14) is invariant under reversion of the order of $t_1, t_2, \ldots t_s$ into $t_s, t_{s-1}, \ldots t_1$. This is due to the reversibility of the micro-motion represented by the unitarity of $\mathbf{U}(t_b, t_a)$. Now if the observer opens the windows in this reversed order, the theoretician may equally well start with assigning the final statistical operator $\mathbf{k}(t_f) = \mathbf{1}$ and then derive a statistical operator $\mathbf{k}''_{m_s m_{s-1} \cdots m_{j+1}}(t)$ for $t_j < t < t_{j+1}$ and conditional probabilities $w_{m_1 m_2 \cdots m_j / m_{j+1} m_{j+2} \cdots m_s}$. The latter are entirely consistent with those of (13) and they can even be derived from each other. Only the statistical operators are (if not all measurements are perfectly matched to each other and show identical recordings) entirely different from those of (11) for the same time interval. This is, as indicated by the suffixes, because they represent entirely different acquired information. In particular for two successive non-matched maximal measurements at t_j and t_{j+1} the statistical operator assigned for a time t between is $\mathbf{U}(t, t_j) \,.\, \mathbf{K}_{j,\ m_j} \,.\, \mathbf{U}(t_j, t)$ in the original procedure and $\mathbf{U}(t, t_{j+1}) \,.\, \mathbf{K}_{j+1,\ m_{j+1}} \,.\, \mathbf{U}(t_{j+1}, t)$ in the reversed one.

(14) is not invariant under the other permutations of $t_1, t_2, \ldots t_s$. This is in non-relativistic quantum mechanics the rather trivial expression in terms of recorded measuring results of the principle of unidirectional propagation of action in time, which in relativistic field theories (where it is less trivial) nowadays (without philosophical reminiscences) is called the 'causality condition'. Now let the observer for all that open the sets of windows in haphazard order corresponding to an arbitrary permutation $t_{a_1}, t_{a_2}, \ldots t_{a_s}$. The associate theoretician may calculate the conditional probabilities (9) with the help of (14) anyhow. But in this case it is even of no practical use to try to introduce a statistical operator (which would have a remarkably intricate time dependence anyhow), which represents the acquired information

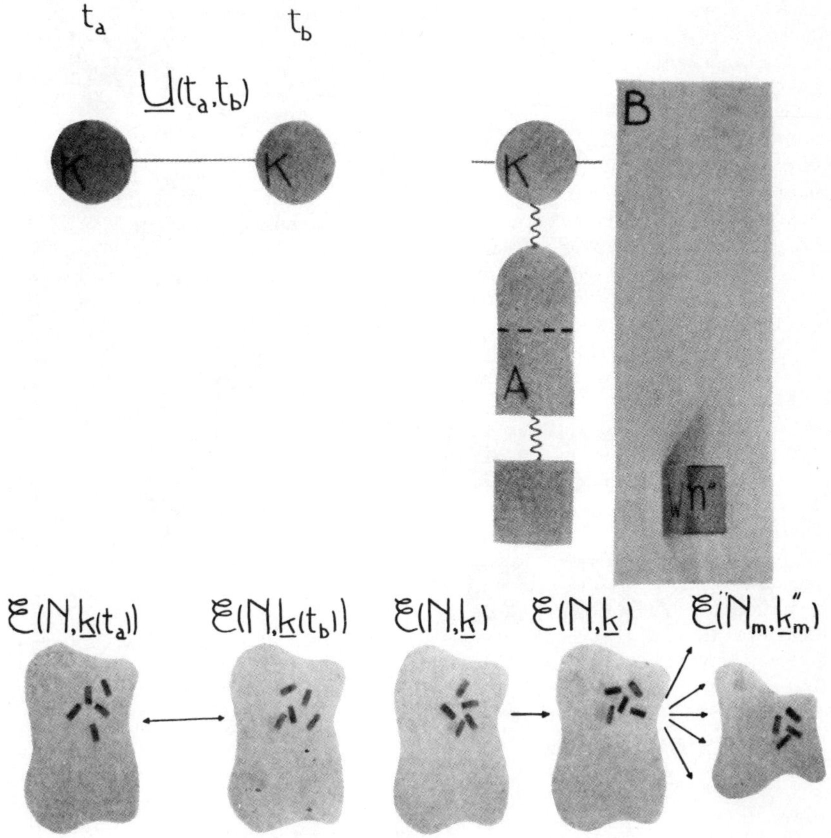

Plate 1

Symbolic illustration of motion (eq. (1)), intervention of the measuring process (eq. (4)) and reading of the recorded measuring result (eq. (6)).

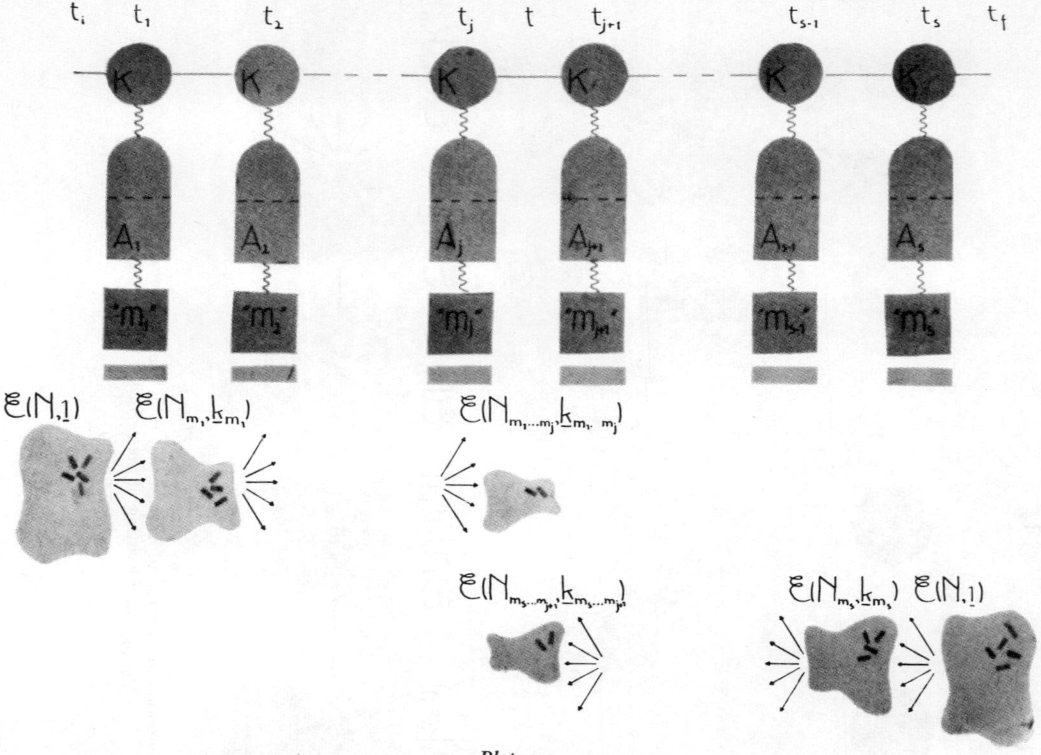

Plate 2.1

Symbolic illustration of a series of various subsequent measurements.

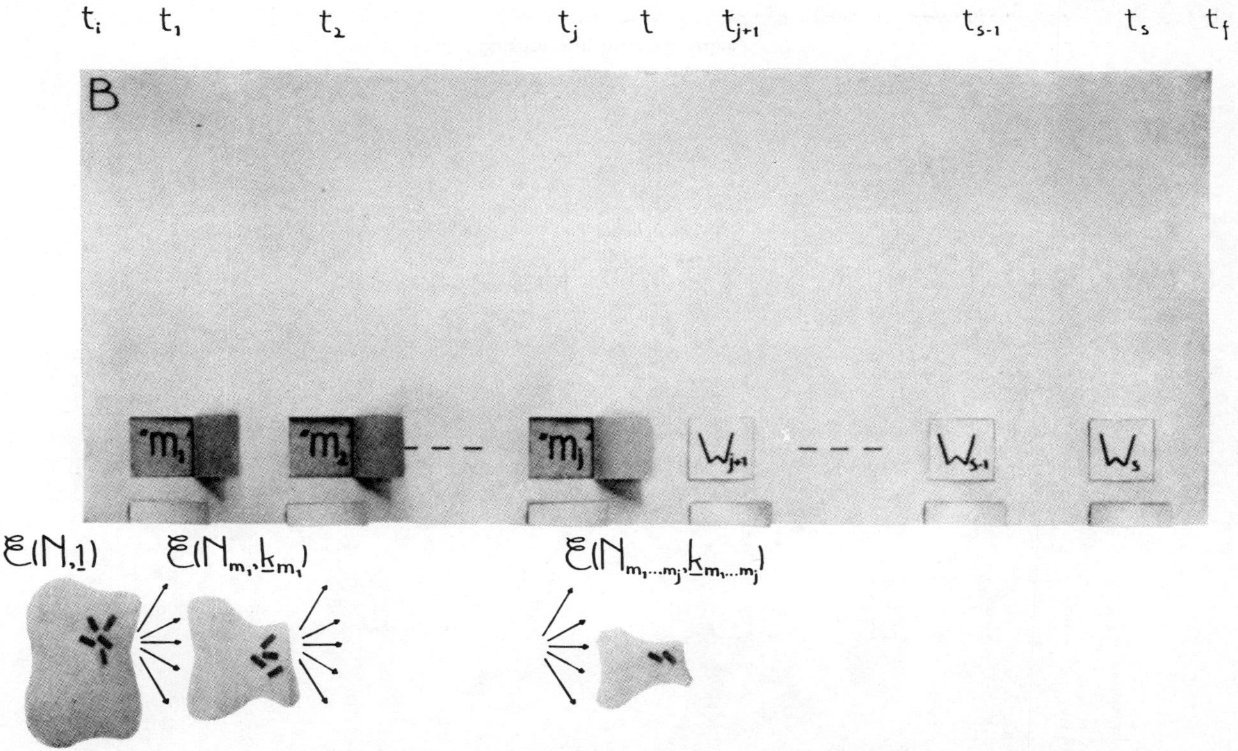

Plate 2.2
Readings in conventional order.

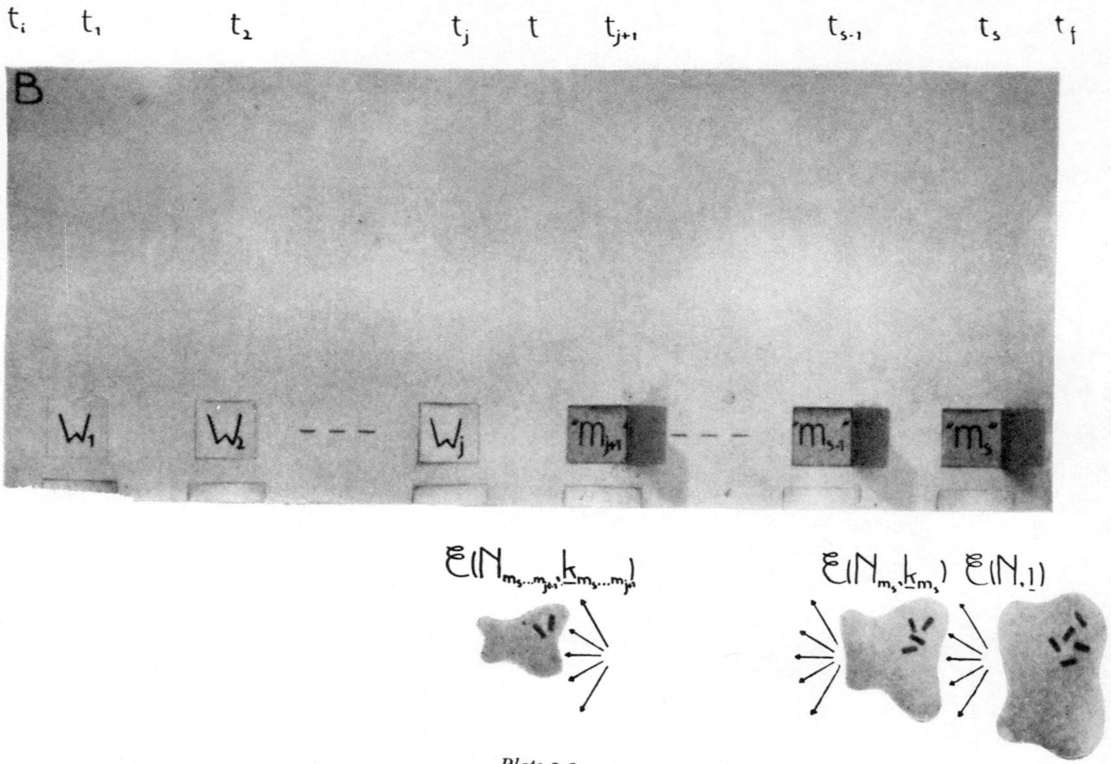

Plate 2.3
Readings in reversed order.

and with the help of which (14) can be split according to the known and unknown '*m*''s.

The way of speaking that the statistical operator (or the state vector) represents the 'quantum state' in which the object system 'is' is (partially because of reminiscences of the classical notion of the state in which a system is) liable to obscure its transient and conditional character. This relative character might even be admitted by some of those, who believe they can go beyond the statistical interpretation but still tolerate it as a consistent interpretation anyhow. The others may really have a hard job to reach anything better than exciting paradoxes.

Now perhaps I ought to point out the objective and subjective aspects. If so, I must apologize. I feel that in my vague and formalistic clumsy scheme with automatically recorded measuring results on one hand and information obtained from their reading on the other hand, with processes of intervention by the measuring apparatus on the one hand and acts of selection by the observer on the other hand and with statistical relations between recordings on the one hand and conditional probability with respect to acquired information on the other hand, I have been less vague and formalistic than for sake of brevity and principle I possibly could have been in the philosophically biassed terms 'objective' and 'subjective'. I leave them for the title only.

Elsasser, W. M., 1937, *Phys. Rev.* **52**, 987
Lüders, G., 1951, *Ann. d. Phys.* **8**, 322.
Wigner, E. P., 1952, *Zs. Phys.* **133**, 101.

Discussion

Fierz. We shall start by discussing Professor Bopp's paper. I have seen his work about a year ago and I want to say that from the mathematical point of view it is quite correct so that one can only discuss whether it is useful or not as a point of view which sheds light on the structure of quantum mechanics.

Rosenfeld. All attempts to give an account of quantum mechanics in terms of statistical ensembles could sooner or later be shown to break down at a certain point. What form does this breakdown take in the case of Bopp's model?

Bopp. This is a mathematical question. Assuming that the distribution function is an essentially positive one, one can say that one of the conditions which cannot be realized is the following one: in this interpretation mean values can be interpreted in the same way as mean values in the usual statistical theory. On the other hand, this theory is mathematically completely equivalent with quantum theory in its usual form and so you can represent mean values also in the usual quantum-mechanical way by forming some traces; hence there must exist correspondences between quantum-mechanical operators and functions of p and q; these correspondences are of the following kind: the operator belonging to the position q is the operator of Schrödinger. The same thing is valid for the momentum. But for the squares the following holds: operator $\underline{q}$ squared in this picture is operator q squared in the Schrödinger picture plus some constant which may be made as small as you want. Operator p squared in this picture is operator p squared in the Schrödinger picture plus a constant which is as large as you want—and the relation is such that Heisenberg's uncertainty principle is satisfied. In order to construct a distribution function in phase space you make any statement on momentum distribution; this statement is a constructed statement which is such that the mean values are the same as usual, whereas the dispersions are much larger within a certain constant; and the meaning is that the momentum in the distribution function is not the momentum you measure.

Rosenfeld. But there I would repeat what I said against Bohm that it is necessary that you make a correspondence between the concepts which are defined in terms of observation, the concepts p and q, and certain variables, which you also call p and q but which are not identifiable with the classical concepts. They are linked by this correspondence to the classical concept, but this link is of an essentially statistical character in order not to contradict the principle of quantization.

Bopp. I don't claim, as the thing stands now, that we have a classical theory—I only claim that it is possible to provide a classical picture of quantum mechanics.

Vigier. If you want to obtain the experimental results of quantum mechanics you have got to take into account the reaction exercised by the apparatus you use on the system you observe. Hence the things which Bohm has called the 'hidden parameters' and which you call 'p' and 'q' behave in such a way that a measurement transforms them into the quantities of quantum mechanics. So basically there is no difference between Professor Bopp's point of view and the point of view we have developed—in both cases we have a picture of sub-quantum mechanical behaviour which when acted upon by the macroscopic apparatus gives you the numerical values obtained by quantum mechanics.

Bopp. I do not introduce hidden parameters because I am studying quantum mechanics as it is. I don't leave the statistical point of view; the question whether it is possible to transform this into a deterministic theory is an altogether different question on which I don't want to say anything at the moment.

Vigier. I think that your ensembles and the Markoff theorem which I have shown the other day are very similar to each other. This random walk of a family of particles, which Bohm and myself have proposed as a possible way of explaining the fundamental statistical behaviour at the quantum level and the quantum numbers, can be represented in phase space, and I don't know whether this random behaviour is going to give you exactly the distribution which you have taken, but it still shows that it is possible to build random ensembles which, whether you take them in phase space or in real space, give you on the average the statistical distribution of quantum mechanics.

Bohm. I read a paper of Professor Bopp's about a year ago. Has the theory which is suggested there been changed since the article was published about a year ago?

Bopp. Yes, and I can say with respect to this point: I have asked myself the question whether it is possible to get stochastic equations which are equivalent to show equations of quantum mechanics in a certain approximation and I succeeded in showing that the differences did not appear before the fourth principle was brought in. The fifth principle could not be satisfied either except in very special cases. Whether or not it can be satisfied in general—this I do not know.

Fierz. Turning to Professor Groenewold's paper, I would like to make a few remarks on the random principle. If you don't know this matrix I think you have no right to make any assumption about it—you can select one of the possible distributions which would give the result and then look at the result and correct accordingly. If, for example, you have a point on a straight line—then there is no *a priori* reason for assuming that the probability of finding the point in a given interval is the same for all intervals. I even think that it is in fact a wrong principle. If you know nothing, you know nothing.

Pryce. But you never know nothing to that extent.

Fierz. No, in fact, I know something and I am guided by the something I know. And in general it is not the random assumption which is the best assumption to make.

Groenewold. If I may start with the last remarks; it is not essential as soon as one of these measurements is maximal. Then from this time on we have all the information that is possible. Now, in case none of the measurements is maximal we can distinguish two extreme cases. In the first case most of the time we know quite a lot about the preparation of a system—this I have called the initial measurement. Of course we do not know quite which operator to use but if we are choosing a certain operator—it doesn't matter which one—and then derive the probabilities from this operator—then, by observing the relative frequencies, we discover whether our choice was appropriate and readjust the operator accordingly; but as I said this is quite a complicated thing—we can account for it by saying that we know more about the initial system and that this knowledge is represented by another still earlier preparation, which also can be taken as a measurement. Now in the case where you have a very complicated system there still remains a great lack of information and one does just the analogue of what is done in thermodynamics in using the Wigner distribution—namely one just chooses the operator in this way and I think this has first been done by Elsasser in the paper which I quoted. Now I don't say that this is a good way to do it. But it turns out that in practice it seems to be the best way one can do it—always better than choosing an arbitrary wave function and calculating from that. Of course one will have to correct it if one gets more information and one will have then to take another operator. But I must stress that one has to do something because otherwise it is completely impossible to calculate these probabilities if there is no maximal measurement in between, and then it is just a practical rule which is an additional rule which does not follow from the other rules of quantum mechanics. It is just a direction for use, which usually turns out to give the best results but need not always do so.

Fierz. I agree to that.

Pryce. I think that I agree with everything—or nearly everything—that Professor Groenewold has said and also I am very thankful to him because it has cleared up a difficulty which I started having this morning when Professor Rosenfeld was talking on the question of the postdiction or retrodiction about the past and prediction about the future and the statement that one frequently makes that the quantum-mechanical measuring process is irreversible, but the sense in which it is irreversible and the sense in which one has to have a time sequence are different. Professor Groenewold has made this very clear by being extremely explicit about this time-sequence in such a way that one could see that one could make statements about the past equally easily as statements about predictions about the future—I think I am not misunderstanding you on that point, although it is hardly an extension of what you said.

Groenewold. That's right. One could say that the processes of the object system along the horizontal lines of the diagrams (Plate 2) are reversible and the irreversibility is along the vertical lines of the measuring devices.

SIR CHARLES DARWIN

Observation and interpretation

Observation and interpretation

by

C. G. DARWIN

THE intention of this address is to explain to you all the outline of the sorts of things that are being discussed at the present meeting of the Colston Research Society. For a great many reasons it is not an easy thing to do. In the first place it is a subject involving a good deal of rather deep philosophy both ancient and modern, and I have no claim to be a philosopher, but only, to use the old term, a Natural Philosopher. I have been listening to discussions among the philosophers, and I have found that they regard as difficult a good many things that have never troubled me, and indeed I come to the conclusion that in some ways the Natural Philosopher, whom we now call physicist, has far fewer troubles than the professional philosopher. No physicist would belittle the enormous difficulties in getting a deep understanding of his subject, but he does seem to have extracted from it new, positive and revolutionary guides to us in our understanding of the world around us. The new outlook, derived from such things as relativity and the quantum theory, seems to me to be a quite fundamental advance, which must have a profound influence on the philosophers, whereas for the most part they seem to be preoccupied with a lot of other difficulties. I ought however to confess that when I reached this conclusion, my satisfaction was marred by a second thought. Might it not be that I was taking up the position like that of the clever adolescent who thinks he knows all about the world, and regards himself as much wiser than his seniors? This may be so, but if it is I can only record that I am quite willing to be an adolescent in this respect.

In reviewing the contributions of the physicists my task has been far easier. I have naturally had to prepare in advance the broad outlines of what I was going to say, and this meant that I had to do it with a knowledge only of the titles they had given for their papers, and without a knowledge of the detail of what they would be saying. This was not so formidable a difficulty as it might appear, because the broad outline of the subject will take me some time to develop, so that it would in any case give me no time to describe the new, more controversial, points that have been under discussion.

The most natural starting point for my subject is the difference between induction and deduction, two terms used in logic. Deduction is the normal process used by the logician; briefly *B* follows out of *A*, and so if *A* is true, *B* must be true. It has its highest development in mathematics, which all comes, or anyhow claims to come, out of a number of axioms; it used I think to be 43 of them, but whether the score is higher or lower now I do not know. But I may quote a comment on the subject made by Russell, who said that the mathematician is not in the least interested in one part of the logical proposition, for he does not care whether *A* is true or not; all he cares about is that if *A* is true—then *B* simply must be true.

Now for all of us in ordinary life the only really interesting thing is to know that A is true, because we have to plan our life accordingly. We form our conduct on our experience, and on the inherited experience we have learnt from our forerunners. From observing various things happening we try to draw universal principles which should tell us that they will happen again. We have seen—or perhaps only been taught—that the path of a projectile is a parabola, and we believe firmly that to-morrow's projectile will also go in a parabola. Indeed we would like to endow this character with the sort of inevitability of deductive logic, but in fact it is quite different. It is *induction* which for my purpose can be described as the forming of universal laws from an inevitably limited amount of experience. Of necessity the experience is always limited—for one thing of necessity it is all in the past—and yet in many cases we believe that the law has the inevitability of logic. In a good many people's minds it is thought of as being a logical process, but it is something quite different. Deduction deals with the proposition: 'If A is true, B follows'. Induction is concerned with the question: Is A likely to be true—and that is entirely different.

I think one could say that the essence of the scientific process is to guess a principle by induction from the observations—which are always necessarily too inadequate to make the principle a certainty—and then to pin one's faith on that guess, and proceed deductively from the principle. This may explain why the scientist is not ashamed when he alters his principles. The politician always lives in fear that someone will remind him of an inconsistency between what he says now and what he said twenty years ago. The scientist does not mind such a charge in the least; indeed he will often regard it as a compliment, because it indicates that his experiments have been improved in their accuracy.

This is all that I shall say about this branch of the subject, and I think I am wise in this, because it has seemed to me that none of the leading philosophers agree about it with one another.

In considering how natural laws can be derived by induction, an important thing to notice is that no observation can ever be exact; it will always be just as precise as the means of measurement allow and no more. This introduces some uncertainty into the verification of the law, which is going to be an important point I shall come to later. This uncertainty calls for consideration of the laws of probability, a subject that has been argued to and fro by philosophers with much the same asperity as induction. I must consider some of its principles.

Instead of starting with a discussion of vague general uncertainties as perhaps strictly I ought, I will begin with the typical action we all at once think of in dealing with probability, the tossing of a coin. We say there is an even chance of heads or tails, and from that alone we can derive a great deal by not very difficult mathematics. The easiest way of thinking about chances is to replace them by frequencies of occurrence. Thus when I say the chance of heads is $\frac{1}{2}$, I mean that if I toss the coin a thousand times I shall expect to get something near five hundred heads—in fact, by counting up the various alternative ways the succession of tosses might go in, we can see that the number of heads is unlikely to be more than about 60 away from the five hundred.

It is curious to speculate why we take the chances of heads or tails as equal, even though it is obviously the common-sense choice to make. I think this can be seen best by considering an actual experiment that was once done. It was felt that it ought to be verified at least once that the accepted probability calculations were correct, and for this purpose a game of dice was used. A die was thrown some 30,000 times. From the experiment it emerged that the face 4 came up just a little more than any other. What inference was drawn? Nobody doubted the laws of probability, but it was simply concluded that there was something wrong with that particular die. The point that this shows is that in any problem of probability there lies at its root what is technically called the *prior probability*, the even chances of heads or tails, or the even chances for the six faces of dice. Once these have been adopted the rest of any problem in probability is a calculation of frequency of occurrence. The mathematics of probability theory mostly consists in calculating these frequencies, but such calculations cannot be done without some sort of basis of equal original chances to start from.

Fortunately for the purposes of the physicist these questions of *prior probability* are often not very difficult, but before coming to physics I will touch for a moment on some of these wider questions. When I say that heads and tails have each the chance $\frac{1}{2}$, I mean that if I toss a thousand times I shall expect to get about 500 heads. But what do I mean when I bet on a horse at 4 to 1 against? Taken on the basis of frequency it ought to mean that if the same horses raced together 100 times, my horse would win about 20 of the races. On the other hand it is perfectly certain that the same horses will not run together a hundred times, so what do I mean in this case by giving a numerical value to the probability? This is a whole subject of study in itself which is closely connected with what is called the problem of inverse probability. Some of the earliest work in it was done about the middle of the eighteenth century by an otherwise unknown Englishman called Bayes. His interest in it arose from thinking about gambling games, and I can illustrate it by a more modern example. In bridge the reward for making a declared slam is very great. I have never seen a correct balance cast up, but if the reward were great enough a point might come where the gain was so much greater than that from other hands, that these other hands would simply not be worth bothering about—the highly skilled player would be only thinking about winning slams or defeating the slams declared by his opponents. In itself this is not a question of inverse probability, but the subject originally arose from Bayes's paper, and it plays a considerable part in modern probability theory. In any problem of inverse probability one knows the frequency with which something happens, and from that one has to derive estimates of the prior probabilities on which it should be based. The subject comes up especially in connexion with many biological problems, because in biology we have no obvious guide as to what are the fundamental equal chances—like the tossed coin—which will determine the prior probabilities. Here however I shall leave this branch of the subject and return to the branch which is more the concern of the physicist.

From the days of Newton till practically the end of the nineteenth century, the science of mechanics was regarded by most people as the science in which one derived exact answers from certain principles, whether it were a matter such as the strength of a bridge, the motion of the parts of an engine, or the orbit of a planet. But about the middle of the nineteenth century Clerk Maxwell and others discovered the kinetic theory of gases. This was certainly a branch of mechanics but it had a very different quality. The idea in this subject is that the molecules of a gas are mechanical bodies perpetually colliding with one another and with the containing walls of the vessel holding them, and the aim of the theory is to explain things like temperature and gas pressure. When a student comes to the subject for the first time he is struck with what a different quality it has from anything in the mechanics he had met before. At first thought he would expect to have to work out elaborately the result of a collision of two molecules, so that, being given their paths of approach, he could answer and say in detail how they would recede from one another after the collision. He is surprised to find that nothing like this is required and that the most general basic principles of mechanics are all that he needs. As he grows in wisdom he gradually realizes that even if the details of the collisions could be accurately solved, they would be no use to him. This is because the number of molecules is so vast that any detailed effects will be smudged out in the enormous averaging that will ensue. However the new subject did demand some form of new principle to base it on, and I must spend a little time describing the various attemps made at getting a deductive basis for gas theory.

In order to justify taking an average of the probabilities of the various states of the gas molecules, there must be an assignment of what I earlier called the prior probabilities. This calls for very deep theory, into which I obviously cannot go, but I can sketch one of the formulations of it. This consists in assuming that the molecules of the gas will, after going through all sorts of interactions, ultimately come back to their original positions. With suitable qualifications it is quite a reasonable thing to believe that they would do so, but with the enormous number of the molecules concerned in any ordinary volume of gas, it would take a fantastically long time before the system actually came back to its starting point.

I can describe this matter by quoting from an example I heard given some years ago in a lecture. If you sit at a typewriter and dab at the keys one after another blindfold you may find by chance that occasionally you have written a real word. If you only do a few dabs you are unlikely to do so, but by the time you have worked at the business for an hour or two it becomes definitely probable that in the untidy mess of what you have written, here and there there will be a real word. The hypothesis needed for the gas theory is equivalent to supposing that an army of monkeys are dabbing at typewriters all the time, and that, if enough of them work long enough, somewhere among their writings there will be found whole sentences, and waiting still a lot longer, it would be found that a whole book had been correctly written by one of them. This is a consequence of pure chance. By applying the strict laws of probability it becomes a practical certainty that, if you waited long enough, in the vast amount of rubbish you would somewhere find that the whole Bible had been written. The only condition is that you must wait long enough, and I can assure you it would be a very, very long time. I once amused myself by seeing how long it might be. I was generous and I did not require that the monkeys should use any capital letters. I took an army of a million monkeys working an eight-hour day, tapping three times a second, and starting 3000 million years ago when the earth first came into existence—of course there were in fact no monkeys till much more modern times, but that does not matter. The first three words of the Bible are (without capitals) 'in the beginning', and I found that even after this immense time and with this immense number of typists, it was no more than about an even chance that these three words would be found somewhere in the texts.

I have described this example because it brings out a difficulty in the argument about the molecules finally returning to their places. They will certainly do so, but only after an absolutely immense time, whereas I can verify the gas laws in a minute or two of time. Most people nowadays therefore take a more useful basis, though it is not so obviously connected with the old mechanics. It was due to the great American physicist Willard Gibbs, and it cannot be proved. He introduced what he called an *ensemble*—from the French word for together, or a group. The ensemble is so to speak a museum full of samples, each of which represents one example of the instantaneous positions of the molecules. The actual gas is one specimen in the museum but, as its molecules move about, it changes into another and then another and so on. But, from what I have said it would take unmeasured ages to go through all the specimens in the museum. Gibbs's assumption is that when we want to know how the gas will behave the answer will come out right if we average over the whole of the ensemble—mathematically an easy thing to do—instead of averaging over the rather few specimens which would correspond to the actual gas at the time it is being studied. This has never been proved according to the rules of the old mechanics, but I think everyone who has studied the subject believes it to be correct.

That is how the matter stood until about 1926 when there was discovered what is known as the New Quantum Theory or the Wave Mechanics. This theory established a synthesis of what up to then had seemed to be two mutually contradictory theories. Up to then it had seemed obvious that things like electrons and atoms were material particles, whereas light and X-rays were waves travelling in a medium which I shall call the aether, though the term has become unfashionable in recent times. The principle which cleared the business up was that in some manner, not clearly understood at first, both atoms and light must each have a dual character showing properties of both particle and wave. The man who started this idea was Louis de Broglie, though in fact he derived much of his work from papers actually written nearly a century earlier by the Irishman Hamilton. Then came the discovery of Schrödinger that by taking certain precise rules for the formulation of a wave equation he could calculate accurately the details of the spectra of the light given out by atoms. There was still a lot of difficulty about the ideas behind this work, but the work gave so much correct information that there never afterwards could be any doubt that it was the beginning of a true theory.

I have been talking about particles and waves, and for those not so familiar with such things I had better describe the characteristic differences between them. I will describe a simplified experiment, so as to see how the differences show themselves. For this I take a wall with a small hole in it. If a particle, say an electron, is shot at this wall from the left-hand side, it may happen to come on a line to the hole and then it will go through to the right-hand side. To see when it has done this I set up a luminous screen made of a special chemical substance which will emit a spark at the place where it is struck by the electron. Since the spark only appears in one place, this seems to show that the electron was a sort of bullet that had gone through the hole. It should be noticed however that the spark will not necessarily be exactly opposite the hole, because if the hole is very small, the bullet can hardly get through and may be knocked off its line by hitting one or other of the sides of the hole as it goes through. A wave behaves quite differently. When the wave comes from the left to the wall all of it is stopped except the part just at the hole, and this spreads out to the right in spherical waves, just as water ripples passing out into a lake from a hole in the bank will travel out in ever-widening circles. The result will be that the whole of the luminous screen will show a faint glow all over it.

Now for the second stage of the experiment I make two holes in the wall a little way apart, and consider what will happen. If I am dealing with a particle, say an electron, it seems obvious that the electron will go through one or other hole and make its spark. But for waves something much more striking will happen. The two ripples will spread out from the holes, but they will *interfere* with one another. This is a technical term, and it means that in some directions the crests coming from both holes will reinforce one another, whereas in other directions they will cancel one another out. The result is that the luminous screen will be crossed by glowing light bands with dark bands in between them.

This is what everyone would have said fifty years ago, but it is changed by the new quantum theory, which is of course confirmed by experiment. This says that both what we used to call particles, and what we used to call waves, possess both properties. If light is sent through the two holes in the wall, it exhibits interference in the sense that there are directions in which the waves cancel one another out, and no light goes in those directions. But in the other directions where the two waves reinforce one another, there is not a steady glow but occasional sparks first in one place and then in another. It would in fact be rather hard to see these sparks for ordinary light, but they could be seen for X-rays, which are much the same thing. These sparks we should certainly regard as characteristics of particles. Even more surprising is the behaviour of an electron, because it is found to do just the same. It produces sparks of course, but none of them come in certain parts of the screen, in fact in the parts where waves going through the two holes would interfere with one another. That can only be explained if each single electron so to speak knows all about both holes simultaneously. It is natural for us to think that when there are two holes the electron must go through one or other of them, but now we can only explain the experimental results by saying that in some fashion it goes through both.

This is of course a much simplified account of what happens, but it has the essence of all the practicable experiments, and it does describe the paradox that in one part of its course the electron seems to be a wave, and yet in another it emits a spark which is typical of a particle. The resolution of this paradox was the formidable task that was set to the exponents of the New Quantum Theory.

One of the most important contributions to the understanding of these difficulties was made by Heisenberg who put forward his Uncertainty Principle not long after the discovery of the Wave Mechanics. To understand the idealized experiment which establishes his principle, it is necessary to know a little about the theory of the microscope and also about a quite different phenomenon known as the Compton effect, and it would take me too long to go into these matters. All that I can do is to give an incomplete idea of it.

Suppose that you want to state accurately where an object lies. Is there any limit to the accuracy that you could attain? There is, but the result is rather unexpected. Suppose the object is lying somewhere on a line and I merely want to be able to say where on the line it is. I should use a foot rule, and see which mark on the rule comes opposite the object. To see exactly I should need to use a microscope and that would lead me into explaining the microscope, a thing I do not propose to do, so I will contrive a way of doing it without the use of light. I will fix the position by using a screw-gauge instead of a foot rule. I screw it along until I suddenly feel, by the extra resistance, that I am pressing on the object, and this tells me its position. But in doing this I have made the assumption that the object will not shift when I touch it, and that will be so if it is heavy. But if the object I am locating is very light, say if it is an electron, my screw-gauge will certainly be a lot heavier than the object it is detecting, and so when it arrives at the electron it cannot help giving it a push. If then the electron was at rest before I got to it, it will get a flip and it will be started moving away by the very act I committed in trying to locate it.

This makes the point that though in ordinary things you can assume that the measuring instrument is so light that it has no effect on the object, in the limit of final precision you cannot overlook the reaction of the measuring instrument on the object. My example of the screw gauge is not good enough to show the peculiar result that does occur, but I am going to ask you to accept Heisenberg's result without explanation. It is that you cannot measure the position, say of an electron, without in the course of the measurement giving it an impulse, and it is an impulse of uncertain amount, that is to say you cannot tell what it will be within certain limits—this is important. Thus the electron will be set in motion by the measurement itself, so that the practical usefulness of the measurement is weakened because all it tells is that the electron *was* there, but not that it will be there if looked for again.

The rule is this. If the position is only measured with rough accuracy, the impulse will be quite small, and so the velocity given to the electron may be negligible, but if high accuracy in position is asked for there is no way of avoiding sending the electron off at a high speed. And I must repeat the point that that speed is not determinate. The rule is that the uncertainty in position, multiplied by the uncertainty in the velocity can never be less than a certain quantity. This quantity is very small, but it is finite, and nothing can reduce it.

The result works either way round. If I make a different kind of experiment in the attempt to measure the speed at which an electron is moving, I cannot at the same time determine exactly where it is, and the more accurately I measure its speed, just so much the less accurately can I determine its position.

There are other things I can measure besides position and speed, for example I might want to measure the time of some occurrence. The general rule is that in mechanics there are conjugate pairs of things, each of which spoils the measurement of the other. One such a pair is position and velocity, though in fact to be precise it is not velocity but the closely related dynamical quantity called momentum, which is the true conjugate to position. Another pair is time and energy, and I can give an example of this which is interesting, by making use of Einstein's result that the mass of a body is really its energy. I therefore say from the Uncertainty Principle that I cannot weigh a body to high accuracy without taking some time to do it. How long will it take?

To see the contrast between what we can do now and the limit of what we might hope for, let us look at a practical case. At the National Physical Laboratory there is what I believe is actually the most precise instrument of any kind for any purpose in the whole world; it is the balance that is used in checking the standards of weight of the pound or the kilogram, which have by Act of Parliament to be reverified every ten years. It can check a weight to one part in a thousand million. To do this the weights are put on the scales and then the door of the room is shut and the balance is left all night so as to settle down to a constant temperature. The weighing done next day takes minutes, and of course is repeated several times. It would be fair to say that even apart from the previous night's settling down, it will take something like an hour to determine the weight accurately to one part in a thousand million. The Uncertainty Principle says that it must *inevitably* take some time to do the weighing to this accuracy, and it gives the answer beyond which it would be impossible in any way to go. The answer for the kilogram weight is about 10^{-42} of a second, that is a millionth of a millionth of a millionth of a . . . seven times over. Evidently we can speed up our processes of weighing quite a lot before coming up against the Uncertainty Principle. The Principle may thus seem to you unimportant, but you ought rather to look at it the other way round, and consider what a wonderful science has been created, when we can with confidence say things about measurements which are so far beyond the actual direct means we have of making them.

The first outcome of the Uncertainty Principle was exciting, because it destroyed the belief we had had in determinism. We always knew that when one calculated the motions of bodies, whether planets at one end or, say, the wind at the other, one could never have the data to start from with perfect accuracy; but we had always felt that this was a mere human weakness in not being able to devise better instruments, and that the bodies were moving inexorably from a definite starting point in an absolutely precise way. It was the predestination of pure mechanics and there seemed no escape from it. Now suddenly we found that the deduction fell down in a respect no one had ever thought of. The starting point may or may not be exact 'really', but it is unknowable, because as soon as we start to measure it, this action itself ensures that the system will start to do something different from what we had intended, and that something is uncertain in amount. It would cost another measurement to determine it, and the second measurement would bring in yet another uncertainty. One will always be one stage behind what one would need for predestination.

I have deliberately used this term predestination with its almost religious meaning, because when the theory was first put forward, some unwise people thought that here was the escape that would clear up the eternal human puzzle about free will. I certainly have no intention to enter that field of discussion, but I would like to insist that it has nothing to do with the subject at all. The behaviour of a single electron may be uncertain because of the principle, the average behaviour of ten electrons is much less so, and by the time you come to a really big body the

Uncertainty Principle plays a quite negligible part. As Eddington magnificently once put it 'You won't hurt the moon by looking at it'.

It was the Uncertainty Principle that gave the key to the difficulty of reconciling the contradictions between wave and particle to which I have referred. The reconciliation was made principally by Niels Bohr, whose name will always rank as the greatest in the development of the new mechanics. He introduced what he called the Principle of Complementarity. You can only know fully the detail of half the things in the world. Every quantity has its complement (also technically called its conjugate); position has velocity as its complement, time has energy and so on. By discussing quite a lot of examples he showed that you could never get experiments which would exactly give both of any pair of them simultaneously, and this means that you can never devise an experiment which will say 'This is a particle and not a wave', or vice versa.

Thus in my example of the electron going through the wall with two holes in it I would say the electron was a particle because I could see the spark. I would then ask the natural question, which of the two holes it went through. I must make a different experiment to test this and the natural one is to set my luminous screen right up against the wall, so as to see by the spark which hole it went through. But by so doing I shall be disturbing its passage through the hole, and that would spoil the interference effects on the other side so that I could not then say it was a wave. I asked it if it was a particle and the answer was 'Yes'. Then I might do another experiment to ask if it was a wave, and again the answer would be 'Yes', but Bohr's point is that they cannot be the same experiment.

For me Bohr's principle is the answer to the whole subject. It was very revolutionary and it calls for difficult thought to follow it through, but it is a self-consistent theory. Briefly to operate it one proceeds like this. Working according to certain well-defined rules, one sets up the equations for a wave system, and one calculates quite exactly and deterministically the progress of the waves in the course of time, but one is not allowed yet to say what 'really' happens. When one wants to know this one makes an *observation*, which tells all the results, but by the very act of observation the system is disturbed, so that it is not possible to follow its further progress, and one must start again from the new data, making it in fact a new system. It is very queer, but I do not think any one has found a fallacy in Bohr's argument, though some of the present discussions show that some people are not satisfied with its finality.

I would also like to refer to one of its deeper aspects. It transforms in a most profitable way the idea I referred to earlier of the *ensemble* of Gibbs. He regarded the actual gas in his vessel as one example of the whole group of possible conditions of the gas molecules. The new principle makes it a much grander idea, because it means that the gas in the vessel is not merely one specimen of the ensemble, it is itself the whole ensemble. In the days of Gibbs physics had not got far enough for him to have dreamt of such a thing, but I like to think that that very great man was struggling towards a greater truth than could be apprehended in his time.

I have spoken long enough and to end I need only say that I have been trying to draw the picture of modern physics, as it is being discussed at this meeting. There are some who try to amplify the principles I have been sketching into directions which will make it easier to follow, and there are some who still deny the validity of Bohr's principle, and still hanker after something like the old determinism. To his dying day Einstein was one of these, and there are many others. If they can succeed they will certainly make it easier for us all to understand intuitively the basic laws of nature, but I can only record my own opinion, that I do not see why nature should have accommodated itself to this human weakness. The past thirty years have been perhaps the greatest age in the development of our understanding of inorganic nature, and I believe that whatever still more wonderful things there may be in store for us to discover, they will come not by reverting to anything like the older views, but by advancing further on the trails that have been laid down by Bohr and his collaborators.

CATALOG OF DOVER BOOKS

BOOKS EXPLAINING SCIENCE AND MATHEMATICS

THE COMMON SENSE OF THE EXACT SCIENCES, W. K. Clifford. Introduction by James Newman, edited by Karl Pearson. For 70 years this has been a guide to classical scientific and mathematical thought. Explains with unusual clarity basic concepts, such as extension of meaning of symbols, characteristics of surface boundaries, properties of plane figures, vectors, Cartesian method of determining position, etc. Long preface by Bertrand Russell. Bibliography of Clifford. Corrected, 130 diagrams redrawn. 249pp. 5⅜ x 8.
T61 Paperbound **$1.60**

SCIENCE THEORY AND MAN, Erwin Schrödinger. This is a complete and unabridged reissue of SCIENCE AND THE HUMAN TEMPERAMENT plus an additional essay: "What is an Elementary Particle?" Nobel Laureate Schrödinger discusses such topics as nature of scientific method, the nature of science, chance and determinism, science and society, conceptual models for physical entities, elementary particles and wave mechanics. Presentation is popular and may be followed by most people with little or no scientific training. "Fine practical preparation for a time when laws of nature, human institutions . . . are undergoing a critical examination without parallel," Waldemar Kaempffert, N. Y. TIMES. 192pp. 5⅜ x 8.
T428 Paperbound **$1.35**

PIONEERS OF SCIENCE, O. Lodge. Eminent scientist-expositor's authoritative, yet elementary survey of great scientific theories. Concentrating on individuals—Copernicus, Brahe, Kepler, Galileo, Descartes, Newton, Laplace, Herschel, Lord Kelvin, and other scientists—the author presents their discoveries in historical order adding biographical material on each man and full, specific explanations of their achievements. The clear and complete treatment of the post-Newtonian astronomers is a feature seldom found in other books on the subject. Index. 120 illustrations. xv + 404pp. 5⅜ x 8. T716 Paperbound **$1.50**

THE EVOLUTION OF SCIENTIFIC THOUGHT FROM NEWTON TO EINSTEIN, A. d'Abro. Einstein's special and general theories of relativity, with their historical implications, are analyzed in non-technical terms. Excellent accounts of the contributions of Newton, Riemann, Weyl, Planck, Eddington, Maxwell, Lorentz and others are treated in terms of space and time, equations of electromagnetics, finiteness of the universe, methodology of science. 21 diagrams. 482pp. 5⅜ x 8. T2 Paperound **$2.00**

THE RISE OF THE NEW PHYSICS, A. d'Abro. A half-million word exposition, formerly titled THE DECLINE OF MECHANISM, for readers not versed in higher mathematics. The only thorough explanation, in everyday language, of the central core of modern mathematical physical theory, treating both classical and modern theoretical physics, and presenting in terms almost anyone can understand the equivalent of 5 years of study of mathematical physics. Scientifically impeccable coverage of mathematical-physical thought from the Newtonian system up through the electronic theories of Dirac and Heisenberg and Fermi's statistics. Combines both history and exposition; provides a broad yet unified and detailed view, with constant comparison of classical and modern views on phenomena and theories. "A must for anyone doing serious study in the physical sciences," JOURNAL OF THE FRANKLIN INSTITUTE. "Extraordinary faculty . . . to explain ideas and theories of theoretical physics in the language of daily life," ISIS. First part of set covers philosophy of science, drawing upon the practice of Newton, Maxwell, Poincaré, Einstein, others, discussing modes of thought, experiment, interpretations of causality, etc. In the second part, 100 pages explain grammar and vocabulary of mathematics, with discussions of functions, groups, series, Fourier series, etc. The remainder is devoted to concrete, detailed coverage of both classical and quantum physics, explaining such topics as analytic mechanics, Hamilton's principle, wave theory of light, electromagnetic waves, groups of transformations, thermodynamics, phase rule, Brownian movement, kinetics, special relativity, Planck's original quantum theory, Bohr's atom, Zeeman effect, Broglie's wave mechanics, Heisenberg's uncertainty, Eigen-values, matrices, scores of other important topics. Discoveries and theories are covered for such men as Alembert, Born, Cantor, Debye, Euler, Foucault, Galois, Gauss, Hadamard, Kelvin, Kepler, Laplace, Maxwell, Pauli, Rayleigh, Volterra, Weyl, Young, more than 180 others. Indexed. 97 illustrations. ix + 982pp. 5⅜ x 8. T3 Volume 1, Paperbound **$2.00**
T4 Volume 2, Paperbound **$2.00**

CONCERNING THE NATURE OF THINGS, Sir William Bragg. Christmas lectures delivered at the Royal Society by Nobel laureate. Why a spinning ball travels in a curved track; how uranium is transmuted to lead, etc. Partial contents: atoms, gases, liquids, crystals, metals, etc. No scientific background needed; wonderful for intelligent child. 32pp. of photos, 57 figures. xii + 232pp. 5⅜ x 8. T31 Paperbound **$1.35**

THE UNIVERSE OF LIGHT, Sir William Bragg. No scientific training needed to read Nobel Prize winner's expansion of his Royal Institute Christmas Lectures. Insight into nature of light, methods and philosophy of science. Explains lenses, reflection, color, resonance, polarization, x-rays, the spectrum, Newton's work with prisms, Huygens' with polarization, Crookes' with cathode ray, etc. Leads into clear statement of 2 major historical theories of light, corpuscle and wave. Dozens of experiments you can do. 199 illus., including 2 full-page color plates. 293pp. 5⅜ x 8. S538 Paperbound **$1.85**

PHYSICS, THE PIONEER SCIENCE, L. W. Taylor. First thorough text to place all important physical phenomena in cultural-historical framework; remains best work of its kind. Exposition of physical laws, theories developed chronologically, with great historical, illustrative experiments diagrammed, described, worked out mathematically. Excellent physics text for self-study as well as class work. Vol. 1: Heat, Sound: motion, acceleration, gravitation, conservation of energy, heat engines, rotation, heat, mechanical energy, etc. 211 illus. 407pp. 5⅜ x 8. Vol. 2: Light, Electricity: images, lenses, prisms, magnetism, Ohm's law, dynamos, telegraph, quantum theory, decline of mechanical view of nature, etc. Bibliography. 13 table appendix. Index. 551 illus. 2 color plates. 508pp. 5⅜ x 8.

Vol. 1 S565 Paperbound **$2.00**
Vol. 2 S566 Paperbound **$2.00**
The set **$4.00**

FROM EUCLID TO EDDINGTON: A STUDY OF THE CONCEPTIONS OF THE EXTERNAL WORLD, Sir Edmund Whittaker. A foremost British scientist traces the development of theories of natural philosophy from the western rediscovery of Euclid to Eddington, Einstein, Dirac, etc. The inadequacy of classical physics is contrasted with present day attempts to understand the physical world through relativity, non-Euclidean geometry, space curvature, wave mechanics, etc. 5 major divisions of examination: Space; Time and Movement; the Concepts of Classical Physics; the Concepts of Quantum Mechanics; the Eddington Universe. 212pp. 5⅜ x 8. T491 Paperbound **$1.35**

THE STORY OF ATOMIC THEORY AND ATOMIC ENERGY, J. G. Feinberg. Wider range of facts on physical theory, cultural implications, than any other similar source. Completely non-technical. Begins with first atomic theory, 600 B.C., goes through A-bomb, developments to 1959. Avogadro, Rutherford, Bohr, Einstein, radioactive decay, binding energy, radiation danger, future benefits of nuclear power, dozens of other topics, told in lively, related, informal manner. Particular stress on European atomic research. "Deserves special mention . . . authoritative," Saturday Review. Formerly "The Atom Story." New chapter to 1959. Index. 34 illustrations. 251pp. 5⅜ x 8. T625 Paperbound **$1.45**

THE STRANGE STORY OF THE QUANTUM, AN ACCOUNT FOR THE GENERAL READER OF THE GROWTH OF IDEAS UNDERLYING OUR PRESENT ATOMIC KNOWLEDGE, B. Hoffmann. Presents lucidly and expertly, with barest amount of mathematics, the problems and theories which led to modern quantum physics. Dr. Hoffmann begins with the closing years of the 19th century, when certain trifling discrepancies were noticed, and with illuminating analogies and examples takes you through the brilliant concepts of Planck, Einstein, Pauli, de Broglie, Bohr, Schroedinger, Heisenberg, Dirac, Sommerfeld, Feynman, etc. This edition includes a new, long postscript carrying the story through 1958. "Of the books attempting an account of the history and contents of our modern atomic physics which have come to my attention, this is the best," H. Margenau, Yale University, in "American Journal of Physics." 32 tables and line illustrations. Index. 275pp. 5⅜ x 8. T518 Paperbound **$1.45**

SPACE AND TIME, Emile Borel. An entirely non-technical introduction to relativity, by world-renowned mathematician, Sorbonne Professor. (Notes on basic mathematics are included separately.) This book has never been surpassed for insight, and extraordinary clarity of thought, as it presents scores of examples, analogies, arguments, illustrations, which explain such topics as: difficulties due to motion; gravitation a force of inertia; geodesic lines; wave-length and difference of phase; x-rays and crystal structure; the special theory of relativity; and much more. Indexes. 4 appendixes. 15 figures. xvi + 243pp. 5⅜ x 8.

T592 Paperbound **$1.45**

THE RESTLESS UNIVERSE, Max Born. New enlarged version of this remarkably readable account by a Nobel laureate. Moving from sub-atomic particles to universe, the author explains in very simple terms the latest theories of wave mechanics. Partial contents: air and its relatives, electrons & ions, waves & particles, electronic structure of the atom, nuclear physics. Nearly 1000 illustrations, including 7 animated sequences. 325pp. 6 x 9.

T412 Paperbound **$2.00**

SOAP SUBBLES, THEIR COLOURS AND THE FORCES WHICH MOULD THEM, C. V. Boys. Only complete edition, half again as much material as any other. Includes Boys' hints on performing his experiments, sources of supply. Dozens of lucid experiments show complexities of liquid films, surface tension, etc. Best treatment ever written. Introduction. 83 illustrations. Color plate. 202pp. 5⅜ x 8. T542 Paperbound **95¢**

SPINNING TOPS AND GYROSCOPIC MOTION, John Perry. Well-known classic of science still unsurpassed for lucid, accurate, delightful exposition. How quasi-rigidity is induced in flexible and fluid bodies by rapid motions; why gyrostat falls, top rises; nature and effect on climatic conditions of earth's precessional movement; effect of internal fluidity on rotating bodies, etc. Appendixes describe practical uses to which gyroscopes have been put in ships, compasses, monorail transportation. 62 figures. 128pp. 5⅜ x 8. T416 Paperbound **$1.00**

MATTER & LIGHT, THE NEW PHYSICS, L. de Broglie. Non-technical papers by a Nobel laureate explain electromagnetic theory, relativity, matter, light and radiation, wave mechanics, quantum physics, philosophy of science. Einstein, Planck, Bohr, others explained so easily that no mathematical training is needed for all but 2 of the 21 chapters. Unabridged. Index. 300pp. 5⅜ x 8. T35 Paperbound **$1.60**

A SURVEY OF PHYSICAL THEORY, Max Planck. One of the greatest scientists of all time, creator of the quantum revolution in physics, writes in non-technical terms of his own discoveries and those of other outstanding creators of modern physics. Planck wrote this book when science had just crossed the threshold of the new physics, and he communicates the excitement felt then as he discusses electromagnetic theories, statistical methods, evolution of the concept of light, a step-by-step description of how he developed his own momentous theory, and many more of the basic ideas behind modern physics. Formerly "A Survey of Physics." Bibliography. Index. 128pp. 5⅜ x 8. S650 Paperbound **$1.15**

THE NATURE OF LIGHT AND COLOUR IN THE OPEN AIR, M. Minnaert. Why is falling snow sometimes black? What causes mirages, the fata morgana, multiple suns and moons in the sky? How are shadows formed? Prof. Minnaert of the University of Utrecht answers these and similar questions in optics, light, colour, for non-specialists. Particularly valuable to nature, science students, painters, photographers. Translated by H. M. Kremer-Priest, K. Jay. 202 illustrations, including 42 photos. xvi + 362pp. 5⅜ x 8. T196 Paperbound **$1.95**

THE STORY OF X-RAYS FROM RONTGEN TO ISOTOPES, A. R. Bleich. Non-technical history of x-rays, their scientific explanation, their applications in medicine, industry, research, and art, and their effect on the individual and his descendants. Includes amusing early reactions to Röntgen's discovery, cancer therapy, detections of art and stamp forgeries, potential risks to patient and operator, etc. Illustrations show x-rays of flower structure, the gall bladder, gears with hidden defects, etc. Original Dover publication. Glossary. Bibliography. Index. 55 photos and figures. xiv + 186pp. 5⅜ x 8. T662 Paperbound **$1.35**

TEACH YOURSELF ELECTRICITY, C. W. Wilman. Electrical resistance, inductance, capacitance, magnets, chemical effects of current, alternating currents, generators and motors, transformers, rectifiers, much more. 230 questions, answers, worked examples. List of units. 115 illus. 194pp. 6⅞ x 4¼. Clothbound **$2.00**

TEACH YOURSELF HEAT ENGINES, E. De Ville. Measurement of heat, development of steam and internal combustion engines, efficiency of an engine, compression-ignition engines, production of steam, the ideal engine, much more. 318 exercises, answers, worked examples. Tables. 76 illus. 220pp. 6⅞ x 4¼. Clothbound **$2.00**

TEACH YOURSELF MECHANICS, P. Abbott. The lever, centre of gravity, parallelogram of force, friction, acceleration, Newton's laws of motion, machines, specific gravity, gas, liquid pressure, much more. 280 problems, solutions. Tables. 163 illus. 271pp. 6⅞ x 4¼. Clothbound **$2.00**

GREAT IDEAS OF MODERN MATHEMATICS: THEIR NATURE AND USE, Jagjit Singh. Reader with only high school math will understand main mathematical ideas of modern physics, astronomy, genetics, psychology, evolution, etc., better than many who use them as tools, but comprehend little of their basic structure. Author uses his wide knowledge of non-mathematical fields in brilliant exposition of differential equations, matrices, group theory, logic, statistics, problems of mathematical foundations, imaginary numbers, vectors, etc. Original publication. 2 appendixes. 2 indexes. 65 illustr. 322pp. 5⅜ x 8. S587 Paperbound **$1.55**

MATHEMATICS IN ACTION, O. G. Sutton. Everyone with a command of high school algebra will find this book one of the finest possible introductions to the application of mathematics to physical theory. Ballistics, numerical analysis, waves and wavelike phenomena, Fourier series, group concepts, fluid flow and aerodynamics, statistical measures, and meteorology are discussed with unusual clarity. Some calculus and differential equations theory is developed by the author for the reader's help in the more difficult sections. 88 figures. Index. viii + 236pp. 5⅜ x 8. T440 Clothbound **$3.50**

FREE! All you do is ask for it!

A DOVER SCIENCE SAMPLER, edited by George Barkin. 64-page book, sturdily bound, containing excerpts from over 20 Dover books explaining science. Edwin Hubble, George Sarton, Ernst Mach, A. d'Abro, Galileo, Newton, others, discussing island universes, scientific truth, biological phenomena, stability in bridges, etc. Copies limited, no more than 1 to a customer. FREE

THE FOURTH DIMENSION SIMPLY EXPLAINED, edited by H. P. Manning. 22 essays, originally Scientific American contest entries, that use a minimum of mathematics to explain aspects of 4-dimensional geometry: analogues to 3-dimensional space, 4-dimensional absurdities and curiosities (such as removing the contents of an egg without puncturing its shell), possible measurements and forms, etc. Introduction by the editor. Only book of its sort on a truly elementary level, excellent introduction to advanced works. 82 figures. 251pp. 5⅜ x 8. T711 Paperbound **$1.35**

FAMOUS BRIDGES OF THE WORLD, D. B. Steinman. An up-to-the-minute revised edition of a book that explains the fascinating drama of how the world's great bridges came to be built. The author, designer of the famed Mackinac bridge, discusses bridges from all periods and all parts of the world, explaining their various types of construction, and describing the problems their builders faced. Although primarily for youngsters, this cannot fail to interest readers of all ages. 48 illustrations in the text. 23 photographs. 99pp. 6⅛ x 9¼. T161 Paperbound **$1.00**

BRIDGES AND THEIR BUILDERS, David Steinman and Sara Ruth Watson. Engineers, historians, everyone who has ever been fascinated by great spans will find this book an endless source of information and interest. Dr. Steinman, recipient of the Louis Levy medal, was one of the great bridge architects and engineers of all time, and his analysis of the great bridges of history is both authoritative and easily followed. Greek and Roman bridges, medieval bridges, Oriental bridges, modern works such as the Brooklyn Bridge and the Golden Gate Bridge, and many others are described in terms of history, constructional principles, artistry, and function. All in all this book is the most comprehensive and accurate semipopular history of bridges in print in English. New, greatly revised, enlarged edition. 23 photographs, 26 line drawings. Index. xvii + 401pp. 5⅜ x 8. T431 Paperbound **$2.00**

FADS AND FALLACIES IN THE NAME OF SCIENCE, Martin Gardner. Examines various cults, quack systems, frauds, delusions which at various times have masqueraded as science. Accounts of hollow-earth fanatics like Symmes; Velikovsky and wandering planets; Hoerbiger; Bellamy and the theory of multiple moons; Charles Fort; dowsing, pseudoscientific methods for finding water, ores, oil. Sections on naturopathy, iridiagnosis, zone therapy, food fads, etc. Analytical accounts of Wilhelm Reich and orgone sex energy; L. Ron Hubbard and Dianetics; A. Korzybski and General Semantics; many others. Brought up to date to include Bridey Murphy, others. Not just a collection of anecdotes, but a fair, reasoned appraisal of eccentric theory. Formerly titled IN THE NAME OF SCIENCE. Preface. Index. x + 384pp. 5⅜ x 8. T394 Paperbound **$1.50**

See also: **A PHILOSOPHICAL ESSAY ON PROBABILITIES, P. de Laplace; ON MATHEMATICS AND MATHEMATICIANS, R. E. Moritz; AN ELEMENTARY SURVEY OF CELESTIAL MECHANICS, Y. Ryabov; THE SKY AND ITS MYSTERIES, E. A. Beet; THE REALM OF THE NEBULAE, E. Hubble; OUT OF THE SKY, H. H. Nininger; SATELLITES AND SCIENTIFIC RESEARCH, D. King-Hele; HEREDITY AND YOUR LIFE, A. M. Winchester; INSECTS AND INSECT LIFE, S. W. Frost; PRINCIPLES OF STRATIGRAPHY, A. W. Grabau; TEACH YOURSELF SERIES.**

HISTORY OF SCIENCE AND MATHEMATICS

DIALOGUES CONCERNING TWO NEW SCIENCES, Galileo Galilei. This classic of experimental science, mechanics, engineering, is as enjoyable as it is important. A great historical document giving insights into one of the world's most original thinkers, it is based on 30 years' experimentation. It offers a lively exposition of dynamics, elasticity, sound, ballistics, strength of materials, the scientific method. "Superior to everything else of mine," Galileo. Trans. by H. Crew, A. Salvio. 126 diagrams. Index. xxi + 288pp. 5⅜ x 8.
S99 Paperbound **$1.65**

A DIDEROT PICTORIAL ENCYCLOPEDIA OF TRADES AND INDUSTRY, Manufacturing and the Technical Arts in Plates Selected from "L'Encyclopédie ou Dictionnaire Raisonné des Sciences, des Arts, et des Métiers" of Denis Diderot. Edited with text by C. Gillispie. This first modern selection of plates from the high point of 18th century French engraving is a storehouse of valuable technological information to the historian of arts and science. Over 2000 illustrations on 485 full page plates, most of them original size, show the trades and industries of a fascinating era in such great detail that the processes and shops might very well be reconstructed from them. The plates teem with life, with men, women, and children performing all of the thousands of operations necessary to the trades before and during the early stages of the industrial revolution. Plates are in sequence, and show general operations, closeups of difficult operations, and details of complex machinery. Such important and interesting trades and industries are illustrated as sowing, harvesting, beekeeping, cheesemaking, operating windmills, milling flour, charcoal burning, tobacco processing, indigo, fishing, arts of war, salt extraction, mining, smelting, casting iron, steel, extracting mercury, zinc, sulphur, copper, etc., slating, tinning, silverplating, gilding, making gunpowder, cannons, bells, shoeing horses, tanning, papermaking, printing, dyeing, and more than 40 other categories. Professor Gillispie, of Princeton, supplies a full commentary on all the plates, identifying operations, tools, processes, etc. This material, presented in a lively and lucid fashion, is of great interest to the reader interested in history of science and technology. Heavy library cloth. 920pp. 9 x 12. T421 Two volume set **$18.50**

DE MAGNETE, William Gilbert. This classic work on magnetism founded a new science. Gilbert was the first to use the word "electricity", to recognize mass as distinct from weight, to discover the effect of heat on magnetic bodies; invent an electroscope, differentiate between static electricity and magnetism, conceive of the earth as a magnet. Written by the first great experimental scientist, this lively work is valuable not only as an historical landmark, but as the delightfully easy to follow record of a perpetually searching, ingenious mind. Translated by P. F. Mottelay. 25 page biographical memoir. 90 figures. lix + 368pp. 5⅜ x 8. S470 Paperbound **$2.00**

CHARLES BABBAGE AND HIS CALCULATING ENGINES, edited by P. Morrison and E. Morrison. Babbage, leading 19th century pioneer in mathematical machines and herald of modern operational research, was the true father of Harvard's relay computer Mark I. His Difference Engine and Analytical Engine were the first machines in the field. This volume contains a valuable introduction on his life and work; major excerpts from his autobiography, revealing his eccentric and unusual personality; and extensive selections from "Babbage's Calculating Engines," a compilation of hard-to-find journal articles by Babbage, the Countess of Lovelace, L. F. Menabrea, and Dionysius Lardner. 8 illustrations, Appendix of miscellaneous papers. Index. Bibliography. xxxviii + 400pp. 5⅜ x 8. T12 Paperbound **$2.00**

A HISTORY OF ASTRONOMY FROM THALES TO KEPLER, J. L. E. Dreyer. (Formerly A HISTORY OF PLANETARY SYSTEMS FROM THALES TO KEPLER.) This is the only work in English to give the complete history of man's cosmological views from prehistoric times to Kepler and Newton. Partial contents: Near Eastern astronomical systems, Early Greeks, Homocentric Spheres of Eudoxus, Epicycles, Ptolemaic system, medieval cosmology, Copernicus, Kepler, etc. Revised, foreword by W. H. Stahl. New bibliography. xvii + 430pp. 5⅜ x 8. S79 Paperbound **$1.98**

A SHORT HISTORY OF ANATOMY AND PHYSIOLOGY FROM THE GREEKS TO HARVEY, Charles Singer. Corrected edition of THE EVOLUTION OF ANATOMY, classic work tracing evolution of anatomy and physiology from prescientific times through Greek & Roman periods, Dark Ages, Renaissance, to age of Harvey and beginning of modern concepts. Centered on individuals, movements, periods that definitely advanced anatomical knowledge: Plato, Diocles, Aristotle, Theophrastus, Herophilus, Erasistratus, the Alexandrians, Galen, Mondino, da Vinci, Linacre, Sylvius, others. Special section on Vesalius; Vesalian atlas of nudes, skeletons, muscle tabulae. Index of names, 20 plates. 270 extremely interesting illustrations of ancient, medieval, Renaissance, Oriental origin. xii + 209pp. 5⅜ x 8. T389 Paperbound **$1.75**

FROM MAGIC TO SCIENCE, Charles Singer. A great historian examines aspects of medical science from the Roman Empire through the Renaissance. Includes perhaps the best discussion of early herbals, and a penetrating physiological interpretation of "The Visions of Hildegarde of Bingen." Also examined are Arabian and Galenic influences; the Sphere of Pythagoras; Paracelsus; the reawakening of science under Leonardo da Vinci, Vesalius; the Lorica of Gildas the Briton; etc. Frequent quotations with translations. New Introduction by the author. New unabridged, corrected edition. 158 unusual illustrations from classical and medieval sources. Index. xxvii + 365pp. 5⅜ x 8. T390 Paperbound **$2.00**

HISTORY OF MATHEMATICS, D. E. Smith. Most comprehensive non-technical history of math in English. Discusses lives and works of over a thousand major and minor figures, with footnotes supplying technical information outside the book's scheme, and indicating disputed matters. Vol I: A chronological examination, from primitive concepts through Egypt, Babylonia, Greece, the Orient, Rome, the Middle Ages, the Renaissance, and up to 1900. Vol 2: The development of ideas in specific fields and problems, up through elementary calculus. Two volumes, total of 510 illustrations, 1355pp. 5⅜ x 8. Set boxed in attractive container. T429, 430 Paperbound, the set **$5.00**

A SHORT ACCOUNT OF THE HISTORY OF MATHEMATICS, W. W. R. Ball. Most readable non-technical history of mathematics treats lives, discoveries of every important figure from Egyptian, Phoenician mathematicians to late 19th century. Discusses schools of Ionia, Pythagoras, Athens, Cyzicus, Alexandria, Byzantium, systems of numeration; primitive arithmetic; Middle Ages, Renaissance, including Arabs, Bacon, Regiomontanus, Tartaglia, Cardan, Stevinus, Galileo, Kepler; modern mathematics of Descartes, Pascal, Wallis, Huygens, Newton, Leibnitz, d'Alembert, Euler, Lambert, Laplace, Legendre, Gauss, Hermite, Weierstrass, scores more. Index. 25 figures. 546pp. 5⅜ x 8. S630 Paperbound **$2.00**

A SOURCE BOOK IN MATHEMATICS, D. E. Smith. Great discoveries in math, from Renaissance to end of 19th century, in English translation. Read announcements by Dedekind, Gauss, Delamain, Pascal, Fermat, Newton, Abel, Lobachevsky, Bolyai, Riemann, De Moivre, Legendre, Laplace, others of discoveries about imaginary numbers, number congruence, slide rule, equations, symbolism, cubic algebraic equations, non-Euclidean forms of geometry, calculus, function theory, quaternions, etc. Succinct selections from 125 different treatises, articles, most unavailable elsewhere in English. Each article preceded by biographical, historical introduction. Vol. I: Fields of Number, Algebra. Index. 32 illus. 338pp. 5⅜ x 8. Vol. II: Fields of Geometry, Probability, Calculus, Functions, Quaternions. 83 illus. 432pp. 5⅜ x 8.
Vol. 1: S552 Paperbound **$1.85**
Vol. 2: S553 Paperbound **$1.85**
2 vol. set, boxed **$3.50**

A HISTORY OF THE CALCULUS, AND ITS CONCEPTUAL DEVELOPMENT, Carl B. Boyer. Provides laymen and mathematicians a detailed history of the development of the calculus, from early beginning in antiquity to final elaboration as mathematical abstractions. Gives a sense of mathematics not as a technique, but as a habit of mind, in the progression of ideas of Zeno, Plato, Pythagoras, Eudoxus, Arabic and Scholastic mathematicians, Newton, Leibnitz, Taylor, Descartes, Euler, Lagrange, Cantor, Weierstrass, and others. This first comprehensive critical history of the calculus was originally titled "The Concepts of the Calculus." Foreword by R. Courant. Preface. 22 figures. 25-page bibliography. Index. v + 364pp. 5⅜ x 8. S509 Paperbound **$2.00**

A CONCISE HISTORY OF MATHEMATICS, D. Struik. Lucid study of development of mathematical ideas, techniques from Ancient Near East, Greece, Islamic science, Middle Ages, Renaissance, modern times. Important mathematicians are described in detail. Treatment is not anecdotal, but analytical development of ideas. "Rich in content, thoughtful in interpretation," U.S. QUARTERLY BOOKLIST. Non-technical; no mathematical training needed. Index. 60 illustrations, including Egyptian papyri, Greek mss., portraits of 31 eminent mathematicians. Bibliography. 2nd edition. xix + 299pp. 5⅜ x 8. T255 Paperbound **$1.75**

See also: **NON-EUCLIDEAN GEOMETRY, R. Bonola; THEORY OF DETERMINANTS IN HISTORICAL ORDER OF DEVELOPMENT, T. Muir; HISTORY OF THE THEORY OF ELASTICITY AND STRENGTH OF MATERIALS, I. Todhunter and K. Pearson; A SHORT HISTORY OF ASTRONOMY, A. Berry; CLASSICS OF SCIENCE.**

PHILOSOPHY OF SCIENCE AND MATHEMATICS

FOUNDATIONS OF SCIENCE: THE PHILOSOPHY OF THEORY AND EXPERIMENT, N. R. Campbell. A critique of the most fundamental concepts of science in general and physics in particular. Examines why certain propositions are accepted without question, demarcates science from philosophy, clarifies the understanding of the tools of science. Part One analyzes the presuppositions of scientific thought: existence of the material world, nature of scientific laws, multiplication of probabilities, etc.: Part Two covers the nature of experiment and the application of mathematics: conditions for measurement, relations between numerical laws and theories, laws of error, etc. An appendix covers problems arising from relativity, force, motion, space, and time. A classic in its field. Index. xiii + 565pp. 5⅝ x 8⅜. S372 Paperbound **$2.95**

WHAT IS SCIENCE?, Norman Campbell. This excellent introduction explains scientific method, role of mathematics, types of scientific laws. Contents: 2 aspects of science, science & nature, laws of science, discovery of laws, explanation of laws, measurement & numerical laws, applications of science. 192pp. 5⅜ x 8. S43 Paperbound **$1.25**

THE VALUE OF SCIENCE, Henri Poincaré. Many of the most mature ideas of the "last scientific universalist" covered with charm and vigor for both the beginning student and the advanced worker. Discusses the nature of scientific truth, whether order is innate in the universe or imposed upon it by man, logical thought versus intuition (relating to math, through the works of Weierstrass, Lie, Klein, Riemann), time and space (relativity, psychological time, simultaneity), Hertz's concept of force, interrelationship of mathematical physics to pure math, values within disciplines of Maxwell, Carnot, Mayer, Newton, Lorentz, etc. Index. iii + 147pp. 5⅜ x 8. S469 Paperbound **$1.35**

SCIENCE AND METHOD, Henri Poincaré. Procedure of scientific discovery, methodology, experiment, idea-germination—the intellectual processes by which discoveries come into being. Most significant and most interesting aspects of development, application of ideas. Chapters cover selection of facts, chance, mathematical reasoning, mathematics, and logic; Whitehead, Russell, Cantor; the new mechanics, etc. 288pp. 5⅜ x 8. S222 Paperbound **$1.35**

SCIENCE AND HYPOTHESIS, Henri Poincaré. Creative psychology in science. How such concepts as number, magnitude, space, force, classical mechanics were developed, and how the modern scientist uses them in his thought. Hypothesis in physics, theories of modern physics. Introduction by Sir James Larmor. "Few mathematicians have had the breadth of vision of Poincaré, and none is his superior in the gift of clear exposition," E. T. Bell. Index. 272pp. 5⅜ x 8. S221 Paperbound **$1.35**

PHILOSOPHY AND THE PHYSICISTS, L. S. Stebbing. The philosophical aspects of modern science examined in terms of a lively critical attack on the ideas of Jeans and Eddington. Discusses the task of science, causality, determinism, probability, consciousness, the relation of the world of physics to that of everyday experience. Probes the philosophical significance of the Planck-Bohr concept of discontinuous energy levels, the inferences to be drawn from Heisenberg's Uncertainty Principle, the implications of "becoming" involved in the 2nd law of thermodynamics, and other problems posed by the discarding of Laplacean determinism. 285pp. 5⅜ x 8. T480 Paperbound **$1.65**

EXPERIMENT AND THEORY IN PHYSICS, Max Born. A Nobel laureate examines the nature and value of the counterclaims of experiment and theory in physics. Synthetic versus analytical scientific advances are analyzed in the work of Einstein, Bohr, Heisenberg, Planck, Eddington, Milne, and others by a fellow participant. 44pp. 5⅜ x 8. S308 Paperbound **60¢**

THE NATURE OF PHYSICAL THEORY, P. W. Bridgman. Here is how modern physics looks to a highly unorthodox physicist—a Nobel laureate. Pointing out many absurdities of science, and demonstrating the inadequacies of various physical theories, Dr. Bridgman weighs and analyzes the contributions of Einstein, Bohr, Newton, Heisenberg, and many others. This is a non-technical consideration of the correlation of science and reality. Index. xi + 138pp. 5⅜ x 8. S33 Paperbound **$1.25**

THE PHILOSOPHY OF SPACE AND TIME, H. Reichenbach. An important landmark in the development of the empiricist conception of geometry, covering the problem of the foundations of geometry, the theory of time, the consequences of Einstein's relativity, including: relations between theory and observations; coordinate and metrical properties of space; the psychological problem of visual intuition of non-Euclidean structures; and many other important topics in modern science and philosophy. The majority of ideas require only a knowledge of intermediate math. Introduction by R. Carnap. 49 figures. Index. xviii + 296pp. 5⅜ x 8. S443 Paperbound **$2.00**

MATTER & MOTION, James Clerk Maxwell, This excellent exposition begins with simple particles and proceeds gradually to physical systems beyond complete analysis: motion, force, properties of centre of mass of material system, work, energy, gravitation, etc. Written with all Maxwell's original insights and clarity. Notes by E. Larmor. 17 diagrams. 178pp. 5⅜ x 8. S188 Paperbound **$1.35**

THE ANALYSIS OF MATTER, Bertrand Russell. How do our senses concord with the new physics? This volume covers such topics as logical analysis of physics, prerelativity physics, causality, scientific inference, physics and perception, special and general relativity, Weyl's theory, tensors, invariants and their physical interpretation, periodicity and qualitative series. "The most thorough treatment of the subject that has yet been published," THE NATION. Introduction by L. E. Denonn. 422pp. 5⅜ x 8. T231 Paperbound **$1.95**

SUBSTANCE AND FUNCTION, & EINSTEIN'S THEORY OF RELATIVITY, Ernst Cassirer. Two books bound as one. Cassirer establishes a philosophy of the exact sciences that takes into consideration newer developments in mathematics, and also shows historical connections. Partial contents: Aristotelian logic, Mill's analysis, Helmholtz & Kronecker, Russell & cardinal numbers, Euclidean vs. non-Euclidean geometry, Einstein's relativity. Bibliography. Index. xxi + 465pp. 5⅜ x 8. T50 Paperbound **$2.00**

PRINCIPLES OF MECHANICS, Heinrich Hertz. This last work by the great 19th century physicist is not only a classic, but of great interest in the logic of science. Creating a new system of mechanics based upon space, time, and mass, it returns to axiomatic analysis, to understanding of the formal or structural aspects of science, taking into account logic, observation, and a priori elements. Of great historical importance to Poincaré, Carnap, Einstein, Milne. A 20-page introduction by R. S. Cohen, Wesleyan University, analyzes the implications of Hertz's thought and the logic of science. Bibliography. 13-page introduction by Helmholtz. xlii + 274pp. 5⅜ x 8. S316 Clothbound **$3.50**
S317 Paperbound **$1.85**

THE PHILOSOPHICAL WRITINGS OF PEIRCE, edited by Justus Buchler. (Formerly published as THE PHILOSOPHY OF PEIRCE.) This is a carefully balanced exposition of Peirce's complete system, written by Peirce himself. It covers such matters as scientific method, pure chance vs. law, symbolic logic, theory of signs, pragmatism, experiment, and other topics. Introduction by Justus Buchler, Columbia University. xvi + 368pp. 5⅜ x 8. T217 Paperbound **$1.95**

ESSAYS IN EXPERIMENTAL LOGIC, John Dewey. This stimulating series of essays touches upon the relationship between inquiry and experience, dependence of knowledge upon thought, character of logic; judgments of practice, data and meanings, stimuli of thought, etc. Index. viii + 444pp. 5⅜ x 8. T73 Paperbound **$1.95**

LANGUAGE, TRUTH AND LOGIC, A. Ayer. A clear introduction to the Vienna and Cambridge schools of Logical Positivism. It sets up specific tests by which you can evaluate validity of ideas, etc. Contents: Function of philosophy, elimination of metaphysics, nature of analysis, a priori, truth and probability, etc. 10th printing. "I should like to have written it myself," Bertrand Russell. Index. 160pp. 5⅜ x 8. T10 Paperbound **$1.25**

THE PSYCHOLOGY OF INVENTION IN THE MATHEMATICAL FIELD, J. Hadamard. Where do ideas come from? What role does the unconscious play? Are ideas best developed by mathematical reasoning, word reasoning, visualization? What are the methods used by Einstein, Poincaré, Galton, Riemann? How can these techniques be applied by others? Hadamard, one of the world's leading mathematicians, discusses these and other questions. xiii + 145pp. 5⅜ x 8. T107 Paperbound **$1.25**

FOUNDATIONS OF GEOMETRY, Bertrand Russell. Analyzing basic problems in the overlap area between mathematics and philosophy, Nobel laureate Russell examines the nature of geometrical knowledge, the nature of geometry, and the application of geometry to space. It covers the history of non-Euclidean geometry, philosophic interpretations of geometry—especially Kant—projective and metrical geometry. This is most interesting as the solution offered in 1897 by a great mind to a problem still current. New introduction by Prof. Morris Kline of N. Y. University. xii + 201pp. 5⅜ x 8. S232 Clothbound **$3.25**
S233 Paperbound **$1.60**

Relativity, quantum theory, nuclear physics

THE PRINCIPLE OF RELATIVITY, A. Einstein, H. Lorentz, M. Minkowski, H. Weyl. These are the 11 basic papers that founded the general and special theories of relativity, all translated into English. Two papers by Lorentz on the Michelson experiment, electromagnetic phenomena. Minkowski's SPACE & TIME, and Weyl's GRAVITATION & ELECTRICITY. 7 epoch-making papers by Einstein: ELECTROMAGNETICS OF MOVING BODIES, INFLUENCE OF GRAVITATION IN PROPAGATION OF LIGHT, COSMOLOGICAL CONSIDERATIONS, GENERAL THEORY, and 3 others. 7 diagrams. Special notes by A. Sommerfeld. 224pp. 5⅜ x 8.
S81 Paperbound **$1.75**

SPACE TIME MATTER, Hermann Weyl. "The standard treatise on the general theory of relativity," (Nature), written by a world-renowned scientist, provides a deep clear discussion of the logical coherence of the general theory, with introduction to all the mathematical tools needed: Maxwell, analytical geometry, non-Euclidean geometry, tensor calculus, etc. Basis is classical space-time, before absorption of relativity. Partial contents: Euclidean space, mathematical form, metrical continuum, relativity of time and space, general theory. 15 diagrams. Bibliography. New preface for this edition. xviii + 330pp. 5⅜ x 8.
S267 Paperbound **$1.85**

PRINCIPLES OF QUANTUM MECHANICS, W. V. Houston. Enables student with working knowledge of elementary mathematical physics to develop facility in use of quantum mechanics, understand published work in field. Formulates quantum mechanics in terms of Schroedinger's wave mechanics. Studies evidence for quantum theory, for inadequacy of classical mechanics, 2 postulates of quantum mechanics; numerous important, fruitful applications of quantum mechanics in spectroscopy, collision problems, electrons in solids; other topics. "One of the most rewarding features . . . is the interlacing of problems with text," Amer. J. of Physics. Corrected edition. 21 illus. Index. 296pp. 5⅜ x 8. S524 Paperbound **$1.85**

PHYSICAL PRINCIPLES OF THE QUANTUM THEORY, Werner Heisenberg. A Nobel laureate discusses quantum theory; Heisenberg's own work, Compton, Schroedinger, Wilson, Einstein, many others. Written for physicists, chemists who are not specialists in quantum theory, only elementary formulae are considered in the text; there is a mathematical appendix for specialists. Profound without sacrifice of clarity. Translated by C. Eckart, F. Hoyt. 18 figures. 192pp. 5⅜ x 8. S113 Paperbound **$1.25**

SELECTED PAPERS ON QUANTUM ELECTRODYNAMICS, edited by **J. Schwinger.** Facsimiles of papers which established quantum electrodynamics, from initial successes through today's position as part of the larger theory of elementary particles. First book publication in any language of these collected papers of Bethe, Bloch, Dirac, Dyson, Fermi, Feynman, Heisenberg, Kusch, Lamb, Oppenheimer, Pauli, Schwinger, Tomonoga, Weisskopf, Wigner, etc. 34 papers in all, 29 in English, 1 in French, 3 in German, 1 in Italian. Preface and historical commentary by the editor. xvii + 423pp. 6⅛ x 9¼. S444 Paperbound **$2.45**

THE FUNDAMENTAL PRINCIPLES OF QUANTUM MECHANICS, WITH ELEMENTARY APPLICATIONS, E. C. Kemble. An inductive presentation, for the graduate student or specialist in some other branch of physics. Assumes some acquaintance with advanced math; apparatus necessary beyond differential equations and advanced calculus is developed as needed. Although a general exposition of principles, hundreds of individual problems are fully treated, with applications of theory being interwoven with development of the mathematical structure. The author is the Professor of Physics at Harvard Univ. "This excellent book would be of great value to every student . . . a rigorous and detailed mathematical discussion of all of the principal quantum-mechanical methods . . . has succeeded in keeping his presentations clear and understandable," Dr. Linus Pauling, J. of the American Chemical Society. Appendices: calculus of variations, math. notes, etc. Indexes. 611pp. 5⅜ x 8.
S472 Paperbound **$2.95**

ATOMIC SPECTRA AND ATOMIC STRUCTURE, G. Herzberg. Excellent general survey for chemists, physicists specializing in other fields. Partial contents: simplest line spectra and elements of atomic theory, building-up principle and periodic system of elements, hyperfine structure of spectral lines, some experiments and applications. Bibilography. 80 figures. Index. xii + 257pp. 5⅜ x 8. S115 Paperbound **$1.95**

THE THEORY AND THE PROPERTIES OF METALS AND ALLOYS, N. F. Mott, H. Jones. Quantum methods used to develop mathematical models which show interrelationship of basic chemical phenomena with crystal structure, magnetic susceptibility, electrical, optical properties. Examines thermal properties of crystal lattice, electron motion in applied field, cohesion, electrical resistance, noble metals, para-, dia-, and ferromagnetism, etc. "Exposition . . . clear . . . mathematical treatment . . . simple," Nature. 138 figures. Bibliography. Index. xiii + 320pp. 5⅜ x 8. S456 Paperbound **$1.85**

FOUNDATIONS OF NUCLEAR PHYSICS, edited by **R. T. Beyer.** 13 of the most important papers on nuclear physics reproduced in facsimile in the original languages of their authors: the papers most often cited in footnotes, bibliographies. Anderson, Curie, Joliot, Chadwick, Fermi, Lawrence, Cockcroft, Hahn, Yukawa. UNPARALLELED BIBLIOGRAPHY. 122 double-columned pages, over 4,000 articles, books classified. 57 figures. 288pp. 6⅛ x 9¼.
S19 Paperbound **$1.75**

MESON PHYSICS, R. E. Marshak. Traces the basic theory, and explicity presents results of experiments with particular emphasis on theoretical significance. Phenomena involving mesons as virtual transitions are avoided, eliminating some of the least satisfactory predictions of meson theory. Includes production and study of π mesons at nonrelativistic nucleon energies, contrasts between π and μ mesons, phenomena associated with nuclear interaction of π mesons, etc. Presents early evidence for new classes of particles and indicates theoretical difficulties created by discovery of heavy mesons and hyperons. Name and subject indices. Unabridged reprint. viii + 378pp. 5⅜ x 8. S500 Paperbound **$1.95**

See also: **STRANGE STORY OF THE QUANTUM, B. Hoffmann; FROM EUCLID TO EDDINGTON, E. Whittaker; MATTER AND LIGHT, THE NEW PHYSICS, L. de Broglie; THE EVOLUTION OF SCIENTIFIC THOUGHT FROM NEWTON TO EINSTEIN, A. d'Abro; THE RISE OF THE NEW PHYSICS, A. d'Abro; THE THEORY OF GROUPS AND QUANTUM MECHANICS, H. Weyl; SUBSTANCE AND FUNCTION, & EINSTEIN'S THEORY OF RELATIVITY, E. Cassirer; FUNDAMENTAL FORMULAS OF PHYSICS, D. H. Menzel.**

Hydrodynamics

HYDRODYNAMICS, H. Dryden, F. Murnaghan, Harry Bateman. Published by the National Research Council in 1932 this enormous volume offers a complete coverage of classical hydrodynamics. Encyclopedic in quality. Partial contents: physics of fluids, motion, turbulent flow, compressible fluids, motion in 1, 2, 3 dimensions; viscous fluids rotating, laminar motion, resistance of motion through viscous fluid, eddy viscosity, hydraulic flow in channels of various shapes, discharge of gases, flow past obstacles, etc. Bibliography of over 2,900 items. Indexes. 23 figures. 634pp. 5⅜ x 8. S303 Paperbound **$2.75**

A TREATISE ON HYDRODYNAMICS, A. B. Basset. Favorite text on hydrodynamics for 2 generations of physicists, hydrodynamical engineers, oceanographers, ship designers, etc. Clear enough for the beginning student, and thorough source for graduate students and engineers on the work of d'Alembert, Euler, Laplace, Lagrange, Poisson, Green, Clebsch, Stokes, Cauchy, Helmholtz, J. J. Thomson, Love, Hicks, Greenhill, Besant, Lamb, etc. Great amount of documentation on entire theory of classical hydrodynamics. Vol I: theory of motion of frictionless liquids, vortex, and cyclic irrotational motion, etc. 132 exercises. Bibliography. 3 Appendixes. xii + 264pp. Vol II: motion in viscous liquids, harmonic analysis, theory of tides, etc. 112 exercises. Bibliography. 4 Appendixes. xv + 328pp. Two volume set. 5⅜ x 8.

S724 Vol I Paperbound **$1.75**
S725 Vol II Paperbound **$1.75**
The set **$3.50**

HYDRODYNAMICS, Horace Lamb. Internationally famous complete coverage of standard reference work on dynamics of liquids & gases. Fundamental theorems, equations, methods, solutions, background, for classical hydrodynamics. Chapters include Equations of Motion, Integration of Equations in Special Gases, Irrotational Motion, Motion of Liquid in 2 Dimensions, Motion of Solids through Liquid-Dynamical Theory, Vortex Motion, Tidal Waves, Surface Waves, Waves of Expansion, Viscosity, Rotating Masses of liquids. Excellently planned, arranged; clear, lucid presentation. 6th enlarged, revised edition. Index. Over 900 footnotes, mostly bibliographical. 119 figures. xv + 738pp. 6⅛ x 9¼. S256 Paperbound **$2.95**

See also: **FUNDAMENTAL FORMULAS OF PHYSICS, D. H. Menzel; THEORY OF FLIGHT, R. von Mises; FUNDAMENTALS OF HYDRO- AND AEROMECHANICS, L. Prandtl and O. G. Tietjens; APPLIED HYDRO- AND AEROMECHANICS, L. Prandtl and O. G. Tietjens; HYDRAULICS AND ITS APPLICATIONS, A. H. Gibson; FLUID MECHANICS FOR HYDRAULIC ENGINEERS, H. Rouse.**

Acoustics, optics, electromagnetics

ON THE SENSATIONS OF TONE, Hermann Helmholtz. This is an unmatched coordination of such fields as acoustical physics, physiology, experiment, history of music. It covers the entire gamut of musical tone. Partial contents: relation of musical science to acoustics, physical vs. physiological acoustics, composition of vibration, resonance, analysis of tones by sympathetic resonance, beats, chords, tonality, consonant chords, discords, progression of parts, etc. 33 appendixes discuss various aspects of sound, physics, acoustics, music, etc. Translated by A. J. Ellis. New introduction by Prof. Henry Margenau of Yale. 68 figures. 43 musical passages analyzed. Over 100 tables. Index. xix + 576pp. 6⅛ x 9¼.

S114 Paperbound **$2.95**

THE THEORY OF SOUND, Lord Rayleigh. Most vibrating systems likely to be encountered in practice can be tackled successfully by the methods set forth by the great Nobel laureate, Lord Rayleigh. Complete coverage of experimental, mathematical aspects of sound theory. Partial contents: Harmonic motions, vibrating systems in general, lateral vibrations of bars, curved plates or shells, applications of Laplace's functions to acoustical problems, fluid friction, plane vortex-sheet, vibrations of solid bodies, etc. This is the first inexpensive edition of this great reference and study work. Bibliography. Historical introduction by R. B. Lindsay. Total of 1040pp. 97 figures. 5⅜ x 8.
S292, S293, Two volume set, paperbound, **$4.00**

THE DYNAMICAL THEORY OF SOUND, H. Lamb. Comprehensive mathematical treatment of the physical aspects of sound, covering the theory of vibrations, the general theory of sound, and the equations of motion of strings, bars, membranes, pipes, and resonators. Includes chapters on plane, spherical, and simple harmonic waves, and the Helmholtz Theory of Audition. Complete and self-contained development for student and specialist; all fundamental differential equations solved completely. Specific mathematical details for such important phenomena as harmonics, normal modes, forced vibrations of strings, theory of reed pipes, etc. Index. Bibliography. 86 diagrams. viii + 307pp. 5⅜ x 8. S655 Paperbound **$1.50**

WAVE PROPAGATION IN PERIODIC STRUCTURES, L. Brillouin. A general method and application to different problems: pure physics, such as scattering of X-rays of crystals, thermal vibration in crystal lattices, electronic motion in metals; and also problems of electrical engineering. Partial contents: elastic waves in 1-dimensional lattices of point masses. Propagation of waves along 1-dimensional lattices. Energy flow. 2 dimensional, 3 dimensional lattices. Mathieu's equation. Matrices and propagation of waves along an electric line. Continuous electric lines. 131 illustrations. Bibliography. Index. xii + 253pp. 5⅜ x 8.
S34 Paperbound **$1.85**

THEORY OF VIBRATIONS, N. W. McLachlan. Based on an exceptionally successful graduate course given at Brown University, this discusses linear systems having 1 degree of freedom, forced vibrations of simple linear systems, vibration of flexible strings, transverse vibrations of bars and tubes, transverse vibration of circular plate, sound waves of finite amplitude, etc. Index. 99 diagrams. 160pp. 5⅜ x 8. S190 Paperbound **$1.35**

LOUD SPEAKERS: THEORY, PERFORMANCE, TESTING AND DESIGN, N. W. McLachlan. Most comprehensive coverage of theory, practice of loud speaker design, testing; classic reference, study manual in field. First 12 chapters deal with theory, for readers mainly concerned with math. aspects; last 7 chapters will interest reader concerned with testing, design. Partial contents: principles of sound propagation, fluid pressure on vibrators, theory of moving-coil principle, transients, driving mechanisms, response curves, design of horn type moving coil speakers, electrostatic speakers, much more. Appendix. Bibliography. Index. 165 illustrations, charts. 411pp. 5⅜ x 8. S588 Paperbound **$2.25**

MICROWAVE TRANSMISSION, J. S. Slater. First text dealing exclusively with microwaves, brings together points of view of field, circuit theory, for graduate student in physics, electrical engineering, microwave technician. Offers valuable point of view not in most later studies. Uses Maxwell's equations to study electromagnetic field, important in this area. Partial contents: infinite line with distributed parameters, impedance of terminated line, plane waves, reflections, wave guides, coaxial line, composite transmission lines, impedance matching, etc. Introduction. Index. 76 illus. 319pp. 5⅜ x 8.
S564 Paperbound **$1.50**

THE ANALYSIS OF SENSATIONS, Ernst Mach. Great study of physiology, psychology of perception, shows Mach's ability to see material freshly, his "incorruptible skepticism and independence." (Einstein). Relation of problems of psychological perception to classical physics, supposed dualism of physical and mental, principle of continuity, evolution of senses, will as organic manifestation, scores of experiments, observations in optics, acoustics, music, graphics, etc. New introduction by T. S. Szasz, M. D. 58 illus. 300-item bibliography. Index. 404pp. 5⅜ x 8. S525 Paperbound **$1.75**

APPLIED OPTICS AND OPTICAL DESIGN, A. E. Conrady. With publication of vol. 2, standard work for designers in optics is now complete for first time. Only work of its kind in English; only detailed work for practical designer and self-taught. Requires, for bulk of work, no math above trig. Step-by-step exposition, from fundamental concepts of geometrical, physical optics, to systematic study, design, of almost all types of optical systems. Vol. 1: all ordinary ray-tracing methods; primary aberrations; necessary higher aberration for design of telescopes, low-power microscopes, photographic equipment. Vol. 2: (Completed from author's notes by R. Kingslake, Dir. Optical Design, Eastman Kodak.) Special attention to high-power microscope, anastigmatic photographic objectives. "An indispensable work," J., Optical Soc. of Amer. "As a practical guide this book has no rival," Transactions, Optical Soc. Index. Bibliography. 193 diagrams. 852pp. 6⅛ x 9¼. Vol. 1 T611 Paperbound **$2.95**
Vol. 2 T612 Paperbound **$2.95**

THE THEORY OF OPTICS, Paul Drude. One of finest fundamental texts in physical optics, classic offers thorough coverage, complete mathematical treatment of basic ideas. Includes fullest treatment of application of thermodynamics to optics; sine law in formation of images, transparent crystals, magnetically active substances, velocity of light, apertures, effects depending upon them, polarization, optical instruments, etc. Introduction by A. A. Michelson. Index. 110 illus. 567pp. 5⅜ x 8. S532 Paperbound **$2.45**

OPTICKS, Sir Isaac Newton. In its discussions of light, reflection, color, refraction, theories of wave and corpuscular theories of light, this work is packed with scores of insights and discoveries. In its precise and practical discussion of construction of optical apparatus, contemporary understandings of phenomena it is truly fascinating to modern physicists, astronomers, mathematicians. Foreword by Albert Einstein. Preface by I. B. Cohen of Harvard University. 7 pages of portraits, facsimile pages, letters, etc. cxvi + 414pp. 5⅜ x 8.
S205 Paperbound **$2.00**

OPTICS AND OPTICAL INSTRUMENTS: AN INTRODUCTION WITH SPECIAL REFERENCE TO PRACTICAL APPLICATIONS, B. K. Johnson. An invaluable guide to basic practical applications of optical principles, which shows how to set up inexpensive working models of each of the four main types of optical instruments—telescopes, microscopes, photographic lenses, optical projecting systems. Explains in detail the most important experiments for determining their accuracy, resolving power, angular field of view, amounts of aberration, all other necessary facts about the instruments. Formerly "Practical Optics." Index. 234 diagrams. Appendix. 224pp. 5⅜ x 8.
S642 Paperbound **$1.65**

PRINCIPLES OF PHYSICAL OPTICS, Ernst Mach. This classical examination of the propagation of light, color, polarization, etc. offers an historical and philosophical treatment that has never been surpassed for breadth and easy readability. Contents: Rectilinear propagation of light. Reflection, refraction. Early knowledge of vision. Dioptrics. Composition of light. Theory of color and dispersion. Periodicity. Theory of interference. Polarization. Mathematical representation of properties of light. Propagation of waves, etc. 279 illustrations, 10 portraits. Appendix. Indexes. 324pp. 5⅜ x 8.
S178 Paperbound **$1.75**

FUNDAMENTALS OF ELECTRICITY AND MAGNETISM, L. B. Loeb. For students of physics, chemistry, or engineering who want an introduction to electricity and magnetism on a higher level and in more detail than general elementary physics texts provide. Only elementary differential and integral calculus is assumed. Physical laws developed logically, from magnetism to electric currents, Ohm's law, electrolysis, and on to static electricity, induction, etc. Covers an unusual amount of material; one third of book on modern material: solution of wave equation, photoelectric and thermionic effects, etc. Complete statement of the various electrical systems of units and interrelations. 2 Indexes. 75 pages of problems with answers stated. Over 300 figures and diagrams. xix +669pp. 5⅜ x 8.
S745 Paperbound **$2.75**

THE ELECTROMAGNETIC FIELD, Max Mason & Warren Weaver. Used constantly by graduate engineers. Vector methods exclusively: detailed treatment of electrostatics, expansion methods, with tables converting any quantity into absolute electromagnetic, absolute electrostatic, practical units. Discrete charges, ponderable bodies, Maxwell field equations, etc. Introduction. Indexes. 416pp. 5⅜ x 8.
S185 Paperbound **$2.00**

ELECTRICAL THEORY ON THE GIORGI SYSTEM, P. Cornelius. A new clarification of the fundamental concepts of electricity and magnetism, advocating the convenient m.k.s. system of units that is steadily gaining followers in the sciences. Illustrating the use and effectiveness of his terminology with numerous applications to concrete technical problems, the author here expounds the famous Giorgi system of electrical physics. His lucid presentation and well-reasoned, cogent argument for the universal adoption of this system form one of the finest pieces of scientific exposition in recent years. 28 figures. Index. Conversion tables for translating earlier data into modern units. Translated from 3rd Dutch edition by L. J. Jolley. x + 187pp. 5½ x 8¾.
S909 Clothbound **$6.00**

THEORY OF ELECTRONS AND ITS APPLICATION TO THE PHENOMENA OF LIGHT AND RADIANT HEAT, H. Lorentz. Lectures delivered at Columbia University by Nobel laureate Lorentz. Unabridged, they form a historical coverage of the theory of free electrons, motion, absorption of heat, Zeeman effect, propagation of light in molecular bodies, inverse Zeeman effect, optical phenomena in moving bodies, etc. 109 pages of notes explain the more advanced sections. Index. 9 figures. 352pp. 5⅜ x 8.
S173 Paperbound **$1.85**

TREATISE ON ELECTRICITY AND MAGNETISM, James Clerk Maxwell. For more than 80 years a seemingly inexhaustible source of leads for physicists, mathematicians, engineers. Total of 1082pp. on such topics as Measurement of Quantities, Electrostatics, Elementary Mathematical Theory of Electricity, Electrical Work and Energy in a System of Conductors, General Theorems, Theory of Electrical Images, Electrolysis, Conduction, Polarization, Dielectrics, Resistance, etc. "The greatest mathematical physicist since Newton," Sir James Jeans. 3rd edition. 107 figures, 21 plates. 1082pp. 5⅜ x 8.
S636-7, 2 volume set, paperbound **$4.00**

See also: **FUNDAMENTAL FORMULAS OF PHYSICS, D. H. Menzel; MATHEMATICAL ANALYSIS OF ELECTRICAL & OPTICAL WAVE MOTION, H. Bateman.**

Mechanics, dynamics, thermodynamics, elasticity

MECHANICS VIA THE CALCULUS, P. W. Norris, W. S. Legge. Covers almost everything, from linear motion to vector analysis: equations determining motion, linear methods, compounding of simple harmonic motions, Newton's laws of motion, Hooke's law, the simple pendulum, motion of a particle in 1 plane, centers of gravity, virtual work, friction, kinetic energy of rotating bodies, equilibrium of strings, hydrostatics, sheering stresses, elasticity, etc. 550 problems. 3rd revised edition. xii + 367pp. 6 x 9.
S207 Clothbound **$3.95**

MECHANICS, J. P. Den Hartog. Already a classic among introductory texts, the M.I.T. professor's lively and discursive presentation is equally valuable as a beginner's text, an engineering student's refresher, or a practicing engineer's reference. Emphasis in this highly readable text is on illuminating fundamental principles and showing how they are embodied in a great number of real engineering and design problems: trusses, loaded cables, beams, jacks, hoists, etc. Provides advanced material on relative motion and gyroscopes not usual in introductory texts. "Very thoroughly recommended to all those anxious to improve their real understanding of the principles of mechanics." MECHANICAL WORLD. Index. List of equations. 334 problems, all with answers. Over 550 diagrams and drawings. ix + 462pp. 5⅜ x 8.
S754 Paperbound **$2.00**

THEORETICAL MECHANICS: AN INTRODUCTION TO MATHEMATICAL PHYSICS, J. S. Ames, F. D. Murnaghan. A mathematically rigorous development of theoretical mechanics for the advanced student, with constant practical applications. Used in hundreds of advanced courses. An unusually thorough coverage of gyroscopic and baryscopic material, detailed analyses of the Corilis acceleration, applications of Lagrange's equations, motion of the double pendulum, Hamilton-Jacobi partial differential equations, group velocity and dispersion, etc. Special relativity is also included. 159 problems. 44 figures. ix + 462pp. 5⅜ x 8.
S461 Paperbound **$2.00**

THEORETICAL MECHANICS: STATICS AND THE DYNAMICS OF A PARTICLE, W. D. MacMillan. Used for over 3 decades as a self-contained and extremely comprehensive advanced undergraduate text in mathematical physics, physics, astronomy, and deeper foundations of engineering. Early sections require only a knowledge of geometry; later, a working knowledge of calculus. Hundreds of basic problems, including projectiles to the moon, escape velocity, harmonic motion, ballistics, falling bodies, transmission of power, stress and strain, elasticity, astronomical problems. 340 practice problems plus many fully worked out examples make it possible to test and extend principles developed in the text. 200 figures. xvii + 430pp. 5⅜ x 8. S467 Paperbound **$2.00**

THEORETICAL MECHANICS: THE THEORY OF THE POTENTIAL, W. D. MacMillan. A comprehensive, well balanced presentation of potential theory, serving both as an introduction and a reference work with regard to specific problems, for physicists and mathematicians. No prior knowledge of integral relations is assumed, and all mathematical material is developed as it becomes necessary. Includes: Attraction of Finite Bodies; Newtonian Potential Function; Vector Fields, Green and Gauss Theorems; Attractions of Surfaces and Lines; Surface Distribution of Matter; Two-Layer Surfaces; Spherical Harmonics; Ellipsoidal Harmonics; etc. "The great number of particular cases . . . should make the book valuable to geophysicists and others actively engaged in practical applications of the potential theory," Review of Scientific Instruments. Index. Bibliography. xiii + 469pp. 5⅜ x 8. S486 Paperbound **$2.25**

THEORETICAL MECHANICS: DYNAMICS OF RIGID BODIES, W. D. MacMillan. Theory of dynamics of a rigid body is developed, using both the geometrical and analytical methods of instruction. Begins with exposition of algebra of vectors, it goes through momentum principles, motion in space, use of differential equations and infinite series to solve more sophisticated dynamics problems. Partial contents: moments of inertia, systems of free particles, motion parallel to a fixed plane, rolling motion, method of periodic solutions, much more. 82 figs. 199 problems. Bibliography. Indexes. xii + 476pp. 5⅜ x 8. S641 Paperbound **$2.00**

MATHEMATICAL FOUNDATIONS OF STATISTICAL MECHANICS, A. I. Khinchin. Offering a precise and rigorous formulation of problems, this book supplies a thorough and up-to-date exposition. It provides analytical tools needed to replace cumbersome concepts, and furnishes for the first time a logical step-by-step introduction to the subject. Partial contents: geometry & kinematics of the phase space, ergodic problem, reduction to theory of probability, application of central limit problem, ideal monatomic gas, foundation of thermo-dynamics, dispersion and distribution of sum functions. Key to notations. Index. viii + 179pp. 5⅜ x 8.
S147 Paperbound **$1.35**

ELEMENTARY PRINCIPLES IN STATISTICAL MECHANICS, J. W. Gibbs. Last work of the great Yale mathematical physicist, still one of the most fundamental treatments available for advanced students and workers in the field. Covers the basic principle of conservation of probability of phase, theory of errors in the calculated phases of a system, the contributions of Clausius, Maxwell, Boltzmann, and Gibbs himself, and much more. Includes valuable comparison of statistical mechanics with thermodynamics: Carnot's cycle, mechanical definitions of entropy, etc. xvi + 208pp. 5⅜ x 8. S707 Paperbound **$1.45**

THE DYNAMICS OF PARTICLES AND OF RIGID, ELASTIC, AND FLUID BODIES; BEING LECTURES ON MATHEMATICAL PHYSICS, A. G. Webster. The reissuing of this classic fills the need for a comprehensive work on dynamics. A wide range of topics is covered in unusually great depth, applying ordinary and partial differential equations. Part I considers laws of motion and methods applicable to systems of all sorts; oscillation, resonance, cyclic systems, etc. Part 2 is a detailed study of the dynamics of rigid bodies. Part 3 introduces the theory of potential; stress and strain, Newtonian potential functions, gyrostatics, wave and vortex motion, etc. Further contents: Kinematics of a point; Lagrange's equations; Hamilton's principle; Systems of vectors; Statics and dynamics of deformable bodies; much more, not easily found together in one volume. Unabridged reprinting of 2nd edition. 20 pages of notes on differential equations and the higher analysis. 203 illustrations. Selected bibliography. Index. xi + 588pp. 5⅜ x 8. S522 Paperbound **$2.35**

A TREATISE ON DYNAMICS OF A PARTICLE, E. J. Routh. Elementary text on dynamics for beginning mathematics or physics student. Unusually detailed treatment from elementary definitions to motion in 3 dimensions, emphasizing concrete aspects. Much unique material important in recent applications. Covers impulsive forces, rectilinear and constrained motion in 2 dimensions, harmonic and parabolic motion, degrees of freedom, closed orbits, the conical pendulum, the principle of least action, Jacobi's method, and much more. Index. 559 problems, many fully worked out, incorporated into text. xiii + 418pp. 5⅜ x 8.
S696 Paperbound **$2.25**

DYNAMICS OF A SYSTEM OF RIGID BODIES (Elementary Section), E. J. Routh. Revised 7th edition of this standard reference. This volume covers the dynamical principles of the subject, and its more elementary applications: finding moments of inertia by integration, foci of inertia, d'Alembert's principle, impulsive forces, motion in 2 and 3 dimensions, Lagrange's equations, relative indicatrix, Euler's theorem, large tautochronous motions, etc. Index. 55 figures. Scores of problems. xv + 443pp. 5⅜ x 8. S664 Paperbound **$2.35**

DYNAMICS OF A SYSTEM OF RIGID BODIES (Advanced Section), E. J. Routh. Revised 6th edition of a classic reference aid. Much of its material remains unique. Partial contents: moving axes, relative motion, oscillations about equilibrium, motion. Motion of a body under no forces, any forces. Nature of motion given by linear equations and conditions of stability. Free, forced vibrations, constants of integration, calculus of finite differences, variations, precession and nutation, motion of the moon, motion of string, chain, membranes. 64 figures. 498pp. 5⅜ x 8. S229 Paperbound **$2.35**

DYNAMICAL THEORY OF GASES, James Jeans. Divided into mathematical and physical chapters for the convenience of those not expert in mathematics, this volume discusses the mathematical theory of gas in a steady state, thermodynamics, Boltzmann and Maxwell, kinetic theory, quantum theory, exponentials, etc. 4th enlarged edition, with new material on quantum theory, quantum dynamics, etc. Indexes. 28 figures. 444pp. 6⅛ x 9¼.
S136 Paperbound **$2.45**

FOUNDATIONS OF POTENTIAL THEORY, O. D. Kellogg. Based on courses given at Harvard this is suitable for both advanced and beginning mathematicians. Proofs are rigorous, and much material not generally avialable elsewhere is included. Partial contents: forces of gravity, fields of force, divergence theorem, properties of Newtonian potentials at points of free space, potentials as solutions of Laplace's equations, harmonic functions, electrostatics, electric images, logarithmic potential, etc. One of Grundlehren Series. ix + 384pp. 5⅜ x 8.
S144 Paperbound **$1.98**

THERMODYNAMICS, Enrico Fermi. Unabridged reproduction of 1937 edition. Elementary in treatment; remarkable for clarity, organization. Requires no knowledge of advanced math beyond calculus, only familiarity with fundamentals of thermometry, calorimetry. Partial Contents: Thermodynamic systems; First & Second laws of thermodynamics; Entropy; Thermodynamic potentials: phase rule, reversible electric cell; Gaseous reactions: van't Hoff reaction box, principle of LeChatelier; Thermodynamics of dilute solutions: osmotic & vapor pressures, boiling & freezing points; Entropy constant. Index. 25 problems. 24 illustrations. x + 160pp. 5⅜ x 8 S361 Paperbound **$1.75**

THE THERMODYNAMICS OF ELECTRICAL PHENOMENA IN METALS and A CONDENSED COLLECTION OF THERMODYNAMIC FORMULAS, P. W. Bridgman. Major work by the Nobel Prizewinner: stimulating conceptual introduction to aspects of the electron theory of metals, giving an intuitive understanding of fundamental relationships concealed by the formal systems of Onsager and others. Elementary mathematical formulations show clearly the fundamental thermodynamical relationships of the electric field, and a complete phenomenological theory of metals is created. This is the work in which Bridgman announced his famous "thermomotive force" and his distinction between "driving" and "working" electromotive force. We have added in this Dover edition the author's long unavailable tables of thermodynamic formulas, extremely valuable for the speed of reference they allow. Two works bound as one. Index. 33 figures. Bibliography. xviii + 256pp. 5⅜ x 8. S723 Paperbound **$1.65**

REFLECTIONS ON THE MOTIVE POWER OF FIRE, by Sadi Carnot, and other papers on the 2nd law of thermodynamics by E. Clapeyron and R. Clausius. Carnot's "Reflections" laid the groundwork of modern thermodynamics. Its non-technical, mostly verbal statements examine the relations between heat and the work done by heat in engines, establishing conditions for the economical working of these engines. The papers by Clapeyron and Clausius here reprinted added further refinements to Carnot's work, and led to its final acceptance by physicists. Selections from posthumous manuscripts of Carnot are also included. All papers in English. New introduction by E. Mendoza. 12 illustrations. xxii + 152pp. 5⅜ x 8.
S661 Paperbound **$1.50**

TREATISE ON THERMODYNAMICS, Max Planck. Based on Planck's original papers this offers a uniform point of view for the entire field and has been used as an introduction for students who have studied elementary chemistry, physics, and calculus. Rejecting the earlier approaches of Helmholtz and Maxwell, the author makes no assumptions regarding the nature of heat, but begins with a few empirical facts, and from these deduces new physical and chemical laws. 3rd English edition of this standard text by a Nobel laureate. xvi + 297pp. 5⅜ x 8. S219 Paperbound **$1.75**

THE THEORY OF HEAT RADIATION, Max Planck. A pioneering work in thermodynamics, providing basis for most later work. Nobel Laureate Planck writes on Deductions from Electrodynamics and Thermodynamics, Entropy and Probability, Irreversible Radiation Processes, etc. Starts with simple experimental laws of optics, advances to problems of spectral distribution of energy and irreversibility. Bibliography. 7 illustrations, xiv + 224pp. 5⅜ x 8.
S546 Paperbound **$1.50**

A HISTORY OF THE THEORY OF ELASTICITY AND THE STRENGTH OF MATERIALS, I. Todhunter and K. Pearson. For over 60 years a basic reference, unsurpassed in scope or authority. Both a history of the mathematical theory of elasticity from Galileo, Hooke, and Mariotte to Saint Venant, Kirchhoff, Clebsch, and Lord Kelvin and a detailed presentation of every important mathematical contribution during this period. Presents proofs of thousands of theorems and laws, summarizes every relevant treatise, many unavailable elsewhere. Practically a book apiece is devoted to modern founders: Saint Venant, Lame, Boussinesq, Rankine, Lord Kelvin, F. Neumann, Kirchhoff, Clebsch. Hundreds of pages of technical and physical treatises on specific applications of elasticity to particular materials. Indispensable for the mathematician, physicist, or engineer working with elasticity. Unabridged, corrected reprint of original 3-volume 1886-1893 edition. Three volume set. Two indexes. Appendix to Vol. I. Total of 2344pp. 5⅜ x 8⅜.
S914–916 The set, Clothbound **$12.50**

THE MATHEMATICAL THEORY OF ELASTICITY, A. E. H. Love. A wealth of practical illustration combined with thorough discussion of fundamentals—theory, application, special problems and solutions. Partial Contents: Analysis of Strain & Stress, Elasticity of Solid Bodies, Elasticity of Crystals, Vibration of Spheres, Cylinders, Propagation of Waves in Elastic Solid Media, Torsion, Theory of Continuous Beams, Plates. Rigorous treatment of Volterra's theory of dislocations, 2-dimensional elastic systems, other topics of modern interest. "For years the standard treatise on elasticity," AMERICAN MATHEMATICAL MONTHLY. 4th revised edition. Index. 76 figures. xviii + 643pp. 6⅛ x 9¼.
S174 Paperbound **$2.95**

RAYLEIGH'S PRINCIPLE AND ITS APPLICATIONS TO ENGINEERING, G. Temple & W. Bickley. Rayleigh's principle developed to provide upper and lower estimates of true value of fundamental period of a vibrating system, or condition of stability of elastic systems. Illustrative examples; rigorous proofs in special chapters. Partial contents: Energy method of discussing vibrations, stability. Perturbation theory, whirling of uniform shafts. Criteria of elastic stability. Application of energy method. Vibrating systems. Proof, accuracy, successive approximations, application of Rayleigh's principle. Synthetic theorems. Numerical, graphical methods. Equilibrium configurations, Ritz's method. Bibliography. Index. 22 figures. ix + 156pp. 5⅜ x 8.
S307 Paperbound **$1.50**

INVESTIGATIONS ON THE THEORY OF THE BROWNIAN MOVEMENT, Albert Einstein. Reprints from rare European journals. 5 basic papers, including the Elementary Theory of the Brownian Movement, written at the request of Lorentz to provide a simple explanation. Translated by A. D. Cowper. Annotated, edited by R. Fürth. 33pp. of notes elucidate, give history of previous investigations. Author, subject indexes. 62 footnotes. 124pp. 5⅜ x 8.
S304 Paperbound **$1.25**

See also: **FUNDAMENTAL FORMULAS OF PHYSICS, D. H. Menzel.**

ENGINEERING

THEORY OF FLIGHT, Richard von Mises. Remains almost unsurpassed as balanced, well-written account of fundamental fluid dynamics, and situations in which air compressibility effects are unimportant. Stressing equally theory and practice, avoiding formidable mathematical structure, it conveys a full understanding of physical phenomena and mathematical concepts. Contains perhaps the best introduction to general theory of stability. "Outstanding," Scientific, Medical, and Technical Books. New introduction by K. H. Hohenemser. Bibliographical, historical notes. Index. 408 illustrations. xvi + 620pp. 5⅜ x 8⅜.
S541 Paperbound **$2.85**

THEORY OF WING SECTIONS, I. H. Abbott, A. E. von Doenhoff. Concise compilation of subsonic aerodynamic characteristics of modern NASA wing sections, with description of their geometry, associated theory. Primarily reference work for engineers, students, it gives methods, data for using wing-section data to predict characteristics. Particularly valuable: chapters on thin wings, airfoils; complete summary of NACA's experimental observations, system of construction families of airfoils. 350pp. of tables on Basic Thickness Forms, Mean Lines, Airfoil Ordinates, Aerodynamic Characteristics of Wing Sections. Index. Bibliography. 191 illustrations. Appendix. 705pp. 5⅜ x 8.
S558 Paperbound **$2.95**

SUPERSONIC AERODYNAMICS, E. R. C. Miles. Valuable theoretical introduction to the supersonic domain, with emphasis on mathematical tools and principles, for practicing aerodynamicists and advanced students in aeronautical engineering. Covers fundamental theory, divergence theorem and principles of circulation, compressible flow and Helmholtz laws, the Prandtl-Busemann graphic method for 2-dimensional flow, oblique shock waves, the Taylor-Maccoll method for cones in supersonic flow, the Chaplygin method for 2-dimensional flow, etc. Problems range from practical engineering problems to development of theoretical results. "Rendered outstanding by the unprecedented scope of its contents . . . has undoubtedly filled a vital gap," AERONAUTICAL ENGINEERING REVIEW. Index. 173 problems, answers. 106 diagrams. 7 tables. xii + 255pp. 5⅜ x 8.
S214 Paperbound **$1.45**

K. Pearson; THEORY AND OPERATION OF THE SLIDE RULE, J. P. Ellis; DIFFERENTIAL EQUATIONS FOR ENGINEERS, P. Franklin; MATHEMATICAL METHODS FOR SCIENTISTS AND ENGINEERS, L. P. Smith; APPLIED MATHEMATICS FOR RADIO AND COMMUNICATIONS ENGINEERS, C. E. Smith; MATHEMATICS OF MODERN ENGINEERING, E. G. Keller, R. E. Doherty; THEORY OF FUNCTIONS AS APPLIED TO ENGINEERING PROBLEMS, R. Rothe, F. Ollendorff, K. Pohlhausen.

CHEMISTRY AND PHYSICAL CHEMISTRY

ORGANIC CHEMISTRY, F. C. Whitmore. The entire subject of organic chemistry for the practicing chemist and the advanced student. Storehouse of facts, theories, processes found elsewhere only in specialized journals. Covers aliphatic compounds (500 pages on the properties and synthetic preparation of hydrocarbons, halides, proteins, ketones, etc.), alicyclic compounds, aromatic compounds, heterocyclic compounds, organophosphorus and organometallic compounds. Methods of synthetic preparation analyzed critically throughout. Includes much of biochemical interest. "The scope of this volume is astonishing," INDUSTRIAL AND ENGINEERING CHEMISTRY. 12,000-reference index. 2387-item bibliography. Total of x + 1005pp. 5⅜ x 8. Two volume set.
S700 Vol I Paperbound **$2.00**
S701 Vol II Paperbound **$2.00**
The set **$4.00**

THE PRINCIPLES OF ELECTROCHEMISTRY, D. A. MacInnes. Basic equations for almost every subfield of electrochemistry from first principles, referring at all times to the soundest and most recent theories and results; unusually useful as text or as reference. Covers coulometers and Faraday's Law, electrolytic conductance, the Debye-Hueckel method for the theoretical calculation of activity coefficients, concentration cells, standard electrode potentials, thermodynamic ionization constants, pH, potentiometric titrations, irreversible phenomena, Planck's equation, and much more. "Excellent treatise," AMERICAN CHEMICAL SOCIETY JOURNAL. "Highly recommended," CHEMICAL AND METALLURGICAL ENGINEERING. 2 Indices. Appendix. 585-item bibliography. 137 figures. 94 tables. ii + 478pp. 5⅝ x 8⅜.
S52 Paperbound **$2.35**

THE CHEMISTRY OF URANIUM: THE ELEMENT, ITS BINARY AND RELATED COMPOUNDS, J. J. Katz and E. Rabinowitch. Vast post-World War II collection and correlation of thousands of AEC reports and published papers in a useful and easily accessible form, still the most complete and up-to-date compilation. Treats "dry uranium chemistry," occurrences, preparation, properties, simple compounds, isotopic composition, extraction from ores, spectra, alloys, etc. Much material available only here. Index. Thousands of evaluated bibliographical references. 324 tables, charts, figures. xxi + 609pp. 5⅜ x 8.
S757 Paperbound **$2.95**

KINETIC THEORY OF LIQUIDS, J. Frenkel. Regarding the kinetic theory of liquids as a generalization and extension of the theory of solid bodies, this volume covers all types of arrangements of solids, thermal displacements of atoms, interstitial atoms and ions, orientational and rotational motion of molecules, and transition between states of matter. Mathematical theory is developed close to the physical subject matter. 216 bibliographical footnotes. 55 figures. xi + 485pp. 5⅜ x 8.
S94 Clothbound **$3.95**
S95 Paperbound **$2.45**

POLAR MOLECULES, Pieter Debye. This work by Nobel laureate Debye offers a complete guide to fundamental electrostatic field relations, polarizability, molecular structure. Partial contents: electric intensity, displacement and force, polarization by orientation, molar polarization and molar refraction, halogen-hydrides, polar liquids, ionic saturation, dielectric constant, etc. Special chapter considers quantum theory. Indexed. 172pp. 5⅜ x 8.
S64 Paperbound **$1.50**

ELASTICITY, PLASTICITY AND STRUCTURE OF MATTER, R. Houwink. Standard treatise on rheological aspects of different technically important solids such as crystals, resins, textiles, rubber, clay, many others. Investigates general laws for deformations; determines divergences from these laws for certain substances. Covers general physical and mathematical aspects of plasticity, elasticity, viscosity. Detailed examination of deformations, internal structure of matter in relation to elastic and plastic behavior, formation of solid matter from a fluid, conditions for elastic and plastic behavior of matter. Treats glass, asphalt, gutta percha, balata, proteins, baker's dough, lacquers, sulphur, others. 2nd revised, enlarged edition. Extensive revised bibliography in over 500 footnotes. Index. Table of symbols. 214 figures. xviii + 368pp. 6 x 9¼.
S385 Paperbound **$2.45**

THE PHASE RULE AND ITS APPLICATION, Alexander Findlay. Covering chemical phenomena of 1, 2, 3, 4, and multiple component systems, this "standard work on the subject" (NATURE, London), has been completely revised and brought up to date by A. N. Campbell and N. O. Smith. Brand new material has been added on such matters as binary, tertiary liquid equilibria, solid solutions in ternary systems, quinary systems of salts and water. Completely revised to triangular coordinates in ternary systems, clarified graphic representation, solid models, etc. 9th revised edition. Author, subject indexes. 236 figures. 505 footnotes, mostly bibliographic. xii + 494pp. 5⅜ x 8.
S91 Paperbound **$2.45**

TERNARY SYSTEMS: INTRODUCTION TO THE THEORY OF THREE COMPONENT SYSTEMS, G. Masing. Furnishes detailed discussion of representative types of 3-components systems, both in solid models (particularly metallic alloys) and isothermal models. Discusses mechanical mixture without compounds and without solid solutions; unbroken solid solution series; solid solutions with solubility breaks in two binary systems; iron-silicon-aluminum alloys; allotropic forms of iron in ternary system; other topics. Bibliography. Index. 166 illustrations. 178pp. 5⅝ x 8⅜. S631 Paperbound **$1.45**

THE STORY OF ALCHEMY AND EARLY CHEMISTRY, J. M. Stillman. An authoritative, scholarly work, highly readable, of development of chemical knowledge from 4000 B.C. to downfall of phlogiston theory in late 18th century. Every important figure, many quotations. Brings alive curious, almost incredible history of alchemical beliefs, practices, writings of Arabian Prince Oneeyade, Vincent of Beauvais, Geber, Zosimos, Paracelsus, Vitruvius, scores more. Studies work, thought of Black, Cavendish, Priestley, Van Helmont, Bergman, Lavoisier, Newton, etc. Index. Bibliography. 579pp. 5⅜ x 8. S628 Paperbound **$2.45**

See also: **ATOMIC SPECTRA AND ATOMIC STRUCTURE, G. Herzberg; INVESTIGATIONS ON THE THEORY OF THE BROWNIAN MOVEMENT, A. Einstein; TREATISE ON THERMODYNAMICS, M. Planck.**

ASTRONOMY AND ASTROPHYSICS

AN ELEMENTARY SURVEY OF CELESTIAL MECHANICS, Y. Ryabov. Elementary exposition of gravitational theory and celestial mechanics. Historical introduction and coverage of basic principles, including: the elliptic, the orbital plane, the 2- and 3-body problems, the discovery of Neptune, planetary rotation, the length of the day, the shapes of galaxies, satellites (detailed treatment of Sputnik I), etc. First American reprinting of successful Russian popular exposition. Elementary algebra and trigonometry helpful, but not necessary; presentation chiefly verbal. Appendix of theorem proofs. 58 figures. 165pp. 5⅜ x 8. T756 Paperbound **$1.25**

THE SKY AND ITS MYSTERIES, E. A. Beet. One of most lucid books on mysteries of universe; deals with astronomy from earliest observations to latest theories of expansion of universe, source of stellar energy, birth of planets, origin of moon craters, possibility of life on other planets. Discusses effects of sunspots on weather; distances, ages of several stars; master plan of universe; methods and tools of astronomers; much more. "Eminently readable book," London Times. Extensive bibliography. Over 50 diagrams. 12 full-page plates, fold-out star map. Introduction. Index, 238pp. 5¼ x 7½. T627 Clothbound **$3.00**

THE REALM OF THE NEBULAE, E. Hubble. One of the great astronomers of our time records his formulation of the concept of "island universes," and its impact on astronomy. Such topics are covered as the velocity-distance relation; classification, nature, distances, general field of nebulae; cosmological theories; nebulae in the neighborhood of the Milky Way. 39 photos of nebulae, nebulae clusters, spectra of nebulae, and velocity distance relations shown by spectrum comparison. "One of the most progressive lines of astronomical research," The Times (London). New introduction by A. Sandage. 55 illustrations. Index. iv + 201pp. 5⅜ x 8. S455 Paperbound **$1.50**

OUT OF THE SKY, H. H. Nininger. A non-technical but comprehensive introduction to "meteoritics", the young science concerned with all aspects of the arrival of matter from outer space. Written by one of the world's experts on meteorites, this work shows how, despite difficulties of observation and sparseness of data, a considerable body of knowledge has arisen. It defines meteors and meteorites; studies fireball clusters and processions, meteorite composition, size, distribution, showers, explosions, origins, craters, and much more. A true connecting link between astronomy and geology. More than 175 photos, 22 other illustrations. References. Bibliography of author's publications on meteorites. Index. viii + 336pp. 5⅜ x 8. T519 Paperbound **$1.85**

SATELLITES AND SCIENTIFIC RESEARCH, D. King-Hele. Non-technical account of the manmade satellites and the discoveries they have yielded up to the spring of 1959. Brings together information hitherto published only in hard-to-get scientific journals. Includes the life history of a typical satellite, methods of tracking, new information on the shape of the earth, zones of radiation, etc. Over 60 diagrams and 6 photographs. Mathematical appendix. Bibliography of over 100 items. Index. xii + 180pp. 5⅜ x 8½. T703 Clothbound **$4.00**

Dover publishes books on art, music, philosophy, literature, languages, history, social sciences, psychology, handcrafts, orientalia, puzzles and entertainments, chess, pets and gardens, books explaining science, intermediate and higher mathematics mathematical physics, engineering, biological sciences, earth sciences, classics of science, etc. Write to:

Dept. catrr.
Dover Publications, Inc.
180 Varick Street, N. Y. 14, N. Y.